A FLOWER BOOK
FOR THE POCKET

A FLOWER BOOK
FOR THE POCKET

By

MACGREGOR SKENE
MELVILLE WILLS PROFESSOR OF BOTANY
IN THE UNIVERSITY OF BRISTOL
AUTHOR OF 'SCHOOL BOTANY'

With Illustrations by
CHARLOTTE GEORGIANA TROWER
and
RUTH WESTON

OXFORD UNIVERSITY PRESS
LONDON: HUMPHREY MILFORD

OXFORD UNIVERSITY PRESS
AMEN HOUSE, E.C. 4
London Edinburgh Glasgow New York
Toronto Melbourne Capetown Bombay
Calcutta Madras
HUMPHREY MILFORD
PUBLISHER TO THE UNIVERSITY

FIRST PRINTED 1935
SECOND (CORRECTED) IMPRESSION 1936
THIRD IMPRESSION 1937
FOURTH IMPRESSION 1941

PRINTED IN GREAT BRITAIN

PREFACE

THE production of this book, with its large number of coloured illustrations, has been possible only through the generosity of the executors of the late Dr. G. Claridge Druce in placing at the disposal of the Oxford University Press a collection of paintings of British plants made by the late Miss C. G. Trower and left by her to Dr. Druce. A few gaps have been filled by Miss Ruth Weston and the black and white drawings of the grasses are from her pen, but 483 of the paintings are Miss Trower's work.

The choice of species has not been easy. The number of flowering plants illustrated in colour is 501, and 28 species of grasses are illustrated in black and white, making the total number of illustrated species 529. In addition 315 species, not illustrated, are briefly described in the text, making the total number of plants described 844. As a great many of the plants not dealt with are either very rare or belong to such genera as the blackberries and the hawkweeds, the numerous species of which can be identified only by specialists, it may be claimed that the *Flower Book for the Pocket* deals with most of the British plants likely to attract the attention of those who are not botanists.

The majority of the 529 species illustrated are, naturally, 'common' species; but a number of them are comparatively rare, or at least less common than some of the species not illustrated and only described in the text. Frequently one, not necessarily the commonest, of two or more similar plants has been chosen, reference being made in the text to the characters of the others. Plants abundant in some localities only or otherwise striking or interesting have been freely chosen.

It is hoped, therefore, that the book may be a useful Flora for those who are interested in plants but have little botanical knowledge. The descriptions have been kept simple by using few technical terms and by dealing as far as possible with characters easy to observe. Such characters have been used, too, in compiling the keys to the families and the genera, even though this entails a certain lack of precision in some groups where accurate distinctions can be made only with the help of rather obscure botanical characters.

It is hoped that the book may also serve as a first Flora for use in schools. To extend its usefulness in this respect the keys have been made to include all the British families and all the important British genera. To make reference to more complete works easy the sequence of families is that of the standard British Floras. For the same reason the Latin names adopted have been taken, with very few exceptions, from the latest edition of Bentham and Hooker's *British Flora*. Notes have been added in many places on points of biological interest.

It is a great pleasure to acknowledge the help and advice I have received throughout the preparation of this book from Mr. A. L. P. Norrington of the Clarendon Press. My thanks are also due to Mr. H. E. Barrow, of Thos. Forman & Sons Ltd., for the care and skill he has brought to the solution of the many difficulties in reproducing the coloured illustrations. I am indebted for many valuable suggestions to Mr. H. Stuart Thompson who read the proofs and compiled the Index.

April 1935   M. S.

The issue of a new impression has afforded the opportunity of correcting a number of errors which have come to notice. Brief notes have also been added on several plants whose omission from the first edition had been criticized.

October 1935   M. S.

HOW TO USE THIS BOOK

THIS book is intended for the beginner, and at the same time it has also been kept as concise as possible in order to make it a true 'pocket book'. While, therefore, many of the technical terms commonly employed in botanical works have been avoided (in describing leaves, for example, such simple English terms as 'arrow-shaped' and 'heart-shaped' have been substituted for the scientific terms 'sagittate' and 'cordate'), the use of a certain number of technical terms has been unavoidable in the interests of brevity. Therefore, before reading the descriptions of the species (or genera or families), the reader should master the contents of the brief section on Botanical Terms and Characters on pp. 10–17, in which the various technical terms used are described. By doing this the reader will also learn the general characteristics of the structure of a flowering plant.

Illustrations and Descriptions.[1]

The main part of the book consists of the coloured plates, each faced by a page of text, containing a brief description of each of the *Species* illustrated on the opposite plate. A species is just a kind of plant, e.g. a Bulbous Buttercup or Meadow Buttercup (p. 105). A *Genus* (plural *genera*) is a group of species which resemble each other in their important characters, especially in those of the flower, but differ in minor ways. All the plants illustrated on p. 105 clearly have flowers very much alike and they all belong to one genus. But their foliage is quite different and each is a separate species. At the beginning of the description are given the English and the Latin names. The Latin name consists of two words of which the first is the name of the genus and the second is the distinguishing name of the species. Thus *Ranunculus acris* and *Ranunculus auricomus* are two species belonging to the genus *Ranunculus*.

[1] For a further note on the descriptions see p. 97.

The genera are grouped in *Families*. A family is a group of genera which resemble each other in some important characters. But the beginner should be warned that these characters are not always very apparent. The family name is a feminine plural Latin word, always ending in -ae and nearly always in -aceae. Thus Papaveraceae is the Latin name of the Poppy Family (papaver = poppy; papaveraceae = poppy-like plants). The family is generally named after a typical genus; e.g. the Papaveraceae include the genus Papaver and the Ranunculaceae the genus Ranunculus, and so on. Families are arranged in still larger groups. Of these we need only mention the three principal which concern the plants dealt with in this book. The Conifers (p. 98) are plants in which the seeds are naked. The Dicotyledons (pp. 101–318) are plants in which the seeds are enclosed in fruits. They possess two seed-leaves (dicotyledon = two cotyledons or seed-leaves) and can generally be recognized by certain other characters. The petals and sepals, for example, are nearly always four or five in number. The Monocotyledons (p. 318) have also seeds enclosed in fruits. They possess one seed-leaf, and the petals and sepals are nearly always three or six. Classification is the process of arranging plants in genera, families, and larger groups.

Identifying an unknown species.

The first step is to identify the family. For this purpose the keys to the families on pp. 18–26 should be referred to. At the beginning of these keys will be found a number of groups based chiefly on obvious leaf and flower characters. When the plant has been assigned to one of these groups, refer to the key of that group, and when the family has thus been found, the result may be checked by the detailed family description, to which a page reference is given in each case.

The genus may next be found by referring to the key to the genera of the family, which follows the family description, and once the genus has been established, a reference to the illustrations and descriptions of the species will complete the process of identification. The position in the text of the species of any genus is found by referring to the index at the end of the book.

This process may perhaps be made more clear by taking a definite example. Suppose that the plant is *Ononis repens*, the Restharrow. Since it is a shrub and has alternate leaves it falls into the third Group. Reference to the key to this group shows us that we must first make a choice between the headings A, B, and C. The plant falls under heading C, as it has conspicuous, coloured flowers. We must then select either *a* or *b*, and since the flowers are irregular the plant comes under *a* and proves to belong to the family Leguminosae. Turning to p. 39 we can check this result by reading the description of the family and then refer to the key to the genera. As the plant is a shrub it comes under A, and as some leaves have three leaflets under *b*. We have then a choice between plants with yellow flowers and plants with pink flowers. As the flowers are pink the plant falls under II and belongs to the genus Ononis. It may then be compared with the description and illustration on p. 153.

For the sake of greater completeness the names of certain families and genera, which are not represented in the text, are printed in their proper places in the keys, and are always enclosed in square brackets, thus: [Meconopsis].

In order to avoid using obscure characters and making the keys too complicated they have not, in all cases, been brought down to a single genus; a choice is sometimes left between two or three genera. The final decision must then be made by reference to the descriptions of the genera in question.

Species described but not illustrated.

In addition to descriptions of the 529 illustrated species, the text contains also descriptions of a number of allied species (315). These are not numbered (as the illustrated species are), but they occur in their proper places in the keys and are also indexed. When, in the final process of identification, the plant is being compared with the illustrations and descriptions in the text, the possibility that it belongs to one of the species described, but not illustrated, or even to a species not dealt with, must not be overlooked.

Botanical Terms and Characters.

The flowering plant normally consists of a root system and a shoot system. The former is underground. The characters of the roots are not much used in plant description, though the possession of *tuberous* (swollen and fleshy) roots (Lesser Celandine) is a feature to be noted.

The conspicuous part of the shoot system is above ground, though many plants possess underground shoots, as we shall see later. The shoot consists of the stem and its branches, leaves, and flowers.

The stem of a plant may be *branched* or *simple* (without branches). The stem and its branches may be *erect* (upright) or *prostrate* (trailing). Often the base of the stem is prostrate and the apex more or less erect. Many plants (Strawberry, Silverweed) have special slender shoots growing along the surface of the soil, rooting at intervals and so giving rise to new plants at some distance from the parent. Such shoots are called *runners*. Similar shoots arising below the soil and growing up into new plants at some distance from the parent are *suckers* (some Willow-herbs). A horizontal underground stem is a *rhizome* (Wood Anemone). A more or less vertical underground stem is a *root-stock* (Primrose). A tuberous underground stem is a *corm* (Crocus). A *bulb* is a very short stem crowned by a number of fleshy, scale leaves. A *crown* is a bud with some roots. Underground stems often resemble roots superficially, but may be distinguished by the possession of buds and of leaves in the form of scales. As regards their duration plants may be *annual*, *biennial*, or *perennial*. Perennials the stems of which are green and not woody are *herbaceous* or *herbs*. The term herb is also applied to annuals and biennials. Herbaceous plants often die down and pass the winter in the form of a leaf rosette (Plantain) or as a crown, bulb, corm, &c. Many perennials have woody stems which persist through the winter. If the stem is much branched from near the base and the plant is small or of moderate size it is a *shrub*. If the stem runs up for some height unbranched and the plant is large it is a *tree*.

Leaves arise from the stem at points called *nodes*, and in many plants (Grasses, Pinks) the nodes are swollen. The angle between leaf and stem is the leaf *axil*, and in it stands a bud which may develop into a branch or a flower. A flower or inflorescence in the axil of a leaf is called *axillary*, while one ending the stem is *terminal*. Leaves may stand opposite each other in pairs, when they are *opposite* (Maple). They may arise in whorls at the same level, when they are *whorled* (Woodruff, Fig. 228). Leaves which are neither opposite nor whorled are *alternate* (Oak). Alternate leaves may be in two rows, if each is on the opposite side of the stem from that at a higher, or lower, level; but usually they are arranged in a spiral. In some plants a number of leaves rise from a short portion of the stem at ground level; such leaves are called *radical*, as they seem to come from the root. If the stem does not elongate, the radical leaves may form a rosette on the surface of the soil (Plantain).

A leaf may consist of a *stalk* and a *blade*. Or there may be no stalk, when the leaf is *sessile*. At the base of the stalk in many leaves there is a pair of outgrowths, one on each side, the *stipules*. These may be green, leafy, and large (Heartsease) or small (Violet) and are often thin and dry or *membranous* (Spurrey). Sometimes they fall off as the leaf expands (Beech).

The margin of a leaf may be quite even, when it is *entire* (Plantain), or it may be indented in various ways. The indentations may take the form of numerous small teeth, when the leaf is *toothed* (Nettle). They may go deeper, dividing the leaf into several lobes, when it is *notched* or *lobed* (Oak). They may divide the leaf deeply, nearly to the midrib or base, when it is *segmented* or *cut* or *deeply divided* (Milfoil). The leaf may be divided completely into separate leaflets, when it is *compound* (Vetch). A compound leaf is defined strictly as one in which the parts may be pulled off without tearing, but this distinction is not always sharp. All leaves which are not compound are *simple*.

A leaf may possess one main vein, the *midrib*, running from base to tip, with smaller veins running off from it arranged like the plumes of a feather. In such a leaf the divisions are arranged like the veins, and the leaf is said to be *pinnate* or *pinnately compound*, *lobed*, or *cut* (Vetch); or there may be several nearly equal veins running out from the tip of the stalk, like the fingers of a hand (Ivy), and the leaf is then described as *palmately compound*, &c. The leaflets, segments, &c., may be again divided in various ways, and the process may be repeated a third time. We then have leaves which may be described as *twice pinnate*, *thrice pinnately cut*, and so on. A compound leaf with three leaflets is said to be *trifoliate* (Clover).

The surface of a leaf may be *hairy* or without hairs, when it is *glabrous*. Leaves with a 'bloom' giving them a bluish tint are called *glaucous* (Carnation). The hairs of some plants act as *glands* producing a sticky or scented secretion. Leaves or stems with such hairs are said to be *glandular* (Pelargonium). Glands may take many other forms. *Nectaries* are glands and secrete the sugary *nectar* which is the raw material of honey. Nectaries may occur on the axis of the flower, the petals, the sepals, the stamens, or the carpels. In some flowers there are small scale-like *nectar-leaves* (Christmas Rose).

The shape of a leaf is described by a number of terms, the meanings of which may be better understood from the diagrams on the opposite page than from descriptions.

The stalk or blade of a leaf may more or less encircle the stem, when it is said to be *sheathing*. Between the blade and the sheath of the leaf of many grasses is a small scale called the *ligule*. A leaf or part of a leaf or a branch is replaced in some plants (Vetch) by a whip-like structure called a *tendril*. This is sensitive to touch, and, twining round other objects, supports the plant. Tendrils may be branched.

The flower consists of a number of parts inserted on the tip of a shoot. This tip is the *axis* or *receptacle* of the flower. To the outside, in a flower like that of the buttercup, is a circle

LEAF SHAPES

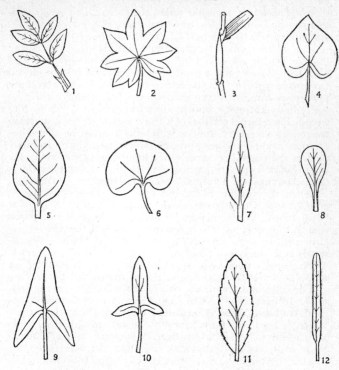

1. Pinnately compound with stipules.
2. Palmately lobed.
3. Grass leaf with sheath and ligule.
4. Heart-shaped.
5. Ovate.
6. Kidney-shaped.

7. Lance-shaped.
8. Spoon-shaped.
9. Arrow-shaped.
10. Halbert-shaped.
11. Elliptical, toothed.
12. Linear.

or *whorl* of *sepals*, together called the *calyx*. The sepals protect the bud and are usually small, greenish leaves. Within and above this is a whorl of coloured *petals*, together the *corolla*, which forms a landmark and landing-stage for visiting insects. Within and above this are numerous *stamens* each with a stalk or *filament* and a head or *anther* in which is produced the powdery *pollen*. In the centre and at the highest level are numerous carpels, within each of which is a small green or white body, the *ovule*, which, after fertilization, develops into a seed. Each carpel consists of a body or *ovary* bearing at its tip the *stigma*, a receptive spot on which pollen must be placed before fertilization and seed production can take place. In many flowers the stigma is carried on a longer or shorter stalk, the *style*. *Pollination* is the placing of pollen on the stigma, and it is carried out in some flowers by insects and in others by the wind.

When the various parts, but especially the petals, are of equal size and evenly spaced the flower is said to be *regular* (Buttercup). When they are of unequal size and so disposed that the flower is bilaterally symmetrical the flower is *irregular* (Broom). In some flowers (Violet) a petal is produced backwards at the base into a narrow tube or *spur* containing nectar.

The sepals may be *free* from each other (Buttercup) or *united* together (Daffodil), and this is true of the petals also.

The calyx and corolla are referred to collectively as the *perianth*. In many flowers the calyx (Hemlock) or corolla (Anemone) or both (Willow) are absent. It is not always easy to say which of the two whorls is absent, since some coloured parts which seem to be petals have been shown on botanical grounds to be really sepals (Anemone). Further, two whorls may be present, both green, like sepals (Dock) or both coloured, like petals (Tulip). In such cases it is often convenient to use the words *perianth* and *perianth segments* or *leaves*.

The stamens are usually free, but may be united either by their stalks (Mallow) or by their anthers (Cornflower). The carpels may be free (Buttercup), but are usually united (Daffodil, Foxglove). United carpels may be spoken of together as the *pistil*. The part of the pistil containing the seeds is then the ovary. The number of carpels, when they are united, may be indicated by the number of stigmas, or of styles, or by the number of ribs or angles of the ovary. Sometimes the ovary is divided by internal partitions or *septa* (singular *septum*) into a number of chambers equal to the number of carpels; or it may have only one chamber with one or more rows of seeds.

The carpels, or ovary, may stand at a higher level than the other parts of the flower, when they are *superior* (Buttercup, Foxglove). The axis of the flower may expand into a disk, or cup, or flask (Strawberry, Cherry, Rose) bearing the sepals, petals, and stamens on its rim; here again the ovary is superior. Or the axis may entirely enclose the ovary, becoming one with its wall. The sepals, &c., then rise from the top of the ovary and the ovary is *inferior* (Daffodil, Honey-suckle). Most flowers possess both stamens and carpels and are *hermaphrodite* or 2-sexual. In some plants the flowers are 1-sexual and of two kinds. Those with carpels only are called *pistillate* or female, those with stamens only are *staminate* or male or *sterile*.

After fertilization the sepals, petals, and stamens usually fall off and the ovary develops into a fruit. A fruit enclosing a single seed may be a small, leathery, seed-like body, when it is called an *achene* (Buttercup). When it is large and hard it is a *nut* (Oak); a small hard fruit is called a *nutlet* (Dock). A fruit containing several seeds may dry out and open as it ripens, or it may become fleshy. A dry fruit which opens by splitting right down one or both edges is a *pod* (Broom). A fruit which opens by small holes or *pores*, teeth, large flaps or *valves*, or by a lid is a *capsule* (Poppy). Some dry fruits instead of opening break up, when ripe, into separate 1-seeded portions (Maple, Crane's-bill).

Fleshy fruits which are soft throughout are *berries* (Bilberry); those with a hard stone are *drupes* (cherry).

A fruit may consist of a collection of achenes (Buttercup), drupes (Blackberry), or pods (Marsh Marigold).

Ripe fruits may possess expanded wings or tufts of hair which aid in dispersal by wind. Such structures may arise from the wall of the ovary (wing of Ash), from the calyx (hairs, or *pappus*, of Thistle), or from the style (hairs of Clematis). Seeds may also have tufts of hairs (Willow-herb). The fruit may have little hooks which catch in the fur of animals so that

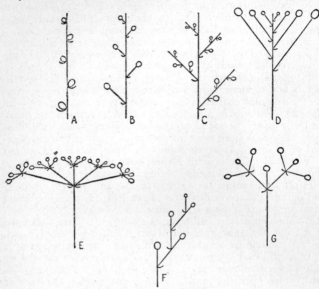

Diagrams of inflorescences
A, Spike. *B*, Raceme. *C*, Panicle. *D*, Corymb. *E*, Compound umbel. *F* and *G*, Two types of cyme.

the fruit is carried about (Cleavers, Agrimony). The bristle or stout hair which tips some fruits and is developed from the style is called an *awn* (Crane's-bill), and the same term is applied to similar bristles in the flowers of the grasses. The style or apical part of the ovary may develop into a spike or *beak*, when the fruit is said to be *beaked*. A pod is sometimes constricted so as to appear *beaded*. A fruit may be surrounded by a cup or *cupule* of enlarged bracts (Hazel).

Flowers may occur singly in the axil of a leaf or at the tip of a shoot, when they are *solitary*. Or they may be grouped on special shoots forming an *inflorescence*. When the flowers are sessile on a simple stem the inflorescence is a *spike*. When they are stalked on a simple stem, it is a *raceme*. When they are stalked on a branched stem, it is a *panicle*. When the stalks of a raceme or the branches of a panicle, though arising at different levels, are of such lengths as to bring the flowers into a flat head the inflorescence is a *corymb*. When the stalks all arise at the same level the inflorescence is an *umbel*. An umbel is compound when it is repeatedly branched. A large number of small flowers may be crowded into a close *head* (Daisy). A *catkin* (Willow) is a close spike which falls as a whole.

In all these inflorescences the oldest flowers are at the base, and the tip goes on forming new flowers. There is another kind of inflorescence in which the axis ends with a flower and the younger flowers are formed on side branches. Such inflorescences are *cymes*, and two types are shown in the diagram. Cymes may be much branched and may assume forms very similar to panicles, corymbs, and umbels; such inflorescences are termed *false panicles*, &c.

The individual flower of an inflorescence often stands in the axil of a leaf, which often differs from an ordinary foliage leaf in size—it is usually smaller—in texture, or in colour. Such a leaf with a flower in its axil is called a *bract*. Small scales on the flower stalk are called *bracteoles*. The word *scale* is widely used for structures arising from the stem like leaves, but unlike leaves in their appearance, being small or membranous or fleshy or lacking green colour.

Parasites are plants which attach themselves to other plants and draw nourishment from them. They may be green (Mistletoe) or not (Dodder). *Saprophytes* are plants which draw nourishment from decaying matter in the soil; they are never green (Bird's Nest). *Insectivorous* plants capture and digest small insects (Sundew).

KEYS TO THE FAMILIES

THE MAIN GROUPS

Plants without green colour—parasites and saprophytes   .   .   .   .   1ST GROUP   (*p*. 19)

Woody plants, trees or shrubs (sometimes very small):
(*a*) leaves opposite or whorled   .   .   2ND GROUP   (*p*. 19)
(*b*) leaves alternate   .   .   .   3RD GROUP   (*p*. 19)

Herbs with greenish or brownish flowers, sometimes tinged with red or yellow; sometimes white or pinkish, but in that case minute, inconspicuous and not massed in groups   .   4TH GROUP   (*p*. 20)

Herbs with white or coloured petals and with a distinct calyx of green or greenish, or small and whitish, sepals:
(*a*) petals free   .   .   .   .   5TH GROUP   (*p*. 23)
(*b*) petals united   .   .   .   .   6TH GROUP   (*p*. 24)

Herbs with white or coloured flowers. No green calyx (or at most only minute teeth); apparently only white or coloured petals present, which may be in 2 whorls, but both whorls nearly alike:
(*a*) petals free   .   .   .   .   7TH GROUP   (*p*. 25)
(*b*) petals united   .   .   .   .   8TH GROUP   (*p*. 25)

NOTE. The beginner should note that in the Daisy family, and some others, the 'flower' commonly so called is really an inflorescence of many small flowers in a close head. In the Keys the word 'flower' refers to these small flowers.

FIRST GROUP

Parasites and saprophytes without green colour

A. Small twining plant   CONVOLVULACEAE, p. 67
B. Upright rather fleshy plants:
  (*a*) Stamens 1   ORCHIDACEAE, p. 82
  (*b*) Stamens 4   OROBANCHACEAE, p. 70
  (*c*) Stamens 8–10   ERICACEAE, p. 61

SECOND GROUP

Trees and shrubs with opposite or whorled leaves

A. Flowers small, green, or tinged with red or yellow:
  (*a*) Evergreen
    1. Leaves narrow, needle-like   CONIFERAE, p. 27
    2. Leaves broad   EUPHORBIACEAE, p. 77
    3. Parasite on trees   [LORANTHACEAE]
  (*b*) Deciduous
    1. Leaves compound   OLEACEAE, p. 64
    2. Leaves lobed   ACERACEAE, p. 38
    3. Leaves finely toothed   CELASTRACEAE, p. 38
    4. Leaves entire   CORNACEAE, p. 51
B. Flowers white or coloured:
  (*a*) Petals free or absent
    1. Climber   RANUNCULACEAE, p. 27
    2. Tall tree   OLEACEAE, p. 64
    3. Small shrubs
      I. Flowers pink   FRANKENIACEAE, p. 34
      II. Flowers white or yellow
        Style 1   CISTACEAE, p. 33
        Styles 3–5   HYPERICACEAE, p. 36
  (*b*) Petals united
    1. Flowers, in umbels   CAPRIFOLIACEAE, p. 51
    2. Flowers bell-shaped, in pairs CAPRIFOLIACEAE, p. 51
    3. Flowers otherwise arranged
      I. Twining plants   CAPRIFOLIACEAE, p. 51
      II. Not twining
        Stamens 5–10   ERICACEAE, p. 61
        Stamens 2   OLEACEAE, p. 64

THIRD GROUP

Trees and shrubs with alternate leaves

A. Flowers small, green or tinged with red or yellow, in cones or catkins:
  (*a*) Evergreens, leaves narrow   CONIFERAE, p. 27
  (*b*) Evergreen, leaves broad   FAGACEAE, p. 79

 (c) Deciduous
  1. Leaves aromatic when crushed MYRICACEAE, p. 78
  2. Leaves not aromatic when crushed
   I. Male and female catkins on separate plants
              SALICACEAE, p. 80
   II. Male and female catkins on same plant
     Fruit in a woody cup FAGACEAE, p. 79
     Fruit not in woody cup BETULACEAE, p. 79
B. Flowers inconspicuous, green or tinged with white, red, or yellow, not in cones or catkins:
 (a) Evergreen
  1. Leaves spiny or with sharp points
   I. Small tree [AQUIFOLIACEAE]
   II. Small shrub LILIACEAE, p. 85
  2. Leaves lobed, climber [ARALIACEAE]
  3. Leaves entire, small shrubs THYMELEACEAE, p. 76
  4. Leaves minute, trailing shrub EMPETRACEAE, p. 81
 (b) Deciduous
  1. Leaves lobed RIBESACEAE, p. 44
  2. Leaves heart-shaped [TILIACEAE], ULMACEAE, p. 78
  3. Leaves oval RHAMNACEAE, p. 38
  4. Leaves lance-shaped ELAEAGNACEAE, p. 76
C. Flowers conspicuous, white or coloured:
 (a) Flowers irregular LEGUMINOSAE, p. 39
 (b) Flowers regular
  1. Petals absent, sepals pink or green
   I. Tree ULMACEAE, p. 78
   II. Shrub THYMELEACEAE, p. 76
  2. Petals and sepals present
   I. Petals united
    Corolla flat SOLANACEAE, p. 68
    Corolla bell- or urn-shaped ERICACEAE, p. 61
   II. Petals free
    Stamens 4–5 RIBESACEAE, p. 44, [TAMARICACEAE]
    Stamens 6 [BERBERIDACEAE]
    Stamens numerous ROSACEAE, p. 41

FOURTH GROUP

Herbaceous plants with usually greenish or brownish flowers, or with minute coloured flowers

A. Fleshy plant with jointed stems and without leaves
              CHENOPODIACEAE, p. 75
B. Plants with narrow, rather grass-like leaves, or with rush-like leaves or stems:
 (a) Floating or submerged aquatics
  1. Leaves in a rosette

      I. Flowers few or solitary   PLANTAGINACEAE, p. 74, CRUCIFERAE, p. 30
      II. Flowers many in a head   [ERIOCAULACEAE]
  2. Leaves not in a rosette
      I. Flowers in spiky balls   SPARGANIACEAE, p. 87
      II. Flowers not in spiky balls
             Leaf sheath not split   CYPERACEAE, p. 90
             Leaf sheath split, with ligule GRAMINEAE, p. 91
             Leaf sheath split, or none, no ligule
                      NAIADACEAE, p. 89

(b) Not as in (a)
  1. Flowers with definite perianth
      I. Flowers in spiky balls   SPARGANIACEAE, p. 87
      II. Flowers solitary   RANUNCULACEAE, p. 27,
                                CARYOPHYLLACEAE, p. 34

     III. Flowers in close, or open panicles
                         JUNCACEAE, p. 87

    IV. Flowers in simple spikes
             Tall plant, leaves fragrant when crushed
                        ARACEAE, p. 88
             Small plant, leaves 2-ranked LILIACEAE, p. 85
             Small plant, stamen stalks short
                        JUNCAGINACEAE, p. 89
             Small plant, stamen stalks long, threadlike
                        PLANTAGINACEAE, p. 74

  2. Flowers without definite perianth
      I. Flowers in a massive chocolate club
                        TYPHACEAE, p. 87
      II. Not as in I, leaves 2-ranked, sheaths split
                        GRAMINEAE, p. 91
     III. Not as I, leaves 3-ranked, sheaths not split
                        CYPERACEAE, p. 90

C. Leaves opposite or whorled, not grass-like:
  (a) Aquatic with erect shoots above water HALORAGACEAE, p. 45
  (b) Submerged or floating aquatics
    1. Leaves whorled
      I. Leaves finely toothed   NAIADACEAE, p. 89
      II. Leaves finely forked   CERATOPHYLLACEAE, p. 81
     III. Leaves finely pinnately cut HALORAGACEAE, p. 45
    IV. Leaves short, entire   HYDROCHARIDACEAE, p. 81
    2. Leaves opposite
      I. Leaves more than ½ in. long NAIADACEAE, p. 89
      II. Leaves ½ in. long or less PORTULACACEAE, p. 36, HALO-
             RAGACEAE, p. 45, LYTHRACEAE, p. 46, ONAGRACEAE, p. 46
             [ELATINACEAE]
  (c) Small or minute, prostrate or creeping plants.
    1. Plants of damp or wet places
      I. Leaves 1/10 in. long.   LINACEAE, p. 37, CRASSULACEAE, p. 44

II. Leaves ¼ to ½ in. long   HALORAGACEAE, p. 45, PORTULACACEAE, p. 36, LYTHRACEAE, p. 46, ILLECEBRACEAE, p. 74, CARYOPHYLLACEAE, p. 34

  2. Plants of dry places
    I. Styles 2   ILLECEBRACEAE, p. 74
    II. Styles 3–5   CARYOPHYLLACEAE, p. 34
(d) Plants erect, or if prostrate, with erect tips
  1. Juice milky   EUPHORBIACEAE, p. 77
  2. Juice not milky
    I. Leaves entire   LILIACEAE, p. 85, ORCHIDACEAE, p. 87
    II. Leaves toothed, with stinging hairs
                           URTICACEAE, p. 78
    III. Leaves toothed, no stinging hairs EUPHORBIACEAE, p. 77
    IV. Leaves with shallow lobes   SAXIFRAGACEAE, p. 44
    V. Leaves compound   CAPRIFOLIACEAE, p. 51
(e) Climbing plant   URTICACEAE, p. 78

D. Leaves alternate, not grass-like:
  (a) Submerged or floating aquatics
    1. Minute floating plants without true leaves
                          LEMNACEAE, p. 88
    2. Submerged plants with much divided leaves
                       LENTIBULARIACEAE, p. 71
    3. Submerged or floating plants with undivided leaves
                       NAIADACEAE, p. 89
  (b) Small prostrate or creeping plants of damp or wet places
    1. Leaves with stipules   ILLECEBRACEAE, p. 74
    2. Leaves without stipules
      I. Stamens 4   SCROPHULARIACEAE, p. 68
      II. Stamens 5   PRIMULACEAE, p. 63
    3. Leaves without stipules, lobed SCROPHULARIACEAE, p. 68
  (c) Small prostrate plants of fields or mountains
                       ROSACEAE, p. 41
  (d) Climbing plant   DIOSCOREACEAE, p. 84
  (e) Leaves all radical   PLANTAGINACEAE, p. 74
  (f) Not as in (a) to (e)
    1. Flowers in close heads   COMPOSITAE, p. 54
    2. Flowers in a spike, surrounded by a large hood
                       ARACEAE, p. 88
    3. Flowers otherwise arranged
      I. Plants with milky juice   EUPHORBIACEAE, p. 77
      II. Plants with compound leaves RANUNCULACEAE, p. 27
      III. Plants with very narrow, entire leaves
         SANTALACEAE, p. 77, RANUNCULACEAE, p. 27
      IV. Plant with hairy leaves URTICACEAE, p. 78
      V. Not as I to IV
        Leaves with stipules   POLYGONACEAE, p. 76

Leaves without stipules, stamens many
     RESEDACEAE, p. 33
Leaves without stipules, stamens few
   CHENOPODIACEAE, p. 75, SAXIFRAGACEAE, p. 44
Leaves without stipules, stamen 1
     ORCHIDACEAE, p. 82

FIFTH GROUP

Herbs with coloured flowers, a distinct calyx and free petals

A. Plant with rosettes of leaves having red, glandular hairs
      DROSERACEAE, p. 45

B. Leaves fleshy:
 (*a*) Sepals 5   CRASSULACEAE, p. 44
 (*b*) Sepals 4   CRUCIFERAE, p. 30
 (*c*) Sepals 2   PORTULACACEAE, p. 36

C. Flowers irregular; not as A and B:
 (*a*) Flowers with spur
  1. Leaves with stipules   VIOLACEAE, p. 33
  2. No stipules, leaves much divided or compound
         FUMARIACEAE, p. 30
  3. No stipules, leaves not divided BALSAMINACEAE, p. 38
 (*b*) Flowers not spurred
  1. Stamens exposed   RESEDACEAE, p. 33
  2. Stamens enclosed, leaves entire POLYGALACEAE, p. 34
         (see also Fig. 132)
  3. Stamens enclosed, leaves compound LEGUMINOSAE, p. 39

D. Flowers regular; not as A and B:
 (*a*) Flowers with 3 petals   ALISMACEAE, p. 88
 (*b*) Flowers with petals of other numbers
  1. Stamens 2   ONAGRACEAE, p. 46
  2. Stamens 5
   I. Leaves entire, narrow   LINACEAE, p. 37
   II. Leaves entire, broad   SAXIFRAGACEAE, p. 44
   III. Leaves divided   GERANIACEAE, p. 37
  3. Stamens 4 or 6
   I. Style short or 0   CRUCIFERAE, p. 30
   II. Style long   LYTHRACEAE, p. 46
   III. Styles long   CARYOPHYLLACEAE, p. 34
  4. Stamens 8 or 10
   I. Leaves opposite, entire or toothed
    Ovary inferior   ONAGRACEAE, p. 46
    Ovary superior, style 1 LYTHRACEAE, p. 46
    Ovary superior, styles 2–5 CARYOPHYLLACEAE, p. 34
    Ovary superior, 2-beaked SAXIFRAGACEAE, p. 44.
   II. Leaves opposite, lobed, divided, or compound
         GERANIACEAE, p. 37

III. Leaves alternate, entire or toothed
   Ovary inferior   ONAGRACEAE, p. 46
   Ovary superior, style 1 ERICACEAE, p. 61
   Ovary superior, styles 2 SAXIFRAGACEAE, p. 44
IV. Leaves alternate, divided   GERANIACEAE, p. 37
V. Leaves alternate compound OXALIDACEAE, p. 38
5. Stamens 12   LYTHRACEAE, p. 46
6. Stamens numerous, united   MALVACEAE, p. 36
7. Stamens numerous, free or nearly so
 I. Leaves opposite   HYPERICACEAE, p. 36
 II. Leaves opposite and alternate CISTACEAE, p. 33
 III. Leaves alternate
   Sepals 2   PAPAVERACEAE, p. 29
   Sepals 5, leaves with stipules ROSACEAE, p. 41
   Sepals 3–5, leaves without stipules RANUNCULACEAE, p. 27

SIXTH GROUP

Herbs with coloured flowers, a distinct calyx and united petals

A. Leaves whorled
 (a) Aquatic   PRIMULACEAE, p. 63
 (b) Land Plant   RUBIACEAE, p. 52
B. Leaves opposite:
 (a) Flowers in close heads
  1. Style simple   DIPSACEAE, p. 53
  2. Style forked   LABIATAE, p. 72
 (b) Flowers not in close heads, regular
  1. Sepals 2   PORTULACACEAE, p. 36
  2. Sepals 5, juice milky   APOCYNACEAE, p. 65
  3. Sepals 5, fruit a berry SOLANACEAE, p. 68
  4. Sepals 5, not as in 2 and 3 GENTIANACEAE, p. 65, PRIMU-
              LACEAE, p. 63
 (c) Flowers not in close heads, irregular
  1. Fruit a capsule   SCROPHULARIACEAE, p. 68
  2. Fruit 4 nutlets LABIATAE, p. 72, VERBENACEAE, p. 71
C. Leaves alternate:
 (a) Climbing plants
  1. With tendrils   CUCURBITACEAE, p. 47
  2. Without tendrils, flowers purple SOLANACEAE, p. 68
  3. Without tendrils, flowers pink or white CONVOLVULACEAE, p. 67
 (b) Aquatic plants
  1. Leaves compound   GENTIANACEAE, p. 65
  2. Leaves very finely divided LENTIBULARIACEAE, p. 71
  3. Leaves undivided
   I. Stamens 2   SCROPHULARIACEAE, p. 68
   II. Stamens 5   CAMPANULACEAE, p. 60
 (c) Plants with slimy leaves in a rosette LENTIBULARIACEAE, p. 71

(d) Plants with fleshy leaves   CRASSULACEAE, p. 44, CON-
                                               VOLVULACEAE, p. 67

  (e) Not as in (a) to (d)
      1. Ovary inferior   CAMPANULACEAE, p. 60
      2. Ovary superior stamens opposite petals
          I. Style 1   PRIMULACEAE, p. 63
          II. Styles 3–5   PLUMBAGINACEAE, p. 63
      3. Ovary superior, stamens alternate with petals
          I. Fruit 1–4 nutlets   BORAGINACEAE, p. 66
          II. Fruit a berry   SOLANACEAE, p. 68
        III. Fruit a capsule
            Stamens 2 or 4   SCROPHULARIACEAE, p. 68
            Stamens 5, flowers blue   [POLEMONIACEAE]
            Stamens 5, flowers yellow   SCROPHULARIACEAE, p. 68
            Stamens 5, flowers yellowish, irregular
                                    SOLANACEAE, p. 68
            Stamens 5, flowers white or pink   CONVOLVULACEAE, p. 67

SEVENTH GROUP

Flowers without a distinct green calyx and with free petals

A. Petals or perianth leaves 3 or 6:
  (a) Ovary inferior
      1. Aquatics   HYDROCHARIDACEAE, p. 81
      2. Land plants   AMARYLLIDACEAE, p. 84
  (b) Ovary superior
      1. Stamens 6   LILIACEAE, p. 85
      2. Stamens 9   ALISMACEAE, p. 88
B. Petals or perianth segments of other numbers:
  (a) Stamens many
      1. Aquatics with entire, floating leaves   NYMPHAEACEAE, p. 29
      2. Land or water plants, no floating leaves   RANUNCULACEAE, p. 27
  (b) Stamens 8 or fewer
      1. Ovary superior   POLYGONACEAE, p. 76
      2. Ovary inferior   UMBELLIFERAE, p. 47, CORNACEAE, **p. 51**

EIGHTH GROUP

Flowers without a distinct green calyx and with united petals

A. Petals or perianth segments 3 or 6:
  (a) Flowers irregular
      1. Stamens 3   IRIDACEAE, p. 84
      2. Stamens 1 or 2   ORCHIDACEAE, p. 82
  (b) Flowers regular, 2-sexual
      1. Stamens 3   IRIDACEAE, p. 84

    2. Stamens 6
       I. Ovary superior   LILIACEAE, p. 85
       II. Ovary inferior   AMARYLLIDACEAE, p. 84
  (c) Flowers regular, 1-sexual   HYDROCHARIDACEAE, p. 81
B. Petals or perianth segments of other numbers:
  (a) Flowers in close heads
      1. Stamens united   COMPOSITAE, p. 54
      2. Stamens free   DIPSACEAE, p. 53
  (b) Flowers not in a close head
      1. Flowers irregular   VALERIANACEAE, p. 53
      2. Flowers regular
         I. Leaves whorled   RUBIACEAE, p. 52
        II. Leaves not whorled   PRIMULACEAE, p. 63, VALERIANACEAE, p. 53

KEYS TO THE GENERA

CONIFERAE. PINE FAMILY (p. 98)

Trees or shrubs with narrow or needle-shaped, leathery, evergreen leaves. Ovules and stamens in separate cones; no true flowers. Staminate cones small and falling off. Ovules usually on opposite or spirally arranged scales, naked, not enclosed in an ovary. Pollination by wind; pollen dusty and very abundant.

A. Leaves in threes   JUNIPERUS, 1
B. Leaves in 2 rows   TAXUS, 2
C. Leaves in twos   PINUS, 3

1. JUNIPERUS (p. 98)
Shrubs or small trees. Male and female cones usually on separate plants. Ovules surrounded by 3 fleshy scales, with several sterile scales below. The Latin name.

2. TAXUS (p. 98)
Small tree. Leaves spirally arranged but flattened into 2 rows. Male and female cones on separate plants. Female cone with 1 terminal ovule in a cup. Greek, toxon, a bow, for which the wood was used.

3. PINUS (p. 98)
Trees. The needle leaves are borne singly in seedlings and in groups of 2 or more in older plants. Male and female cones on the same tree. Female cone with numerous, spirally arranged scales, each with 2 ovules. Mature cone woody. The Latin name.

RANUNCULACEAE. BUTTERCUP FAMILY (p. 101)

Usually perennial herbs. Leaves usually alternate, palmately divided, and without stipules. (Clematis is woody with opposite leaves.) Flowers usually regular (irregular in Aconitum and Delphinium). Sepals 4, 5, or more, free, often brightly coloured. Petals 0, or 5 or more, sometimes in the form of nectar-leaves. Stamens many, spirally arranged. Carpels usually many, free, superior. Fruit a collection of 1-seeded achenes or many-seeded pods or rarely a berry.

A. Flowers White:
    (a) Climber   CLEMATIS, 1
    (b) Aquatic   RANUNCULUS, 4
    (c) Herb   ANEMONE, 3, [ACTAEA]
B. Flowers green   HELLEBORUS, 7
C. Flowers purple   ANEMONE, 3
D. Flowers blue   [DELPHINIUM, ACONITUM, AQUILEGIA]
E. Flowers scarlet   [ADONIS]

F. Flowers yellow:
  (*a*) Green sepals present   RANUNCULUS, **4**, [MYOSURUS]
  (*b*) No green sepals
    1. Flowers, small, numerous   THALICTRUM, **2**
    2. Flowers large, few
      I. Leaves divided   TROLLIUS, **6**
      II. Leaves undivided   CALTHA, **5**

1. CLEMATIS (p. 101)

Shrubby climber. Leaves opposite. Sepals 4, white. Petals o. Greek, klema, a shoot or tendril.

2. THALICTRUM (p. 101)

Perennial herbs. Leaves compound, with stipules. Flowers small, in showy panicles. Sepals small, yellowish. Petals o. Stamens many, conspicuous. Fruit a group of achenes. Greek, thallein, to bloom, because of the numerous flowers.

3. ANEMONE (p. 101)

Perennial herbs with rhizomes or tubers. Leaves radical, divided. Flowers solitary surrounded by leafy bracts. Sepals 6 or more, coloured. Petals o. Fruit a group of achenes. The Greek name, from anemos, wind, because some species thrive in exposed situations.

4. RANUNCULUS (p. 102)

Herbs, usually perennial. Leaves entire or more usually lobed or compound. Flowers white or yellow in loose inflorescences or solitary. Sepals 3–5. Petals usually 5 with a nectary near the base, naked or covered by a scale. Fruit a collection of achenes. The Latin name, from rana, a frog, as some species grow in ponds or marshes.

5. CALTHA (p. 106)

Herbs with a stout rhizome. Leaves undivided. Flowers large. Sepals yellow. Petals o. Fruit a collection of pods. Greek, kalathos, a cup, from the form of the flower.

6. TROLLIUS (p. 106)

Herbs, erect from a root-stock. Leaves divided. Flowers large. Sepals 5 or more, yellow. Petals represented by 5 or more small nectaries. Fruit a collection of pods. Latin, trulleus, a bowl, from the form of the flower.

7. HELLEBORUS (p. 109)

Herbs with coarse, divided, light-green leaves. Sepals large, green or coloured. Petals small nectar-pouches. Fruit a collection of pods. The Greek name helleboros.

NYMPHAEACEAE. WATER-LILY FAMILY (p. 109)

Aquatic perennials, with large rounded floating leaves. Flowers large, solitary, regular. Sepals about 5, free. Petals 5 or more, free. Stamens numerous. Carpels numerous, united, superior, or embedded in a disk, from which arise the petals and stamens. Stigma a rayed disk. Fruit rather fleshy, often liberating the seeds by rotting away.

A. Flowers yellow   NUPHAR, **1**
B. Flowers white   [NYMPHAEA]

1. NUPHAR (p. 109)

Flowers yellow. Petals and stamens arise below the carpels. Fruit ripens above water and splits irregularly. The Arabic name, naufar.

PAPAVERACEAE. POPPY FAMILY (p. 109)

Annual or perennial, often hairy, herbs with milky juice. Leaves alternate, divided, without stipules. Flowers regular. Sepals 2, falling early. Petals 4, crumpled in the bud. Stamens very numerous. Carpels 2 or more, united and superior; stigma a rayed disk. Fruit a pod opening by valves, or a capsule opening by pores. Seeds small and numerous.

A. Flowers red   PAPAVER, **1**
B. Flowers yellow:
  (a) Leaves bluish-green   GLAUCIUM, **2**
  (b) Leaves green; bluish below only   CHELIDONIUM, **3**, [MECONOPSIS]

1. PAPAVER (p. 109)

Annual herbs with white milky juice. Leaves divided. Flowers regular on long stalks, nodding in the bud. Ovary with many partitions projecting towards, but not meeting in, the centre and bearing many small seeds. Stigmas 4–20, forming rays on a disk on the top of the ovary. Fruit a capsule, opening by pores. The Latin name.

2. GLAUCIUM (p. 110)

Biennial herbs with yellow juice. Leaves bluish-green. Fruit a very long pod, divided into 2 compartments by a rather fleshy septum in which the numerous seeds are sunk, and opening by 2 valves. Greek, glaukos, blue-green, from the colour of the leaves.

3. CHELIDONIUM (p. 110)

Perennial herbs with orange juice. Fruit a slender pod with a single cavity, opening by 2 valves which separate from the base up. Greek, chelidon, a swallow, perhaps because of the time of flowering.

FUMARIACEAE. FUMITORY FAMILY (p. 110)

*Annual or perennial glabrous herbs. Leaves much divided, or compound,
alternate, without stipules. Flowers small, irregular, twisted sideways on their
stalks. Sepals 2, scale-like. Petals 4, in 2 unequal pairs, the outer larger
and one of them spurred. Stamens 6, in 2 groups of 3. Carpels 2, united,
superior. Fruit a pod with several seeds, or a nutlet with 1 seed.*

A. Fruit a pod   CORYDALIS, **1**
B. Fruit a nutlet   FUMARIA, **2**

1. CORYDALIS (p. 110)

*Annual or perennial. Fruit a pod opening by valves with several seeds. Greek,
korydalis, the crested lark, from the shape of the flower.*

2. FUMARIA (p. 110)

Annual. Fruit a nutlet. Latin, fumus, smoke, perhaps because of the smell.

CRUCIFERAE. WALLFLOWER FAMILY (p. 113)

*Herbs with alternate, often divided leaves, without stipules. Flowers regular,
usually small, in racemes without bracts. Sepals 4, free. Petals 4, free,
forming a cross. Stamens 6, 4 long and 2 short. Carpels 2, united, superior;
ovary divided into 2 compartments by a thin partition. Fruit a pod, opening
by 2 valves which leave the partition as a frame with the seeds attached to
it; rarely breaking into joints. A large family of very uniform floral structure,
and including many important vegetables.*

A. Pod not opening when ripe:
  (a) Pod round, less than 1/10 in.   CORONOPUS, **13**
  (b) Pod much larger
    1. Pod with wide wing   [ISATIS]
    2. Pod 2-jointed, 1 seed, flowers white CRAMBE, **17**
    3. Pod 2-jointed, 1 or 2 seeds, flowers purple CAKILE, **18**
    4. Pod 2-jointed, 2 or more seeds, flowers white or yellow
                                   RAPHANUS, **19**
B. Pod opening by valves, more than four times as long as broad:
  (a) Leaves compound or deeply lobed
    1. Flowers white or pink NASTURTIUM, **1** or CARDAMINE, **4**
    2. Flowers yellow
      I. Fruit beaked BRASSICA, **10** or DIPLOTAXIS, **11**
      II. Fruit not beaked NASTURTIUM, **1** or BARBAREA, **2** or
                                  SISYMBRIUM, **7**
  (b) Leaves undivided, at most notched
    1. Flowers white, leaves large   SISYMBRIUM, **7**
    2. Flowers white, leaves small   ARABIS, **3**
    3. Flowers yellow   ERYSIMUM, **8**

C. Pods opening by valves, short, broad:
   (a) Small aquatic   SUBULARIA, 9
   (b) Fleshy-leaved plant   COCHLEARIA, 6
   (c) Neither aquatic nor fleshy-leaved
     1. Leaves deeply lobed or notched   CAPSELLA, 12 or
                          TEESDALIA, 16, [HUTCHINSIA]
     2. Leaves at most slightly notched.
      I. Pods with wing or flat border   LEPIDIUM, 14 or THLASPI, 15
      II. Pods not winged   DRABA, 5

1. NASTURTIUM (p. 113)

Perennial, aquatic or terrestrial, glabrous herbs. Leaves compound or deeply cut. Flowers small, white or yellow. Pods stout, somewhat curved, with 2 rows of seeds. Latin, nasus, the nose, and torquere, to twist, as the acrid flavour makes one screw up the nose.

2. BARBAREA (p. 113)

Glabrous biennial herbs distinguished from Nasturtium by having straight slender pods with only 1 row of seeds. Said to be called after St. Barbara.

3. ARABIS (p. 113)

Annual or perennial herbs, usually hairy. Leaves in a rosette and also on the stem. Flowers white. Pods flattened, each valve with a definite vein. From Arabia, where many species are native.

4. CARDAMINE (p. 113)

Annual or perennial herbs, glabrous or only slightly hairy. Leaves compound or deeply lobed. Flowers white or pink. Pods flattened; valves without veins, springing open. Greek, kardia, the heart, and damao, to quieten, referring to medicinal properties.

5. DRABA (p. 114)

Small herbs with a rosette of simple leaves. Flowers in small racemes usually on leafless stems. Pods oval flattened; seeds in 2 rows; partition broad, membranous. Greek, drabe, pungent, and also used for a kind of cress.

6. COCHLEARIA (p. 114)

Perennial herbs with simple, glabrous, often fleshy leaves. Flowers small, white. Pods swollen, with a broad partition and several seeds. Latin, cochlear, a spoon, from the leaf-shape.

7. SISYMBRIUM (p. 117)

Usually rather tall biennials with hairy leaves of varied form. Flowers small, yellow or white. Pod long, narrow, rounded. Seeds in 1 row. Greek, sisymbrion, a plant mentioned by Theophrastus.

8. ERYSIMUM (p. 117)

Annuals or perennials, with short hairs. Leaves undivided, at most toothed. Flowers small, yellow. Pods slender, markedly 4-angled; seeds in 1 row. Greek, eruo, I draw, the plant having been used for blistering.

9. SUBULARIA (p. 118)

A small submerged plant. Flowers minute, white. Pod oval, somewhat flattened. Seeds few. Latin, subula, an awl, from the leaf-shape.

10. BRASSICA (p. 118)

Annuals, biennials, or perennials usually with branched, upright stems and rough hairs. Lower leaves usually lobed. Flowers rather large, yellow. Pods long, stout, with a more or less distinct beak, often beaded when dry. Seeds large, in 1 row. Latin, brassica, a cabbage.

11. DIPLOTAXIS (p. 118)

Herbs like Brassica, usually with pinnately cut leaves and with small seeds in 2 rows. Greek, diplos, double, and taxis, a rank, from the arrangement of the seeds.

12. CAPSELLA (p. 118)

Annual herbs, with rosette and stem leaves. Flowers small, white. Pods flattened, triangular or heart-shaped, broadest at the tip. Partition narrow, valves boat-shaped, seeds many, small. Latin, capsula, a box, from the shape of the pod.

13. CORONOPUS (p. 121)

Annual, prostrate herbs. Leaves much divided. Flowers minute, white. Racemes opposite the leaves. Pods consist of 2 rounded, seed-like portions with 1 seed in each, joined side by side and separating without opening. Greek, korone, a crow, pous, a foot, from the shape of the foliage.

14. LEPIDIUM (p. 121)

Branched annuals or perennials. Leaves entire or divided, hairy or glabrous. Flowers small, numerous, white. Pod more or less oval, more or less flattened, often winged; partition narrow; 1 seed in each division. Greek, lepis, a scale, from the shape of the pods.

15. THLASPI (p. 121)

Annual or perennial herbs. Leaves undivided. Flowers white. Pods oval with a prominent wing; partition narrow; more than 1 seed in each division. Greek, thlao, to flatten, from the shape of the pod.

16. TEESDALIA (p. 121)

Small annuals with a rosette of notched leaves. Flowers white. 2 petals longer than the other 2. Pod round, notched, with 2 seeds in each division. Called after Teesdale, an English botanist.

17. CRAMBE (p. 122)

Large coarse perennials. Leaves large, notched. Flowers white in large inflorescences. The pod does not open; it consists of 2 joints, the upper with a single seed, the lower forming a stalk. Greek, krambos, dry, the plants growing in sandy places.

18. CAKILE (p. 122)

Seashore annuals with fleshy leaves. Flowers white or purple. Pod not opening, 2-jointed; upper joint with 1 seed, falling off; lower joint remaining on stalk and often without a seed. From the Arabic name, kakeleh.

19. RAPHANUS (p. 122)

Tall coarse annuals or biennials. Lower leaves deeply divided. Flowers yellow, white, or lilac. Pods divided into 2 or more 1-seeded joints. Greek, raphanos, radish.

RESEDACEAE. MIGNONETTE FAMILY (p. 122)

RESEDA (Only British genus)

Annual or biennial herbs. Leaves alternate, with stipules, often divided. Flowers irregular, small, numerous in conspicuous racemes; bracts present. Sepals 4–7 united, unequal. Petals 4–7 free, unequal, fringed. Stamens many on a nectar disk. Carpels 2–6 united superior, the ovary open at the top. Fruit a capsule with 1 compartment and several rows of seeds on the walls. Latin, resedare, to allay, from supposed medicinal qualities.

CISTACEAE. ROCK-ROSE FAMILY (p. 125)

HELIANTHEMUM (Only British genus)

Small shrubs or herbs. Leaves opposite, entire, with or without stipules. Flowers regular, in terminal racemes. Sepals 5, free, 2 smaller than the others. Petals 5, free. Stamens many. Carpels 3, united, superior; style single. Fruit a capsule opening by 3 valves with 3 rows of seeds on the walls. Greek, helios, sun, and anthemon, flower.

VIOLACEAE. VIOLET FAMILY (p. 125)

VIOLA (Only British genus)

Annual or perennial herbs. Leaves alternate, with stipules. Flowers irregular, solitary, with 2 small bracteoles on the stalk. Sepals 5, united, each with a backward projection. Petals 5, free, unequal, the lower with a spur. Stamens 5 with short, broad stalks, more or less united; the 2 lower with nectar-producing spurs projecting into the spur of the petal. Carpels 3, united, superior. Style single. Fruit a capsule opening by 3 valves, with 3 rows of seeds on the walls. The Latin name.

POLYGALACEAE.　MILKWORT FAMILY (p. 129)

POLYGALA (Only British genus)

Herbs or shrubs with alternate or opposite, entire leaves, without stipules. Flowers irregular, in racemes. Sepals 5, of which 2 are large and petal-like, free. Petals 3 or 5 free, the lower large, fringed and folded to form a keel enclosing the stamens and ovary. Stamens 8, united in 2 groups. Carpels 2, united, superior; style single; stigma spoon-shaped. Fruit a pod with 2 chambers and 1 seed in each. Greek, polus, many, and gala, milk, from its effect on cows. ∴

FRANKENIACEAE.　SEA-HEATH FAMILY (p. 129)

FRANKENIA (Only British genus)

Small shrubs or herbs. Leaves small, simple, narrow, with margins rolled back; opposite, but apparently in tufts since they bear very short, leafy branches in their axils. Flowers regular, solitary. Sepals 4–6, united. Petals 4–6, free. Stamens about 6. Carpels usually 3, united, superior. Fruit a capsule with 1 chamber, 3 rows of seeds on the walls, opening by valves, enclosed in the calyx. Called after the Swedish botanist, Franken.

CARYOPHYLLACEAE.　CAMPION FAMILY (p. 129)

Herbs. Leaves entire, opposite at the swollen nodes; stipules usually absent. Flowers regular. Sepals 4–5, free or united. Petals 4–5, free. Stamens 8–10. Carpels 3–5, united and superior. Styles 2–5. Ovary with a single chamber, sometimes partitioned at the base. Fruit a capsule opening by apical teeth, usually with numerous seeds attached to a central column.

A. Stipules absent:
  (a) Sepals united
    1. Styles 2　　　　　　　　　　　　　　　　DIANTHUS, **1**
    2. Styles 3　　　　　　　　　　　　　　　　SILENE, **2**
    3. Styles 4 or 5　　　　　　　　　　　　　LYCHNIS, **3**
  (b) Sepals free
    1. Petals notched　　　　　CERASTIUM, **4** or STELLARIA, **5**
    2. Petals entire　　　　　　　SAGINA, **7** or ARENARIA, **6**
B. Membranous stipules present:
  (a) Flowers pink　　　　　　　　　　　　SPERGULARIA, **9**
  (b) Flowers white　　　　　　　　　　　　SPERGULA, **8**

1. DIANTHUS (p. 129)

Annual or perennial herbs with narrow leaves. Calyx with 5 teeth and surrounded at the base by 2 or more sepal-like bracts. Petals toothed or fringed. Styles 2. Capsule on a stalk and opening by 4 teeth. Seeds flat. From the Greek dios, divine, and anthos, a flower.

2. SILENE (p. 130)

Annual or perennial herbs. Flowers usually in loose, terminal cymes. Calyx inflated, with 5 teeth. Petals with 2 scales at the mouth of the corolla tube. Capsules opening by 6 teeth. Styles 3. Perhaps from the Greek, silene, the moon, the flowers of some opening at night.

3. LYCHNIS (p. 133)

Annual or perennial with the same floral characters as Silene, from which genus it is distinguished by the possession of 5 styles. Greek, luchnos, a torch, from the flower colour.

4. CERASTIUM (p. 133)

Small, softly hairy annual or perennial herbs. Sepals usually 5, free. Petals usually 5, notched; sometimes absent. Stamens usually 5 or 10. 5 small nectaries at base of stamens. Capsule nearly cylindrical, often bent and projecting beyond the calyx, opening by short teeth. Greek, keras, a horn, from the shape of the capsule.

5. STELLARIA (p. 134)

Annual or perennial herbs, usually glabrous. Flowers in loose cymes. Sepals 5, free. Petals 5, deeply notched. Stamens 10, sometimes fewer. Styles usually 3. Capsule ovoid, opening to half-way down by 6 teeth. Latin, stella, a star, from the flower shape.

6. ARENARIA (p. 137)

Small annuals or perennials usually with narrow glabrous leaves. Sepals 5, free. Petals 5, entire. Stamens usually 10. Styles usually 3. Capsule opening by 3 or 6 teeth. Latin, arena, sand, some species growing in sandy places.

7. SAGINA (p. 137)

Small, annual or perennial, often tufted, herbs with awl-shaped leaves. Sepals 4–5, free. Petals 4–5 or absent. Stamens 4 or 10. Styles 4–5. Latin, sagina, fattening, a plant formerly called this having been used as fodder.

8. SPERGULA (p. 138)

Annual herbs with forked branches. Leaves apparently in clusters with small membranous stipules fused in pairs. Flowers white, in leafless cymes. Petals and sepals 5. Stamens usually 5. Styles 5. Capsule opening by 5 valves. Seeds many, flattened, with a rim. Latin, spargo, I spread, referring to the abundant seeds.

9. SPERGULARIA (p. 138)

Small prostrate herbs. Leaves apparently tufted, with membranous stipules. Flowers pink; sepals and petals 5. Styles 3. Capsules opening by 3 valves; seeds often winged. The name is formed from Spergula.

PORTULACACEAE. BLINKS FAMILY (p. 141)

Herbs with opposite, glabrous, entire leaves. Flowers regular. Sepals 2, free. Petals 5, free or united. Stamens 3 or 5. Carpels 3, united and superior; styles 3. Fruit a capsule with 1 chamber, opening by 3 valves, with 3 seeds on a central knob.

A. Land plants   CLAYTONIA, **1**
B. Plants of wet places   MONTIA, **2**

1. CLAYTONIA (p. 141)

Herbs, rather fleshy. Petals 5. Stamens 5, opposite and united to the petals. Called after Clayton, an American botanist.

2. MONTIA (p. 141)

A small aquatic plant with inconspicuous flowers, usually solitary in the leaf axils. The 5 petals are united and the corolla is split down one side. Stamens, 3. Called after Monti, an Italian botanist.

HYPERICACEAE. ST. JOHN'S-WORT FAMILY (p. 141)

HYPERICUM (Only British genus)

Herbs or shrubs with opposite leaves, often with small glands seen as clear dots when held to the light; stipules o. Flowers regular, usually in conspicuous panicles (cymose). Sepals 5, free or united at the base. Petals 5, free. Stamens many, united at the base in 3 or 5 bundles. Carpels 3 or 5, united and superior; styles 3 or 5. Fruit usually a capsule, more or less divided into 3 or 5 chambers, with numerous ovules on the walls or partitions, opening by valves. Greek, hyperikon, a plant name used by Dioscorides.

MALVACEAE. MALLOW FAMILY (p. 142)

Coarse herbs with alternate, palmate leaves; stipules falling early. Flowers regular. Sepals 5, united, with 3 or more sepal-like bracts just below. Petals 5, free. Stamens many, united in a tube. Carpels many, united, superior, separating in the fruit into 1-seeded portions; styles as many as the carpels.

A. Bracts 5 or more   ALTHAEA, **1**
B. Bracts 3, free   MALVA, **3**
C. Bracts 3, united   LAVATERA, **2**

1. ALTHAEA (p. 142)

Herbs with large, lobed leaves. Bracts 5 or more, united. Greek, althein, to heal, in allusion to medicinal properties.

2. LAVATERA (p. 142)

Herbs with large, lobed leaves. Bracts 3, united, much larger than the sepals. Called after the Swiss naturalists Lavater.

3. MALVA (p. 142)

Erect or prostrate herbs with lobed or cut, hairy or glabrous, leaves. Bracts 3, small, separate, inserted on the calyx. Greek, malake, soft, in allusion to soothing medicinal properties.

LINACEAE. FLAX FAMILY (p. 145)

Herbs with entire, usually alternate leaves. Flowers regular. Sepals and petals 5, free. Stamens 5, free, with 5 small teeth between them. Carpels 5, united, superior; styles 5, free. Fruit a 5-chambered capsule breaking into 5 portions each of which splits open; in each chamber there are 2 flat seeds which are sometimes partially separated by a partition. Radiola is exceptional with 4 sepals, &c. Nectaries 5 at the base of the stamens.

A. Parts of flower in fours [RADIOLA]
B. Parts of flower in fives LINUM, 1

1. LINUM (p. 145)

Herbs with the characters of the family; parts of flower in fives; capsule with 5 complete and 5 nearly complete partitions. The Latin name.

GERANIACEAE. CRANE'S-BILL FAMILY (p. 145)

Herbs with opposite or alternate leaves, usually lobed, cut or compound; stipules present. Flowers regular or irregular; sepals usually 5, free. Petals usually 5, free, twisted in the bud. Stamens 5 or 10, often united below. Carpels 5, united and superior; styles 5, united in a long column. Fruit breaks up into 5 portions each with 1 seed, and tipped with the persistent style which forms an awn; the awn twists up when dry and uncurls when wet, and these movements probably assist in dispersing and burying the seeds. Nectaries 5 at the base of the stamens.

A. Leaves palmate GERANIUM, 1
B. Leaves pinnate ERODIUM, 2

1. GERANIUM (p. 145)

Herbs with opposite, usually palmately lobed leaves; nodes often markedly swollen. Flowers solitary or in twos. Stamens 10. Awns curling outwards. Greek, geranos, a crane, from the form of the fruits.

2. ERODIUM (p. 146)

Prostrate herbs with alternate, pinnate leaves. 5 stamens and 5 sterile stalks. Awn of fruit twisting spirally. Greek, erodios, a heron, from the form of the fruit.

OXALIDACEAE. WOOD-SORREL FAMILY (p. 149)

OXALIS (Only British genus)

Herbs with compound leaves; stipules present or absent. Flowers regular. Sepals 5, free. Petals 5, free, twisted in the bud. Stamens 10, united below. Carpels 5, united, superior; styles 5. Fruit a capsule with 5 compartments, opening by 5 slits. Greek, oxus, acid, and halos, salt, from the taste.

BALSAMINACEAE. BALSAM FAMILY (p. 149)

IMPATIENS (Only genus)

Herbs with undivided leaves. Flowers irregular. Sepals 3 or 5, free, the upper produced into a long spur, coloured. Petals 3. Stamens 5, the anthers united. Carpels 5, united and superior. Fruit a pod with 5 chambers, each with many seeds, opening explosively by elastic valves. Latin, impatiens, impatient, from the explosive fruits.

CELASTRACEAE. SPINDLE-TREE FAMILY (p. 149)

EUONYMUS (Only British genus)

Shrubs or trees. Leaves undivided; stipules small and falling. Flowers regular, inconspicuous. Sepals 4, united. Petals 4, free. Stamens 4, alternating with the petals and, with them, set on the edge of a broad, ring-like nectar disk. Carpels 4, united, superior. Fruit a 4-lobed capsule with 4 chambers, each with 1 seed, opening by 4 valves. Perhaps from Euonyme, the mother of the Furies, the fruit being poisonous.

RHAMNACEAE. BUCKTHORN FAMILY (p. 149)

RHAMNUS (Only British genus)

Shrubs or trees. Leaves undivided alternate; stipules small. Flowers regular, inconspicuous, in small inflorescences in the leaf axils. Sepals 4–5, free, set on a tube surrounding the ovary. Petals 4–5, free, or absent; along with and opposite the stamens on the top of the tube. Carpels 3, united, superior. Fruit a berry with 3 compartments, each with 1 seed. From the Greek name, rhamnos.

ACERACEAE. MAPLE FAMILY (p. 150)

ACER (Only British genus)

Trees. Leaves opposite, palmate; stipules absent. Flowers regular, inconspicuous. Petals and sepals usually 5. Stamens usually 8, inserted on a broad, ring-like nectar disk surrounding the ovary. Carpels 2, united, superior. Fruit breaks up into 2, 1-seeded portions, each with a large wing. The Latin name.

LEGUMINOSAE. PEA FAMILY (p. 150)

Herbs, shrubs, or trees. Leaves alternate, usually compound, with stipules.
Flowers irregular. Sepals 5, united. Petals 5, free; the 2 lower, with their
lower margins held firmly together by interlocking hairs, forming a keel, the
2 lateral forming wings, and the upper a more or less erect standard. Stamens
10, the filaments all united to form a tube, or 1 free; set on the cup-shaped
base of the calyx. Carpel 1, superior. Fruit a pod with seeds along 1 edge,
usually splitting along both edges into 2 valves.

A. Shrubs:
   (*a*) Leaves simple   GENISTA, **1** or ULEX, **2**
   (*b*) Leaves, at least some, 3-foliate
     1. Flowers yellow   CYTISUS, **3**
     2. Flowers pink   ONONIS, **4**
B. Herbs:
   (*a*) Leaves 3-foliate
     1. Pods enclosed in calyx   TRIFOLIUM, **6**
     2. Pods longer than calyx, straight   LOTUS, **8**, [MELILOTUS,
                                          TRIGONELLA]
     3. Pods longer than calyx, curved   MEDICAGO, **5**
   (*b*) Leaves with 2 or more than 3 leaflets
     1. Leaves ending in a tendril or small point   VICIA, **12** or LATHYRUS, **13**
     2. Leaves ending in a leaflet
       I. Pod beaded or notched   ORNITHOPUS, **10** or HIPPOCREPIS, **11**
      II. Pod not beaded   ANTHYLLIS, **7** or ASTRAGALUS, **9**
   (*c*) Leaves apparently simple or replaced by a tendril   LATHYRUS, **13**

1. GENISTA (p. 150)

Low shrubs, sometimes with spines; leaves simple; stipules very small or absent.
Calyx divided into 2 lips, the upper with 2 long, and the lower with 3 short,
teeth, green. Stamens all united. Pod much longer than calyx with several
seeds. The Latin name.

2. ULEX (p. 150)

Very spiny shrubs. The stout, often branched, spines are branches; the flat, soft
spines are the leaves; on seedlings 3-foliate leaves may be found. Calyx
yellow, deeply divided into 2 lips, the upper with 2, the lower with 3 minute
teeth. Stamens all united. Pods little longer than calyx. A Latin plant name.

3. CYTISUS (p. 153)

Shrubs with stiff, erect, green, ribbed branches. Leaves small, 3-foliate or simple.
Calyx 2-lipped with minute teeth. Stamens all united. Pod large, flat, with
many seeds. From kytisos, a Greek plant name.

4. ONONIS (p. 153)

Low shrubs with some 3-foliate leaves, stipules leafy; hairy. Flowers in the axils
of foliage leaves. Calyx with 5 long teeth. Keel pointed. All stamens united,
filaments swollen above. Pod short, swollen. The Greek name.

5. Medicago (p. 153)

Herbs with 3-foliate leaves and leafy stipules fused with the leaf-stalks. Calyx 5-toothed. Upper stamen free. Pod with few seeds, much curved or coiled, not opening, longer than the calyx. From Media, the country of origin.

6. Trifolium (p. 154)

Herbs with 3-foliate leaves and leafy stipules united with the leaf-stalks. Flowers in dense heads. Calyx 5-toothed. Upper stamen free. Pod with few seeds, not opening, straight, remaining enclosed in the calyx and sometimes in the corolla, which withers but does not fall. Latin, tres, three, and folium, a leaf, from the three leaflets.

7. Anthyllis (p. 158)

Herbs with pinnate leaves and small stipules. Flowers in crowded heads, a lobed, leafy bract below each head. Calyx swollen, enclosing the pod. Stamens all united. Greek, anthos, a flower, and iulos, down, from the downy flower-heads.

8. Lotus (p. 158)

Herbs with 3-foliate leaves, and large leafy stipules. Flowers in long-stalked heads in the leaf axils, with 3-foliate bracts below the heads. Calyx not swollen. Upper stamen free. Pods much longer than the calyx, straight, cylindrical. Greek, lotos, a name applied to various plants.

9. Astragalus (p. 161)

Herbs with pinnate leaves and small stipules. Flowers in heads or racemes, long-stalked in the leaf-axils or apparently terminal; no leafy bracts. Pods shorter or longer than the calyx, which is not swollen. Upper stamen free. Greek, astragalos, knuckle-bone, from the shape of the pods.

10. Ornithopus (p. 161)

Small herbs with pinnate leaves and minute stipules. Flowers small in small heads in the leaf axils. Pod much longer than the calyx, curved, constricted between the seeds into a number of beads into which it breaks up when ripe. Greek, ornis, a bird, and pous, foot, from the appearance of the pods.

11. Hippocrepis (p. 161)

Herbs with pinnate leaves and small stipules. Flowers yellow, in stalked heads in the leaf axils. Upper stamen free. Pod much longer than the calyx, flattened and bent into several horseshoe-shaped segments into which it breaks when ripe. Greek, hippos, a horse, and krepis, a shoe, from the shape of the pods.

12. Vicia (p. 162)

Herbs, often climbing, with pinnate leaves and half-arrow-shaped stipules; leaflets usually numerous and small; the leaf ends in a branched tendril or small point. Upper stamen usually free. Pod usually many-seeded and longer than the calyx. Style not flattened below the stigma. The Latin name for the tare.

13. LATHYRUS (p. 165)

A genus of herbs resembling Vicia, *distinguished by the style, which is flattened below the stigma; many species have fewer and larger leaflets and so have a distinctive appearance.* Lathyros, *a Greek plant name.*

ROSACEAE. ROSE FAMILY (p. 166)

Herbs, shrubs, or trees. Leaves alternate, often divided or compound, with stipules. Flowers regular. Sepals 4 or 5, free, or united; in some genera the calyx is double with 5 smaller lobes outside and alternating with the sepals. Petals 4 or 5 free. Stamens usually numerous, 10–30 (1 in Alchemilla arvensis). Carpels 1 to many, free or united, superior or inferior. The axis of the flower is usually flattened or forms round the carpels a cup with stamens, &c., on its rim, secreting nectar inside. Fruit a collection of achenes or a fleshy fruit of various kinds.

A. Trees or shrubs:
  (*a*) Leaves undivided, at most toothed
    1. Fleshy stone fruit, 1 seed   PRUNUS, 1
    2. Fleshy fruit, several seeds   PYRUS, **12**, [COTONEASTER]
    3. Dry fruit   DRYAS, 4
  (*b*) Leaves lobed
    1. Plant spiny   CRATAEGUS, 13
    2. Plant not spiny   PYRUS, 12
  (*c*) Leaves compound
    1. Plant with prickles
      I. Fruits many, fleshy   RUBUS, 3
      II. Fruit apparently single, fleshy   ROSA, 11
    2. Plant without prickles
      I. Fruit fleshy   PYRUS, 12
      II. Fruit dry   POTENTILLA, 1
B. Herbs:
  (*a*) Leaves simple, lobed
    1. Flowers yellow or reddish   GEUM, 5
    2. Flowers greenish   ALCHEMILLA, 8
    3. Flowers white, fruit dry   DRYAS, 4
    4. Flowers white, fruit fleshy   RUBUS, 3
  (*b*) Leaves compound or deeply cut
    1. Flowers greenish   ALCHEMILLA, 8
    2. Flowers yellow
      I. Calyx single   AGRIMONIA, 9
      II. Calyx double   POTENTILLA, 7
    3. Flowers red or purple
      I. Calyx single   POTERIUM, 10
      II. Calyx double   POTENTILLA, 7
    4. Flowers white
      I. Calyx single, fruit dry   SPIRAEA, 2
      II. Calyx single, fruit fleshy   RUBUS, 3
      III. Calyx double, fruit dry   POTENTILLA, 7
      IV. Calyx double, fruit fleshy FRAGARIA, 6

1. PRUNUS (p. 166)

Shrubs or trees. Leaves undivided, toothed; stipules small. Sepals, petals, and stamens on the rim of a cup round the single carpel. Stamens numerous. Fruit a drupe, that is a fleshy fruit with a hard stone surrounding the single seed. From the Latin prunus, *a plum tree.*

2. SPIRAEA (p. 169)

Herbs with pinnately compound leaves and small stipules. Flowers in showy, corymbs or panicles. Stamens numerous. Carpels 5 or more in a shallow cup. Fruit a collection of small pods. From speiraia, *a Greek plant name.*

3. RUBUS (p. 170)

Rambling shrubs with weak prickly stems and compound leaves (rarely herbs with lobed leaves). Stamens many. Carpels many, free, superior, on a knob in the centre of the flower. Each carpel develops into a small, fleshy stone-fruit and the collection of these on the central knob forms the familiar blackberry or rasp. The Latin name.

4. DRYAS (p. 170)

Prostrate, tufted perennials with simple leaves and membranous stipules. Flowers large, solitary. Sepals and petals 8-10. Stamens and carpels many. Fruit a collection of achenes; after flowering the style develops into a feathery awn. Greek, dryas, *a wood nymph.*

5. GEUM (p. 173)

Perennial herbs with irregularly pinnate leaves and large leafy stipules. Flowers few, in loose terminal cymes. Calyx with 5 small outer teeth. Stamens and carpels numerous, the latter free and superior. Fruit a collection of achenes on a central knob. After flowering the styles develop into stiff, hooked awns. The Latin name.

6. FRAGARIA (p. 173)

Perennial herbs with 3-foliate leaves and membranous stipules. Flowers in small cymes. Calyx double, the outer teeth nearly as large as the inner. Stamens and carpels many, the latter free and superior on a central knob. The fruit is a collection of achenes on a large fleshy knob which forms the 'berry'. Latin, fraga, *strawberries.*

7. POTENTILLA (p. 173)

Perennial herbs or shrubs. Leaves compound, or very deeply cut. Calyx double, the outer teeth not much smaller than the inner. Stamens and carpels numerous, the latter free and superior on a central knob. Fruit a collection of achenes on a dry knob. Latin, potens, *powerful, referring to medicinal properties.*

8. ALCHEMILLA (p. 177)

Annual or perennial herbs, with leaves palmately lobed or so deeply divided as to be almost compound; stipules large, sheathing. Flowers very small, greenish. Sepals 4, with 4 smaller outer teeth. Petals o. Stamens 1 or 4. Carpels few, free, superior. Fruit 1 or more achenes in a cup. Arabic, alkemelyeh, the name given to the drops of water collecting on the leaves which were used in alchemy.

9. AGRIMONIA (p. 177)

Erect herbs with pinnately compound leaves and leafy stipules. Flowers in terminal racemes. Flower axis forming a spiny cup with a thickened rim. Sepals 5. Petals 5. Stamens about 10. Carpels 2, free and superior. Fruit of 2 achenes in a cup. A Latin plant name.

10. POTERIUM (p. 178)

Upright herbs with pinnately compound leaves; leaflets stalked; stipules leafy. Flowers unisexual or hermaphrodite, in small, dense, terminal heads. Sepals 4. Petals o. Stamens 4 or many. Carpels 1 or 2, free and superior, but surrounded by the tube of the flower axis. Fruit usually a single achene enclosed in the leathery, somewhat winged tube. Greek, poterion, a cup, perhaps because used for flavouring liquours.

11. ROSA (p. 178)

Bushy shrubs, sometimes rambling, with prickly branches. Leaves pinnately compound, with leafy stipules united to the leaf-stalk. Flowers usually in small corymbs. Sepals and petals 5, along with the numerous stamens on the edge of the flask-shaped axis of the flower. Carpels many, free, superior, inside the flask, the styles protruding from its mouth and sometimes fused. Fruit a collection of achenes enclosed in the flask which becomes fleshy. The Latin name.

12. PYRUS (p. 178)

Trees with simple or compound leaves; stipules falling early. Flowers in corymbs. Sepals and petals 5. Stamens many. Carpels 2–5 united, inferior, and fused with the flower axis. In the fruit the carpels, each with two seeds, are separated by stiff membranous partitions (well seen in the apple) and surrounded by the fleshy axis. The Latin name for a pear.

13. CRATAEGUS (p. 181)

Shrubs or small trees with spiny branches. Leaves lobed. Floral structure as in Pyrus, but the carpels have stony walls. Greek, kratos, strength, from the hard wood.

SAXIFRAGACEAE.　SAXIFRAGE FAMILY (p. 181)

Herbs or shrubs. Leaves often palmately lobed, without stipules. Flowers regular. Sepals 5, united. Petals 5, free. Stamens 5 or 10. In one genus sepals 4, petals 0, stamens 8. Carpels 2 or 4, united, inferior or superior. Fruit a capsule with 1 chamber and ovules on the walls, or with 2 chambers and ovules on the partition, or a berry.

A. Petals 0　　　　　　　　　　　　　　　　　CHRYSOSPLENIUM, **2**
B. Petals 5
   (*a*) Leaves heart-shaped, entire　　　　　　PARNASSIA, **3**
   (*b*) Leaves of other shapes　　　　　　　　SAXIFRAGA, **1**

1. SAXIFRAGA (p. 181)

Herbs, often tufted. Flowers either solitary or in terminal cymes. Petals 5, and stamens 10, inserted on the rim of the flat or tubular axis, which is often more or less adherent to the ovary. Styles 2. Fruit a capsule with 2 chambers and many seeds, opening by 2 valves. Latin, saxum, a stone, and frangere, to break, as some species root in crevices of rock and break it up.

2. CHRYSOSPLENIUM (p. 182)

Small herbs. Sepals 4. Petals 0. Stamens 8. Ovary half inferior. Capsule with 1 chamber, opening by 2 valves. Greek, chrysos, golden, and splen, spleen, from the flower colour and medicinal properties.

3. PARNASSIA (p. 185)

Perennial herbs with glabrous leaves and solitary flowers. Sepals and petals 5. 5 fertile stamens, and 5 sterile stalks tipped with branched, glistening glands. Carpels 4; styles 4. Fruit a capsule with 1 chamber opening by 4 valves. Called after Mt. Parnassus.

RIBESACEAE.　CURRANT FAMILY (p. 185)

RIBES (Only genus)

Shrubs with alternate, usually palmately lobed leaves. Flowers regular, usually in racemes. Sepals, petals, and stamens 4 or 5. Ovary with 1 chamber, inferior. Fruit a berry; seeds many, in 2 rows. Arabic, ribas, a plant with acid juice.

CRASSULACEAE.　STONE-CROP FAMILY (p. 185)

Herbs with fleshy, usually alternate leaves. Flowers regular in terminal panicles or cymes. Sepals and petals usually 5 or 6, sometimes 3 or 10–20; sepals united, petals usually free. Stamens as many or twice as many as the petals. Carpels usually about 5, free and superior, each with a small yellow nectary scale at its base. Fruit a collection of pods.

A. Petals united in a tube   COTYLEDON, 1
B. Petals free
  (*a*) Leaves opposite   [TILLAEA]
  (*b*) Leaves alternate
    1. Petals 5–6   SEDUM, 2
    2. Petals 10–20   [SEMPERVIVUM]

1. COTYLEDON (p. 185)

Herbs with alternate leaves and flowers in a panicle. Corolla tubular, with 5 teeth. Stamens 10. Carpels 5. Greek, kotule, a cup, from the leaf-shape.

2. SEDUM (p. 185)

Annual or perennial herbs with fleshy leaves. Flowers in cymes or corymbs. Petals, sepals, and carpels usually 5 or 6; stamens twice as many; petals free. Latin, sedere, to sit, from the prostrate habit.

DROSERACEAE. SUNDEW FAMILY (p. 189)

DROSERA (Only British genus)

Perennial insectivorous plants. Leaves in a rosette, with prominent red, glandular hairs. Flowers regular, in racemes. Sepals and petals 5, free. Stamens 5. Carpels 3 or 4, united and superior. Fruit a capsule with 3 or 4 rows of seeds on the walls, opening by 3 or 4 valves. Greek, droseros, dew, from the glistening leaves.

HALORAGACEAE. MARE'S-TAIL FAMILY (p. 189)

Aquatic herbs with whorled or opposite leaves. Flowers minute, often unisexual. Sepals 2, 4, or 0, united. Petals 2, 4, or 0, free. Stamens 1 or 8. Carpels 1 or 4, united, inferior. Fruit breaking up into 1-seeded portions.

A. Leaves cut into fine segments   MYRIOPHYLLUM, 2
B. Leaves simple, whorled   HIPPURIS, 1
C. Leaves simple, opposite   CALLITRICHE, 3

1. HIPPURIS (p. 189)

Aquatic herbs with erect, hollow, jointed stems, bearing whorls of small leaves. Flowers minute, solitary in the leaf axils, consisting of a single stamen on the edge of a single carpel, with 1 style, or unisexual. Greek, hippos, a horse, and oura, a tail.

2. MYRIOPHYLLUM (p. 189)

Submerged aquatic plants, with whorled, very finely, pinnately divided leaves. Calyx 4-lobed. Male flowers usually with 8 stamens and 4 petals. Female flowers with no petals and 4 carpels. Greek, myrios, many, and phyllon, a leaf, from the appearance of the leaves.

3. CALLITRICHE (p. 189)

Perennial aquatics with opposite leaves. Flowers minute, unisexual, solitary in the leaf axils. Male flower of a single stamen and 2 bracts, female of a 4-ribbed ovary with 2 styles, breaking, when ripe, into four 1-seeded parts. Greek, kalos, beautiful, and trichos, a hair, supposedly from the fine leaves of some species.

LYTHRACEAE. LOOSESTRIFE FAMILY (p. 190)

Herbs. Leaves usually opposite, simple; stipules 0. Flowers regular, solitary, in the leaf axils or in terminal spikes. Sepals united in a tube with 4–6 teeth and an equal number of smaller outer teeth. Petals 4–6 or 0, free, on the rim of the calyx-tube, crumpled in the bud. Stamens as many or twice as many as the petals. Carpels usually 2, united, superior, but enclosed in the calyx tube. Style 1, with a small knob-like stigma. Fruit a capsule with 2 chambers and many seeds on the partition, opening by 2 valves.

A. Creeping aquatic   PEPLIS, **1**
B. Flowering shoots erect   LYTHRUM, **2**

1. PEPLIS (p. 190)

Aquatic herb with opposite, glabrous leaves. Flowers minute, solitary in the leaf axils. Petals minute, or 0. Stamens 6. Style very short. Capsule globular. Perhaps from the Greek peplion, the name of the true purslane.

2. LYTHRUM (p. 190)

Herbs with erect stems and usually opposite leaves. Flowers in leafy terminal spikes. Petals large, 4–6. Style long. Greek, luthron, blood, from the flower colour.

ONAGRACEAE. WILLOW-HERB FAMILY (p. 190)

Herbs with opposite or alternate, undivided leaves, without stipules. Flowers regular usually in terminal racemes. Sepals 2 or 4, united. Petals 2 or 4, free, and, with the 2–8 stamens, inserted on the calyx tube. Carpels 4, united inferior. Style 1; stigma simple or lobed. Fruit a capsule with 2–4 chambers, containing usually many seeds, and opened by 2–4 valves.

A. Flowers pink or purple   EPILOBIUM, **1**
B. Flowers yellow   [OENOTHERA]
C. Flowers white   CIRCAEA, **2**
D. Flowers green   [LUDWIGIA]

1. EPILOBIUM (p. 190)

Herbs with undivided leaves and terminal racemes of purple flowers. Petals 4. Stamens 8. Capsule long, slender, opening by 4 valves. Seeds small, numerous, with tufts of hair which aid in wind dispersal. Greek, epi, on, and lobion, a pod, from the position of the corolla.

2. Circaea (p. 193)

Herbs with opposite leaves. Flowers in terminal and axillary racemes. Sepals, petals, and stamens, 2. Called after Circe, the Greek enchantress.

CUCURBITACEAE. MARROW FAMILY (p. 193)

Bryonia (Only British genus)

Herbs, climbing by tendrils. Leaves alternate, palmately lobed, without stipules. Flowers regular, unisexual. Sepals and petals 5, united. Stamens 3, united. Carpels 3, united and inferior; stigmas 3. Fruit a berry with 3 chambers. Greek, bruo, to shoot up, from the rapid growth.

UMBELLIFERAE. PARSLEY FAMILY (p. 193)

Herbs with alternate leaves, often large and much cut. Leaf stalk often broad and sheathing at the base; no stipules. Flowers regular or somewhat irregular, usually small and white, in large showy compound umbels. There may be a whorl of bracts at the base of the main umbel and of small bracts or bracteoles at the base of the partial umbels. Sepals 5 or 0. Petals 5, free. Stamens 5, alternating with the petals. Carpels 2, united and inferior, crowned by a prominent nectar-disk and 2 styles. The fruit breaks up into two 1-seeded parts. Often aromatic, especially the fruits, from oils formed in internal ducts.

A. Flowers yellow:
  (a) Leaves entire   Bupleurum, 6
  (b) Leaves divided or compound
    1. Segments very narrow
      I. Segments tufted   Meum, 20
      II. Segments not tufted   Foeniculum, 16, [Peucedanum]
    2. Segments not very narrow
      I. Leaves pinnate   [Pastinaca]
      II. Leaves 2-pinnate   Carum, 8, [Silaus]
      III. Leaves 1- or 2-trifoliate   Smyrnium, 5

B. Flowers pink or tinged with blue or pink:
  (a) Leaves round   Hydrocotyle, 1
  (b) Leaves spiny   Eryngium, 2
  (c) Leaves divided, glabrous
    1. Fruit winged   Angelica, 22
    2. Fruit not winged   Ligusticum, 21
  (d) Leaves divided, hairy
    1. Fruit not spiny   Pimpinella, 11
    2. Fruit spiny
      I. Bracts large   Daucus, 24
      II. Bracts small or 0   Caucalis, 25

C. Flowers white:
  (a) Leaves hairy
    1. Fruit with beak   SCANDIX, **14** or CHAEROPHYLLUM, **15**
    2. Fruit with broad wing   HERACLEUM, **23**
    3. Fruit with sharp ridges   MYRRHIS, **13**
    4. Fruit with neither beak, wing, nor sharp ridges CHAEROPHYLLUM, **15**
  (b) Leaves glabrous
    1. Leaves with fine segments or leaflets
      I. Marsh plants   OENANTHE, **18** or APIUM, **7**
      II. Not marsh plants
        Bracteoles o   CONOPODIUM, **12**
        Bracteoles 3   AETHUSA, **19**
        Bracteoles many   CONIUM, **4** or CARUM, **8**
    2. Leaves with broad segments
      I. Fruit prickly   SANICULA, **3**
      II. Fruit winged   [PEUCEDANUM]
      III. Fruit neither winged nor prickly
        Bracts leafy   SIUM, **9**
        Bracts o   APIUM, **7** or AEGOPODIUM, **10**

1. HYDROCOTYLE (p. 193)

Creeping herbs with undivided leaves. Flowers in small, inconspicuous heads on leafless stalks. Carpels flattened, joined edge to edge. Calyx teeth small or absent. Greek, hudor, *water, and* kotule, *a cup, alluding to the station and the leaf shape.*

2. ERYNGIUM (p. 194)

Herbs with stout stems and spiny, glaucous leaves. Flowers in dense heads with spiny calyx teeth and bracts. Greek, eryngano, *referring to use as a cure for flatulence.*

3. SANICULA (p. 194)

Herbs with palmately divided leaves. Flowers in small, rounded heads arranged in open umbels. Fruits covered with hooked prickles. Latin, sano, *I heal, alluding to medicinal properties.*

4. CONIUM (p. 194)

Biennial herb with compound, much divided, glabrous leaves. Fruits small, somewhat compressed, each carpel with 5 prominent ribs. Stem spotted. From koneion, *the Greek name.*

5. SMYRNIUM (p. 194)

Biennials with stout stems and large, compound, sheathing leaves, with broad leaflets. Flowers yellow in compound umbels. Bracts few and small; calyx teeth absent. Fruit round, the halves round in section, each with 3 ridges. Greek, smurna, *myrrh, referring to the bitter taste.*

6. BUPLEURUM (p. 197)

Annual or perennial herbs with entire, glabrous leaves. Bracts usually large and leafy. Flowers yellow. Calyx teeth absent. Carpels with 5 angles or ridges. Greek, bous, ox, and pleuron, rib, perhaps from leaf shape, perhaps because used as a cure for cattle disease.

7. APIUM (p. 197)

Annual or perennial marsh plants with compound, glabrous leaves; stalks with membranous sheaths. Umbels often opposite the leaves; partial umbels with or without bracteoles. Fruit somewhat flattened, with 5 ridges on each half. The Latin name for celery.

8. CARUM (p. 197)

Biennial or perennial herbs. Leaves pinnately compound, the leaflets often much divided, glabrous. Flowers white or yellow. Petals with inturned points, often notched. Calyx teeth small or o. Carpels with 5 blunt ridges. From Caria, whence carroway was brought.

9. SIUM (p. 197)

Perennials of wet places with pinnately compound, glabrous leaves. Bracts and bracteoles many, leafy. Calyx teeth very small. Fruit somewhat compressed; carpels 5-ridged. From sion, the Greek name.

10. AEGOPODIUM (p. 198)

Perennials with glabrous, twice 3-foliate leaves. Bracts, bracteoles, and calyx teeth absent. Fruit somewhat flattened, carpels 5-ridged. Greek, aix, goat, and pous, foot, from the leaf shape.

11. PIMPINELLA (p. 198)

Perennials with pinnately compound, slightly hairy leaves. Bracts, bracteoles, and calyx teeth absent. Fruit somewhat flattened; carpels with 5 ridges. From pipinella, a medieval Latin plant name.

12. CONOPODIUM (p. 198)

Perennials with much cut, glabrous leaves. Flowers white. Bracts and bracteoles absent or few, calyx teeth absent. Fruit not flattened; carpels 5-ridged. Greek, konos, a cone, and pous, a foot, from the conical nectaries.

13. MYRRHIS (p. 198)

Perennials with much divided, softly hairy leaves. Bracts absent, bracteoles small. Calyx teeth o. Fruits very long, each carpel with 5 sharp ridges. A Greek plant name.

14. SCANDIX (p. 201)

Annuals with finely divided leaves. Bracteoles present; calyx teeth absent. Fruit not flattened, each carpel 5-ridged, with a slender beak about 6 times its own length. Greek, xandix, comb, from the appearance of the fruits.

15. CHAEROPHYLLUM (p. 201)

Annuals or perennials with hairy, twice pinnately compound leaves. Bracteoles present; calyx teeth 0. Umbels nodding in the bud. Fruit narrowly flask-shaped, with or without ridges, sometimes beaked. Greek, chairo, I rejoice, and phyllon, a leaf, from the bright green colour, or pleasant smell.

16. FOENICULUM (p. 201)

Perennials with very finely divided, glabrous leaves. Flowers yellow. Bracts, bracteoles, and calyx teeth absent. Fruit oval, carpels 5-ridged. Latin, foenum, hay, from the narrow leaves.

17. CRITHMUM (p. 201)

A fleshy, glabrous perennial, with much divided leaves. Bracts and bracteoles present; calyx teeth 0. Carpels joined by a broad face, 5-ridged. Greek, krithe, barley, perhaps from the shape of the fruits.

18. OENANTHE (p. 202)

Biennials or perennials of wet places. Leaves much divided, glabrous. Bracts and bracteoles present or not. Calyx teeth pointed. Carpels joined by a broad face, 5-ridged. Greek, oinos, wine, and anthos, flower, from the odour.

19. AETHUSA (p. 202)

Annual with finely divided, glabrous leaves. Flowers white. Bracteoles three; bracts and calyx teeth absent. Fruit somewhat flattened, carpels united by a very broad face, 5-ridged. Greek, aitho, I burn, variously supposed to refer to the shining leaves or to the taste.

20. MEUM (p. 202)

Perennial with very finely cut leaves, glabrous. Flowers yellowish. Bracts and calyx teeth absent, bracteoles present. Carpels united by a broad face, each with 5 ridges. From meon, a Greek plant name.

21. LIGUSTICUM (p. 202)

Perennials with glabrous, twice 3-foliate leaves. Bracts and bracteoles present; calyx teeth small. Fruit long, oval; carpels united by a broad face, each with 5 sharp ridges. From Liguria where one sort is found.

22. ANGELICA (p. 205)

Tall, glabrous perennials, with twice pinnate leaves. Bracts few, bracteoles small and narrow; calyx teeth absent. Fruit flattened, the carpels joined by a broad face, each with 5 ridges of which 2 are expanded into thin wings. Greek, angelos, an angel, from its curative properties.

23. HERACLEUM (p. 205)

Perennials with coarse, hairy leaves and stout, furrowed stems. Umbels large and close. Bracts few or o, bracteoles small; calyx teeth absent. Fruit much flattened, carpels united by a very broad face, each with 2 broad wings. Greek, herakles, either from its strong growth or because Hercules discovered its medicinal properties.

24. DAUCUS (p. 205)

Biennial herbs with finely divided, hairy leaves. Umbels close. Bracts and bracteoles large, divided, calyx teeth small or o. Fruit with rows of spines on the ridges. Greek, daukos, a name applied to similar plants.

25. CAUCALIS (p. 205)

Annuals with finely divided, hairy leaves. Bracts and bracteoles usually present, narrow; calyx teeth small or o. Fruits with spines on the ridges. Greek, kaukalis, a name for similar plants.

CORNACEAE. DOGWOOD FAMILY (p. 206)

CORNUS (Only British genus)

Herbs, shrubs, or trees, with opposite, undivided leaves; stipules o. Flowers small, regular, in small umbels. Calyx of 4 teeth. Petals 4, free. Stamens 4. Carpels 2, united and inferior. Fruit fleshy, with a 2-chambered stone. Latin, cornu, horn, from the hard wood.

CAPRIFOLIACEAE. HONEYSUCKLE FAMILY (p. 206)

Herbs, shrubs, trees, or climbers with opposite leaves, usually without stipules. Flowers regular or irregular in corymbs or small groups. Sepals and petals usually 5, united. Stamens 4, 5, or 10, inserted on the corolla. Carpels 2–5, united and inferior, crowned by the 5 calyx teeth. Fruit fleshy, with 1 or several seeds.

A. Corolla tube long
   (*a*) Climbers   LONICERA, **5**
   (*b*) Creeper   LINNAEA, **4**
B. Corolla tube short:
   (*a*) Leaves compound
      1. Flowers green   ADOXA, **1**
      2. Flowers white or pink   SAMBUCUS, **2**
   (*b*) Leaves at most lobed   VIBURNUM, **3**

1. ADOXA (p. 206)

Perennial herb with 3-foliate, glabrous leaves. Flowers in small terminal heads of 5; the terminal flower has 2 sepals, 4 petals, and 8 stamens; the 4 lateral flowers have 3 sepals, 5 petals, and 10 stamens. Styles short 3–5. Fruit green and somewhat fleshy. Greek, adoxos, inglorious.

2. Sambucus (p. 206)

Coarse herbs, shrubs, or trees, with pinnately compound leaves. Stems with very large, spongy pith. Flowers in showy corymbs or panicles. Calyx of 5 teeth. Corolla flat. Stamens 5. Styles very short, 3. Fruit fleshy with 3 small stones. Greek, sambuke, a musical instrument, the wood being used for making this.

3. Viburnum (p. 206)

Large shrubs with simple leaves; stipules small or absent. Flowers in corymbs. Calyx of 5 teeth. Corolla with short tube. Stamens 5. Styles 3, very short. Fruit fleshy with 1 stone. The Latin name.

4. Linnaea (p. 209)

Delicate, creeping shrub. Flowers stalked in pairs. Calyx of 5 large teeth. Corolla tubular, 5-lobed. Stamens 4. Ovary 3-chambered; style single, slender, with a knob-like stigma. Called after the Swedish naturalist Linnaeus, whose favourite flower it was.

5. Lonicera (p. 209)

Shrubs, usually twining. Leaves opposite, entire, without stipules. Flowers in small terminal heads. Calyx teeth small. Corolla irregular, with a long tube. Stamens 5. Style long with knob-like stigma. Fruit a berry with several seeds. Called after Lonicer, a German botanist.

RUBIACEAE. BEDSTRAW FAMILY (p. 209)

Herbs with undivided, whorled leaves, often roughly hairy. Flowers regular, small, in clusters, or panicles. Calyx absent or of 4–5 teeth. Petals 4–5 united. Stamens 4–5, on the corolla. Carpels 2, united and inferior. Fruit usually breaking up into 2 dry 1-seeded portions.

A. Fruit fleshy   RUBIA, **1**
B. Fruit dry
   (*a*) Calyx with 4 teeth   SHERARDIA, **4**
   (*b*) Calyx o
      1. Corolla with short tube   ASPERULA, **3**
      2. Corolla without tube   GALIUM, **2**

1. Rubia (p. 209)

Flowers in panicles, terminal and in the leaf axils. Calyx teeth o. Petals 5. Stamens 5. Fruit fleshy. Latin, ruber, red, giving a red dye.

2. Galium (p. 210)

Herbs with square stems, often weak and rambling. Calyx teeth o. Corolla with a short tube and 4 spreading petals. Fruit dry, breaking into 2 portions. Greek, gala, milk, some kinds curdling milk.

3. ASPERULA (p. 213)

Herbs with upright stems. Calyx teeth 0. Corolla funnel-shaped with a distinct tube. Petals and stamens 4. Latin, asper, rough, from the hairs.

4. SHERARDIA (p. 214)

Annual, differing from Asperula in having 4–6 distinct calyx teeth. Called after the botanist Sherard.

VALERIANACEAE. VALERIAN FAMILY (p. 214)

Perennial or annual herbs with opposite leaves, without stipules. Flowers irregular, in umbels or panicles. Calyx a small ring, usually developing into a crown of feathery hairs in the fruit. Corolla usually of 5 petals, united in a long tube, with a sac or spur at the base. Stamens 1 or 3. Carpels 3, united and inferior; only 1 develops a seed. Fruit a nutlet.

A. Corolla with long spur   [KENTRANTHUS]
B. Corolla without long spur
    (*a*) Upper leaves compound or divided   VALERIANA, **1**
    (*b*) Leaves undivided   VALERIANELLA, **2**

1. VALERIANA (p. 214)

Perennials with opposite leaves, those on the stem usually divided. Flowers in terminal corymbs or panicles, pink. Calyx becoming feathery in the fruit. Corolla pouched at the base, with 5 unequal lobes. Latin, valere, to be well, from medicinal properties.

2. VALERIANELLA (p. 214)

Annuals with entire, rarely toothed, leaves and very small flowers. Corolla tube not spurred. Petals equal. Fruit without pappus. Diminutive of Valeriana.

DIPSACEAE. TEASEL FAMILY (p. 217)

Herbs with opposite leaves, without stipules. Flowers irregular. Calyx a small cup on the top of the ovary, often with long teeth. Corolla tubular, with 4–5 petal-lobes, the outer larger. Stamens 4, free, on the corolla tube. Ovary inferior, with 1 seed and 1 long style. The flowers are massed in dense rounded or conical heads; the head is surrounded by a whorl of large bracts and each flower stands in the axil of a small bract; in addition a cup of united bracteoles surrounds the ovary and has the appearance of an outer calyx.

A. Bracts spiny   DIPSACUS, **1**
B. Bracts not spiny   SCABIOSA, **2**

1. DIPSACUS (p. 217)

Prickly, biennial herbs. Bracts long and spiny. Calyx forming a membranous cup on the top of the fruit. Petals 4. Greek, dipso, I thirst, from the water-filled cup at the leaf bases.

2. SCABIOSA (p. 217)

Perennials with entire or divided leaves and flowers in rounded heads. Bracts not spiny and not projecting beyond the flowers. Calyx forming a crown of teeth on the fruit. Petals 4–5. Latin, scabies, the plant having been used to cure skin diseases.

COMPOSITAE. DAISY FAMILY (p. 218)

Herbs with alternate or opposite, usually simple, leaves, without stipules. Flowers crowded in dense heads, on a flattened or conical receptacle, surrounded by 1 or more series of bracts. Flowers regular, or irregular. Calyx represented by small teeth or hairs on the apex of the ovary, or o. Petals 5, united; the corolla is either tubular with 5 lobes, equal or not, or it has a narrow tubular base widening into a long, strap-shaped portion, toothed at the tip. The flower head may consist of tubular flowers alone, or strap flowers alone, or it may have a central disk of tubular and a marginal ray of strap flowers; in the last case the ray flowers are often female or sterile, their presence adding to the visibility of the head. Stamens 5, inserted in the corolla tube, the anthers united in a tube. Carpels 2, united and inferior; style single, slender, forked, with 2 stigmas. Fruit a 1-seeded achene, often crowned by a hairy pappus developed from the calyx hairs.

A. Flower heads with distinct ray and disk flowers:
   (*a*) Ray flowers purple   ASTER, 4 or ERIGERON, 5
   (*b*) Ray flowers yellow
      1. Pappus of soft smooth hairs   SENECIO, 19
      2. Pappus of rough hairs   INULA, 9 or SOLIDAGO, 2
      3. Pappus o   CHRYSANTHEMUM, 12
   (*c*) Ray flowers white
      1. Leaves in a rosette   BELLIS, 3
      2. Leaves on the stems
         I. Receptacle with scales   ANTHEMIS, 13 or ACHILLEA, 11
        II. Receptacle without scales   MATRICARIA, 14 or
                                         CHRYSANTHEMUM, 12

B. Flowers all strap-shaped:
   (*a*) Pappus of simple hairs
      1. Fruit beaked
        I. Heads solitary   TARAXACUM, 32
        II. Heads many   LACTUCA, 33 or CREPIS, 28
      2. Fruits not beaked
        I. Plant hairy   HIERACIUM, 29
        II. Plant glabrous or nearly so   SONCHUS, 34 or CREPIS, 28

(b) Pappus of feathery hairs
   1. Flowering stems leafy
      I. Plant hairy   PICRIS, 27
      II. Plant glabrous   TRAGOPOGON, 35
   2. Flowering stems naked or with small scales
      I. Fruit with long beak   HYPOCHOERIS, 30
      II. Fruit with short beak or o   LEONTODON, 31
(c) No hairy pappus
   1. Flowers blue   CICHORIUM, 25
   2. Flowers yellow   LAPSANA, 26

C. Flowers all tubular or ray flowers quite inconspicuous
  (a) Leaves opposite
     1. Flowers purple   EUPATORIUM, 1
     2. Flowers yellow   BIDENS, 10
  (b) Leaves alternate
     1. Flowers yellow
       I. Flower-heads solitary   TUSSILAGO, 17
       II. Flower-heads numerous
          Pappus of rough hairs   INULA, 9 or ASTER, 4
          Pappus of smooth soft hairs   SENECIO, 19
          Pappus o   TANACETUM, 15
     2. Flowers purple or blue
       I. Pappus short or absent
          Bracts hooked   ARCTIUM, 21
          Bracts not hooked   CENTAUREA, 24
       II. Pappus of long simple or feathery hairs
          Bracts spiny   CARDUUS, 22
          Bracts not spiny   SERRATULA, 23 or PETASITES, 18
     3. Flower-heads brownish, yellowish, or greyish
       I. Heads large with spiny bracts   CENTAUREA, 24 or CARLINA, 20
       II. Heads small, bracts not spiny
          Leaves divided   ARTEMISIA, 16
          Leaves not divided   GNAPHALIUM, 8 or FILAGO, 7

1. EUPATORIUM (p. 218)

Herbs with opposite, deeply divided leaves and purplish flowers. Flowers all tubular in small heads. Receptacle without scales. Stigmas long, slender, standing out from the corolla. Pappus of simple, rough hairs. From Eupatorion, a Greek plant-name.

2. SOLIDAGO (p. 218)

Herbs with alternate, undivided leaves. Flowers yellow, in small heads with a ray of strap flowers, and a disk of tubular flowers. Anthers without tails. Receptacle without scales. Stigmas short and rather thick. Fruit ribbed, with a pappus of simple hairs. Perhaps from Latin, solidum, solid or whole, with reference to healing properties.

3. BELLIS (p. 218)

Perennials with rosette of simple leaves. Flower heads solitary, with ray and disk. Stigmas short and thick. Fruit flattened, without pappus. Latin, bellus, *fair.*

4. ASTER (p. 218)

Perennials with alternate, undivided leaves. Flowers in small heads, usually with a purplish ray and a yellow disk. Bracts green. Receptacle pitted. Stigmas pointed. Fruits flattened, with a pappus of many rows of simple hairs. Latin, aster, *a star, from the flower form.*

5. ERIGERON (p. 221)

Like Aster, from which it differs in possessing very numerous narrow, or purplish ray flowers and many narrow bracts. Greek, eri, *early, and* geron, *hoar, from the downy pappus.*

6. ANTENNARIA (p. 221)

Perennials with downy, undivided leaves. Flowers all tubular, in small heads; male and female flowers on separate plants; pink or white. Bracts in several series, the inner green at the base, with a white expanded membranous tip. Pappus of 1 row of simple hairs. Fruit rounded. Medieval Latin, antenna, *a feeler, from the appearance of the pappus hairs.*

7. FILAGO (p. 221)

Small annuals with woolly, alternate, entire leaves. Receptacle scaly. Bracts in several series, downy, with membranous margins. Flower heads in clusters, numerous and very small. Flowers few, with tubular corolla, which, in the marginal flowers, is no thicker than a hair. Pappus of rough simple hairs. Latin, filum, *a thread, from the hairy appearance.*

8. GNAPHALIUM (p. 221)

Annuals or perennials, downy, with entire leaves. Flower-heads small, clustered, grey or brown. Bracts in several rows, often with membranous brown or yellow tips. Flowers all tubular, the outer with thread-like corollas. Receptacle naked. Pappus of 1 row of simple hairs. Greek, gnaphalon, *wool.*

9. INULA (p. 222)

Erect herbs with alternate, undivided leaves. Flower-heads small or large, in a terminal corymb or panicle, with a ray of strap-shaped flowers, sometimes inconspicuous, and a disk of tubular flowers, yellow. Anthers with tails. Receptacle without scales. Bracts in several series, not membranous. Pappus a circle of simple, rough hairs, sometimes with an outer ring of minute scales. Perhaps a corruption of Greek, helios, *the sun, from the appearance of the flowers.*

10. BIDENS (p. 222)

Annual with opposite, toothed or divided leaves, glabrous. Flower-heads with or without ray flowers. Receptacle with a scale to each flower. Bracts in several series, leafy. Fruit flattened, ridged. Pappus of 2–4, stiff, barbed spines. Latin, bis, *twice, and* dens, *a tooth, from the two pappus bristles.*

11. ACHILLEA (p. 225)

Perennials with alternate, toothed or compound leaves. Flower-heads small, in terminal corymbs; ray white or pink, disk yellowish. Bracts in several series, green, sometimes with membranous margins. Receptacle with scales. Pappus 0. Called after Achilles.

12. CHRYSANTHEMUM (p. 225)

Annuals or perennials with alternate, toothed or divided leaves. Flower-heads large, with yellow disk and white or yellow ray of many, large, strap-shaped flowers. Bracts in several series, green, with membranous margins. Receptacle without scales. Fruit ribbed, sometimes with a small ring, but without pappus. Greek, chrysos, gold, and anthos, a flower.

13. ANTHEMIS (p. 226)

Aromatic herbs with finely cut, alternate leaves. Flower-heads large, with white ray and yellow disk. Bracts in several series, with membranous margins. Receptacle conical with large, membranous scales. Pappus 0. Greek, anthos, a flower.

14. MATRICARIA (p. 226)

Like Anthemis, from which it differs in the absence of scales on the receptacle. Latin, matrix, the womb, referring to medicinal properties.

15. TANACETUM (p. 226)

Aromatic perennials with much cut, alternate leaves. Flower-heads small, rounded, with a yellow disk and no ray. Bracts in several series, with membranous margins. Receptacle without scales. Pappus 0. Etymology obscure.

16. ARTEMISIA (p. 226)

Shrubby, aromatic perennials with alternate, cut leaves. Heads very small, ovoid, without rays. Bracts in 1–2 series, with membranous margins. Receptacle without scales. Pappus 0. A Greek plant-name.

17. TUSSILAGO (p. 229)

Perennials with large, rounded leaves coming up after the flowers. Flower-heads solitary, with yellow disk and yellow ray of many series of narrow, strap-shaped flowers. Bracts in 1 series. Receptacle naked. Pappus of many rings of fine hairs. Latin, tussis, a cough, for the cure of which it is used.

18. PETASITES (p. 229)

Perennials with large, rounded leaves coming up after the flowers. Flower-heads white or purple, in massive panicles, without rays and with either male or female flowers; male flowers tubular, female tubular but very small and narrow. Bracts in 1–2 series. Receptacle without scales. Pappus of many soft hairs. Greek, petasos, a broad-brimmed hat, from the leaf shape.

19. SENECIO (p. 229)

Herbs with alternate, often divided leaves. Flower-heads with yellow disk and yellow ray of female flowers, the ray sometimes small or absent. Bracts in 1 series, sometimes with a 2nd series of smaller ones outside, green or with brown tips. Receptacle without scales. Fruits ridged. Pappus of many rings of soft, simple hairs. Latin, senex, an old man, from the hoary pappus.

20. CARLINA (p. 230)

Biennial with alternate, spiny leaves. Flower-heads large, few. Flowers all tubular, purple. Outer bracts leafy, spiny, inner with long, narrow, membranous tips. Receptacle with membranous scales. Fruit hairy. Pappus of 1 ring of feathery hairs. Called after Charlemagne.

21. ARCTIUM (p. 230)

Biennials with coarse, alternate leaves. Heads many, round. Flowers all tubular, purple. Receptacle bristly. Bracts numerous, in many series, each narrowed into a long, hooked spine. Pappus of short, stiff hairs. Greek, arktos, a bear, the plant being coarse and rough.

22. CARDUUS (p. 230)

Biennials or perennials with alternate, spiny leaves. Heads rounded, or urn-shaped, purple. Bracts in many series, leafy and often spiny. Receptacle bristly. Flowers all tubular. Pappus of abundant simple or feathery hairs, easily broken off. A Latin name for the thistle.

23. SERRATULA (p. 233)

Perennial with alternate, divided leaves. Heads numerous. Flowers all tubular, purple; corolla regular. Bracts in many series, the inner with membranous tips. Receptacle with scales. Fruit flattened, ridged, glabrous. Pappus of many series of simple hairs, the outer shorter. Latin, serra, a saw, from the toothed leaves.

24. CENTAUREA (p. 233)

Annuals or perennials with simple or divided alternate leaves. Bracts in many series, with membranous, fringed or spiny tips. Flowers all tubular, the outer often sterile, corolla irregular. Pappus of short bristles or o. Called after the Centaurs.

25. CICHORIUM (p. 234)

Perennials with alternate, cut leaves and milky juice. Bracts in 2 series, green, the outer smaller and toothed. Flowers all strap-shaped, blue. Pappus of small scales. From kichoré, a Greek plant-name.

26. LAPSANA (p. 237)

Annual with alternate lobed leaves and milky juice. Flower-heads small, yellow. Bracts green in 2 series, the outer very small. Fruit without a beak or pappus. From lapsané, a Greek plant-name.

27. PICRIS (p. 237)

Annuals or biennials with alternate, toothed, rough leaves and milky juice. Flowers all strap-shaped, yellow. Bracts green, in 2 series. Fruit curved, rough, ridged. Pappus of many feathery hairs, easily falling off. Greek, pikros, *bitter, from the taste.*

28. CREPIS (p. 237)

Annuals, biennials, or perennials, often with cut leaves and with milky juice. Heads numerous, small. Flowers all strap-shaped, yellow. Bracts in 2 series, the inner numerous, the outer fewer and smaller. Fruit ridged with or without a beak. Pappus of abundant, simple, silky hairs, usually white, easily detached. From krepis, a Greek plant-name.

29. HIERACIUM (p. 237)

Perennials with alternate, hairy leaves, toothed or not, and milky juice. Flowers yellow, all strap-shaped. Bracts in about 2 series, the outer smaller, green. Fruit not beaked. Pappus of 1 row of stiff, brittle, brownish hairs. This genus is extremely variable and over 100 species native to Britain have been described; the majority can be distinguished only by specialists. Greek, hierax, *a hawk, perhaps because it grows about cliffs.*

30. HYPOCHOERIS (p. 238)

Annuals or perennials with leaf rosettes, naked flowering shoots, and milky juice. Flowers yellow, all strap-shaped. Bracts in many series, green. Receptacle with scales. At least some of the fruits with a long beak, crowned with a pappus of feathery hairs. From hypochoiris, a Greek plant-name.

31. LEONTODON (p. 238)

Perennial, with leaf rosettes, naked flower stems and milky juice. Flowers all strap-shaped, yellow. Bracts green, in several series, the outer smaller. Receptacle without scales. Pappus of abundant feathery hairs. Fruit not beaked. Greek, leon, *lion, and* odous, *tooth, from the toothed leaves.*

32. TARAXACUM (p. 238)

Perennials with leaves in rosettes, naked, hollow flowering stems and milky juice. Flowers all strap-shaped, yellow. Bracts in 2 series, the inner upright, the outer recurved, green. Receptacle without scales. Fruit tapering to a slender beak, crowned by the pappus of abundant, simple, silky hairs. A corruption of the Arabic name.

33. LACTUCA (p. 241)

Annuals and perennials with alternate, usually lobed, nearly glabrous leaves, and milky juice. Heads small. Flowers all strap-shaped, yellow. Bracts in 2 series, the inner very long and narrow, the outer short. Fruit with a beak, crowned by the pappus of very fine, simple, silky hairs. Latin, lac, milk, from the milky juice.

34. SONCHUS (p. 241)

Annual or perennial, succulent plants, with alternate, toothed or cut leaves and milky juice. Flowers all strap-shaped, yellow. Bracts in several series, green. Receptacle without scales. Fruit ridged and rough, without beak. Pappus of abundant, white, silky, simple hairs. From sonchos, a Greek plant-name.

35. TRAGOPOGON (p. 241)

Biennials or perennials, with grass-like leaves and milky juice. Flowers all strap-shaped, yellow or purple. Bracts in 1 series, longer than the flowers. Fruit with a long beak. Pappus of numerous, long, feathery hairs. Greek tragos, a goat, and pogon, a beard, from the hairy pappus.

CAMPANULACEAE. BELLFLOWER FAMILY (p. 241)

Herbs with alternate leaves, without stipules and with milky juice. Flowers regular or irregular, often blue and sometimes collected in a head. Sepals 5. Petals 5, united. Stamens 5, on the petals or top of the ovary; the anthers in the young state fit closely round the style and are sometimes united. Carpels 2–5, united and inferior; style long, with a lobed stigma. Fruit a capsule 2–5 chambered, usually with many seeds and opening by pores or valves.

A. Corolla irregular   LOBELIA, 1
B. Corolla regular
   (*a*) Flowers in close heads, on leafless stalks
       1. Anthers united   JASIONE, 2
       2. Anthers free   PHYTEUMA, 3
   (*b*) Flowers borne otherwise
       1. Marsh plants   WAHLENBERGIA, 4
       2. Not marsh plants
          I. Sepals longer than petals   SPECULARIA, 6
          II. Sepals shorter than petals   CAMPANULA, 5

1. LOBELIA (p. 241)

Perennials with flowers in racemes. Corolla 2-lipped and split down the back. Anthers united round the style. Called after de l'Obel, a Flemish botanist.

2. JASIONE (p. 242)

Annual with radical leaves in a rosette, and blue flowers in small rounded heads surrounded by bracts. Corolla deeply divided into narrow segments. Anther tips free, united in a tube at the base. Capsule opening by 2 valves inside the sepals. Greek, iasis, healing.

3. PHYTEUMA (p. 242)

Perennials with leafy stems and flowers in dense heads surrounded by bracts. Corolla deeply cut into narrow segments. Anthers free. Capsule opening by slits on the sides below the sepals. A Greek plant-name.

4. WAHLENBERGIA (p. 242)

Small creeping perennial with rounded leaves. Flowers solitary. Corolla bell-shaped. Stamens free. Capsule opening by apical valves inside the sepals. Called after the Swedish botanist Wahlenberg.

5. CAMPANULA (p. 242)

Perennials, rarely biennials or annuals, usually with toothed leaves. Flowers in spikes or racemes, usually blue. Corolla bell-shaped. Anthers free. Capsule opening by pores on the sides below the sepals. Latin, campana, a bell, from the flower shape.

6. SPECULARIA (p. 245)

Annual herbs with leafy stems. Corolla nearly flat, shorter than the sepals. Stamens free. Capsule long, opening by pores on the sides below the sepals. Latin, speculum, a mirror, from the flower shape.

ERICACEAE. HEATH FAMILY (p. 245)

Usually shrubs, with small, leathery, evergreen leaves, without stipules. (Pyrola is herbaceous with large leaves. Monotropa has brown scales.) Flowers regular. Sepals 4–5, united. Petals 4–5, united to form an urn- or bell-shaped corolla, rarely free. Stamens 8–10, opening by pores. Carpels 4–5, united and superior (inferior in Vaccinium). Style single, with a simple or lobed stigma. Fruit a 3–5 chambered capsule, opening by as many valves or a 3–5 chambered berry.

A. Herbs:
  (a) Leaves green   PYROLA, 6
  (b) Leaves not green   MONOTROPA, 7
B. Shrubs:
  (a) Leaves needle-like or small scales
    1. Corolla falling   [DABEOCIA]
    2. Corolla withering, persistent   ERICA, 5 or CALLUNA, 4
  (b) Leaves broader
    1. Fruit a berry
      I. Ovary superior   ARCTOSTAPHYLLOS, 2
      II. Ovary inferior   VACCINIUM, 1
    2. Fruit dry   ANDROMEDA, 3, [LOISELEURIA]

1. VACCINIUM (p. 245)

Small shrubs; leaves often leathery and evergreen. Flowers solitary or in small groups. Corolla often urn-shaped. Anthers prolonged upwards into 2 narrow tubes with pores at the tips, through which the pollen is shed. Ovary inferior. Fruit a berry with the remains of the sepals on its apex. Perhaps a corruption of the Latin, bacca, *a berry.*

2. ARCTOSTAPHYLOS (p. 246)

Shrubs similar in appearance to Vaccinium. The anthers are bent back on the filament and have 2 slender tails, but are not prolonged into tubes. Ovary superior. Fruit a berry with the remains of the sepals at the base. Greek, arktos, *a bear, and* staphylé, *grapes, as being eaten by bears.*

3. ANDROMEDA (p. 246)

Small shrubs with narrow leaves and flowers in small terminal racemes. Corolla urn-shaped. Stamens with hairy filaments and tails to the anthers. Fruit a capsule opening by 5 valves. Called after Andromeda.

4. CALLUNA (p. 249)

Shrubs with scale-like leaves in opposite pairs, closely packed in 4 rows on the shoots. Flowers in crowded spikes. Sepals 4, membranous, pink. Corolla deeply divided into 4 segments, shorter than the sepals. Stamens 8, with spurred anthers. Fruit a 4-chambered superior capsule opening by 4 valves. Greek, calluno, *to sweep, the twigs being used for brooms.*

5. ERICA (p. 249)

Shrubs with small, needle-like leaves, alternate or whorled. Flowers in dense spikes. Sepals 4, green. Corolla urn- or bell-shaped, with 4 small teeth. Stamens 8, with or without spurs. Fruit a superior, 4-valved capsule. From the Greek name, ereike.

6. PYROLA (p. 250)

Perennial herbs, with broad, usually rounded, radical leaves and white flowers in a raceme on a stem bearing only scales. Sepals 5. Petals 5, free or nearly so, forming a globular or bell-shaped corolla. Stamens 10, opening by pores. Fruit a superior capsule, opening by 5 valves. Seeds numerous, minute, with a loose coat. Latin, pirus, *a pear, from the leaf shape.*

7. MONOTROPA (p. 250)

Saprophytes with fleshy, cream-white stems and brownish scale leaves. Flowers in terminal spikes, bell-shaped. Sepals and petals 4–5. Stamens 8–10. Fruit a superior capsule opening by 4–5 valves. Greek, monotropos, *solitary, perhaps as the only plant growing in deep shade.*

PLUMBAGINACEAE. THRIFT FAMILY (p. 250)

Seashore herbs with radical leaves without stipules. Flowers regular, in corymbs or close heads, on leafless stalks. Calyx tubular, expanded and membranous above, with 5 sepal lobes. Petals 5, free or united at the base. Stamens 5, opposite the petals. Ovary superior, with 1 chamber and 1 seed. Styles slender, 5.

A. Flowers in a panicle or corymb   STATICE, 1
B. Flowers in a close head   ARMERIA, 2

1. STATICE (p. 250)

Leaves broad, radical. Flowers in small groups of 1–3, which are arranged along 1 side of the stalks and grouped in forked panicles or corymbs. Calyx membranous, with 5 green veins. Petals united at the very base. Stamens on the petals. Greek, statiké, a name for some plant used to stanch wounds.

2. ARMERIA (p. 250)

Perennials, with numerous tufted, narrow leaves and flowers in close heads on leafless stalks. The heads are surrounded by membranous bracts and the bases of 2 of these are prolonged downwards to form a sheath round the top of the stem. Calyx membranous. Petals united at the very base. Celtic, ar mor, near the sea.

PRIMULACEAE. PRIMROSE FAMILY (p. 253)

Perennial or annual herbs with opposite or alternate leaves, without stipules and usually undivided. Flowers regular. Sepals 5, united. Petals 5, united. Stamens 5, inserted on the corolla tube opposite the petals. Ovary 1-chambered, superior. Style slender, with a knob-like stigma. Fruit a capsule, with many seeds on a basal knob, opening by teeth or a lid. In Glaux there is a coloured calyx and no corolla. In Trientalis petals and sepals are 5–9. In Samolus the ovary is inferior.

A. Leaves deeply divided   HOTTONIA, 1
B. Leaves not deeply divided
  (*a*) Leaves in radical rosette   PRIMULA, 2
  (*b*) Leaves on stem
    1. Flowers white
      I. Leaves whorled   TRIENTALIS, 4
      II. Leaves not whorled   SAMOLUS, 7, [CENTUNCULUS]
    2. Flowers yellow   LYSIMACHIA, 3
    3. Flowers pink, red, or blue   ANAGALLIS, 6 or GLAUX, 5

1. HOTTONIA (p. 253)

Aquatic with submerged, deeply divided leaves. Flowers whorled, in a terminal raceme. Called after the Dutch botanist Hotton.

2. PRIMULA (p. 253)

Perennials with radical leaves. Flowers solitary or in terminal umbels. Corolla salver- or funnel-shaped, with a cylindrical tube. Stigma knob-like. Capsule opening by 5 teeth. Latin, primus, first, as flowering early.

3. LYSIMACHIA (p. 254)

Perennials, creeping or upright, with entire, opposite or whorled leaves. Flowers yellow, solitary or in racemes. Sepals and petals united at the base; corolla widely bell-shaped. Capsule opening by 5 teeth. Called after a Greek king, Lysimachus.

4. TRIENTALIS (p. 254)

Erect perennial, with a whorl of entire leaves and 1 or few terminal, white flowers. Sepals and petals 5–9. Capsule opening by 5 teeth. Etymology obscure.

5. GLAUX (p. 257)

Creeping perennial, with opposite, entire, fleshy leaves and small, pink flowers, solitary in the leaf axils. Corolla 0. Calyx pink. Stamens 5 alternating with the sepals. Capsule opening by 2–5 teeth. Greek, glaukos, blue-green, from the leaf colour.

6. ANAGALLIS (p. 257)

Prostrate annuals or perennials, with entire, opposite leaves and flowers solitary in the leaf axils. Sepals and petals 5, united at the base. Corolla flat or bell-shaped. Capsule opening by a hemispherical lid. The Greek name.

7. SAMOLUS (p. 257)

Perennial, with entire, alternate leaves and white flowers in terminal racemes. Sepals and petals 5. Corolla with 5 small teeth between the petals, bell-shaped. Ovary inferior. Capsule opening by teeth. A Latin plant-name.

OLEACEAE. ASH FAMILY (p. 258)

Trees and shrubs, with opposite, simple or compound leaves. Flowers regular, 1-sexual or hermaphrodite. Sepals and petals 4, united, or both absent. Stamens 2, on the corolla tube when this is present. Carpels 2, united, superior; ovary 2-chambered; stigmas 2, thick and blunt. Fruit a berry, capsule, or winged nut ('key'). Lilac, Jasmine, and Forsythia are commonly grown, exotic shrubs of this family.

A. Tree .... ASH, **1**
B. Shrub .... LIGUSTRUM, **2**

1. FRAXINUS (p. 258)

Tree with opposite, pinnately compound, deciduous leaves. Flowers hermaphrodite, male or female, with or without calyx and corolla. Fruit a winged key. The Latin name of the flowering ash.

2. LIGUSTRUM (p. 258)

Shrubs with opposite, entire leaves and white flowers in terminal panicles.
Fruit a berry. Latin, ligare, to bind, from the use of the twigs.

APOCYNACEAE. PERIWINKLE FAMILY (p. 258)

VINCA (Only British genus)

Herbs with opposite, entire leaves; stipules o; juice milky. Flowers solitary,
regular. Sepals 5, united. Petals 5, united, twisted in the bud; corolla salver-
shaped. Stamens 5, with short, bent filaments and bearded anthers; on the
corolla tube, alternating with the petals. Carpels 2, superior, more or less
free below, united above; style single, stigma disk-like. Latin, vincire, to
twine, from the use of the shoots. The Latin name was vicapervica.

GENTIANACEAE. GENTIAN FAMILY (p. 258)

Herbs with opposite, entire, glabrous leaves without stipules (compound and
alternate in Menyanthes). Flowers regular. Sepals, petals, and stamens 4–5
(up to 8 in Chlora and Limnanthemum). Sepals united. Petals united,
usually twisted in the bud. Carpels 2, united and superior. Stigmas 2. Fruit
a capsule, opening by 2 valves, with 2 rows of seeds and sometimes 2-
chambered.

A. Leaves compound   MENYANTHES, 4
B. Leaves simple
   (a) Flowers yellow   BLACKSTONIA, **1**, [MICROCALA, LIMNANTHEMUM]
   (b) Flowers pink   ERYTHRAEA, **2**, [CICENDIA]
   (c) Flowers blue or purple   GENTIANA, 3

1. BLACKSTONIA (p. 258)

Erect annuals, with opposite bluish-green leaves and yellow flowers in terminal
corymbs. Sepals, petals, and stamens 8. Called after the botanist, Blackstone.

2. ERYTHRAEA (p. 261)

Annuals, with erect stems, opposite leaves, and heads or corymbs of pink flowers.
Sepals, petals, and stamens 5. Calyx divided almost to the base. Corolla
with a long tube and a funnel-shaped limb. Capsule 2-chambered. Greek,
eruthros, red, from the colour of the flowers.

3. GENTIANA (p. 261)

Herbs, with opposite leaves and blue or purple flowers, solitary or in panicles.
Sepals, petals, and stamens 4–5. The stigmas persist on the capsules, which
are 1-chambered. Called after Gentius, a king of Illyria.

4. MENYANTHES (p. 261)

Marsh perennial, with 3-foliate, alternate leaves and white or pink flowers.
A Greek plant-name.

BORAGINACEAE. FORGET-ME-NOT FAMILY (p. 262)

Herbs, annual or perennial, with alternate, simple, and usually entire leaves, without stipules; usually roughly hairy. Inflorescence a cyme, usually with the appearance of a simple or forked, curved spike or raceme. Flowers regular (irregular in Echium). Sepals 5, united. Petals 5, united; corolla bell- or salver-shaped, throat often thickened or with hairs. Stamens 5, on the corolla tube, alternating with the petals. Carpels 2, united and superior, each deeply cleft; style single, with a simple or lobed stigma. Fruit breaking up into four, 1-seeded nutlets.

A. Corolla irregular   ECHIUM, 8
B. Corolla regular, nutlets not prickly:
    (*a*) Each flower with a bract
        1. Scales in corolla throat
            I. Corolla tube bent   LYCOPSIS, 4
            II. Corolla tube straight   ANCHUSA, 3, [BORAGO]
        2. No scales in corolla throat
            I. Leaves fleshy   MERTENSIA, 5
            II. Leaves not fleshy   LITHOSPERMUM, 7
    (*b*) Bracts absent or at base of inflorescence only
        1. Corolla bell-shaped   SYMPHYTUM, 2
        2. Corolla salver-shaped   MYOSOTIS, 6
C. Corolla regular, nutlets prickly   CYNOGLOSSUM, 1

1. CYNOGLOSSUM (p. 262)

Biennials with small, purple flowers in 1-sided racemes. Calyx with deep, broad lobes. Corolla with scales in throat. Nutlets covered with hooked prickles. Greek, kion, a dog, and glossa, a tongue, from the rough leaves.

2. SYMPHYTUM (p. 262)

Coarse perennials, with white, cream, or purple, drooping flowers. Calyx divided half-way down. Corolla bell-shaped, with scales in throat. Greek, sumphuo, to heal, from use as a vulnerary.

3. ANCHUSA (p. 262)

Perennials, with blue flowers in small cymes, each flower with a bract. Corolla salver-shaped; tube straight, with hairy scales. Nutlets rough. The Greek name of such plants.

4. LYCOPSIS (p. 262)

Annuals with small, blue flowers, in small cymes, each flower with a bract. Corolla with a bent tube and scales in the throat. Nutlets rough. The Greek name for some such plant.

5. MERTENSIA (p. 265)

Fleshy, glaucous perennials with blue-purple flowers, each with a bract. Calyx deeply divided into broad lobes. Corolla without scales in throat, bell-shaped. Nutlets rather fleshy. Called after the German botanist, Mertens.

6. MYOSOTIS (p. 265)

Annuals or perennials with blue flowers in terminal cymes, without bracts. Corolla salver-shaped, the throat constricted by 5 thickenings or small scales. Stamens hidden in the tube. Nutlets smooth. Greek, mus, *mouse, and* ous, *ear, from the leaf texture.*

7. LITHOSPERMUM (p. 266)

Annuals or perennials. Flowers in terminal cymes, each with a bract. Calyx deeply divided into narrow sepals. Corolla funnel- to salver-shaped. Nutlets very hard. Greek, lithos, *a stone, and* sperma, *seed, from the hard nutlets.*

8. ECHIUM (p. 266)

Biennials with very bristly hairs. Flowers blue, in small cymes grouped in terminal panicles. Calyx deeply divided. Corolla irregular, with 5 unequal lobes. Stamens protruding. Nutlets wrinkled and rough. Greek, echis, *a viper, from the twisted inflorescences.*

CONVOLVULACEAE. BINDWEED FAMILY (p. 266)

Herbs, usually twining, with alternate, undivided leaves, lacking stipules; or parasites without green leaves; often with milky juice. Flowers solitary, or clustered, regular. Sepals 5 or 4, free. Petals 5 or 4, united in a bell- or urn-shaped corolla, often twisted in the bud. Stamens 5 or 4, alternating with the petals and inserted at the base of the corolla tube. Carpels 2, united, superior; style slender with 2 stigmas. Fruit a 2-chambered capsule with 4 seeds, opening by valves or a lid.

A. Leaves large green   CONVOLVULUS, **1**
B. Leaves 0, or small scales, not green   CUSCUTA, **2**

1. CONVOLVULUS (p. 266)

Twining herbs, with milky juice and alternate leaves. Flowers large. Sepals 5. Petals 5, forming a bell-shaped corolla, plaited and twisted in the bud. Fruit opening by 2 valves. Latin, convolvere, *to twine round, from the twining habit or perhaps the twisted corolla.*

2. CUSCUTA (p. 269)

Twining, pinkish or yellow parasites. Leaves absent or minute scales. Flowers in small, rounded clusters. Sepals, petals, and stamens 4–5; corolla urn-shaped with 5 scales in the throat. Capsule opening by a lid. From the Arabic name.

SOLANACEAE. NIGHTSHADE FAMILY (p. 269)

Herbs, shrubs, or climbers, with alternate leaves, lacking stipules. Flowers solitary, or in false corymbs, regular or nearly so. Sepals 5, united. Petals 5, united. Stamens 5, on the corolla tube, alternating with the petals. Carpels 2, united and superior; ovary 2-chambered. Style simple, stigma forked. Fruit a berry or capsule opening by valves or a lid; seeds numerous.

A. Fruit a capsule, flowers irregular   HYOSCYAMUS, 3
B. Fruit a berry, flowers regular
   (*a*) Flowers solitary   ATROPA, 2
   (*b*) Flowers in clusters   SOLANUM, 1

1. SOLANUM (p. 269)

Annual or perennial herbs or shrubs. Flowers in small false corymbs, which do not stand in the leaf axils. Corolla wheel-shaped, with the stamens standing out from it in a cone. Stamens opening by pores. Fruit a berry. A Latin plant-name.

2. ATROPA (p. 269)

Perennial, with undivided leaves. Flowers solitary. Corolla bell-shaped. Fruit a berry, with the persistent calyx at its base. Called after Atropos, *one of the fates, in allusion to poisonous properties.*

3. HYOSCYAMUS (p. 270)

Biennials, with sticky hairs and an unpleasant odour. Flowers in 1-sided, false spikes. Calyx urn-shaped, with sharply pointed teeth. Corolla bell-shaped, with 5 unequal lobes. Fruit a capsule, with many seeds, opening by a lid. Greek, hus, *a pig, and* kuamos, *a bean; reason obscure.*

SCROPHULARIACEAE. FOXGLOVE FAMILY (p. 270)

Herbs, with opposite or alternate, usually undivided, leaves, without stipules. Flowers solitary or in spikes, racemes, or panicles, usually irregular. Sepals 5, rarely 4, united. Petals 5, rarely 4, united; corolla often 2-lipped. Stamens 2, or 4 in 2 pairs, or 5, on the corolla tube. Carpels 2, united and superior; style slender; stigma forked. Fruit a 2-chambered capsule, containing several or many seeds and opening by 2 valves.

A. Stamens 5   VERBASCUM, 1
B. Stamens 2   VERONICA, 7
C. Stamens 4
   (*a*) Leaves, at least the upper, alternate
     1. Corolla pursed up, spurred   LINARIA, 2
     2. Corolla pursed up, with sac   ANTIRRHINUM, 3
     3. Corolla not pursed up
        I. Leaves much cut   PEDICULARIS, 10
        II. Leaves not cut   DIGITALIS, 6
     4. Flowers minute   [SIBTHORPIA, LIMOSELLA]

(b) Leaves opposite
  1. Calyx teeth 5
     I. Flowers large, bright yellow   MIMULUS, 5
     II. Flowers small, yellow or dingy   SCROPHULARIA, 4
     III. Flowers small, white, lilac, or pink   EUPHRASIA, 8
  2. Calyx teeth 4
     I. Flowers yellow, calyx inflated   RHINANTHUS, 11
     II. Flowers yellow or yellow and purple, mouth of corolla pursed up
                               MELAMPYRUM, 12
     III. Flowers yellow, lilac, red or white, mouth of corolla open
                    BARTSIA, 9 or EUPHRASIA, 8

1. VERBASCUM (p. 270)

Tall biennials, with woolly hair, alternate leaves, and flowers in terminal racemes or panicles. Flowers nearly regular. Sepals, petals, and stamens 5; corolla wheel-shaped; stalks of stamens with long, juicy hairs. The Latin name.

2. LINARIA (p. 270)

Annuals or perennials, erect or prostrate, with at least the upper leaves alternate. Flowers solitary or in terminal racemes. Corolla pursed up, so that the mouth is closed, and with a definite spur at the base. Latin, linum, flax, which some species resemble in the leaf.

3. ANTIRRHINUM (p. 273)

Annuals or perennials with entire leaves, the upper alternate. Flowers solitary or in terminal racemes. Corolla pursed up so that the mouth is closed, with a bulge at the base of the tube in front. Greek anthos, flower, and rhinos, the nose, from the flower shape.

4. SCROPHULARIA (p. 273)

Perennials, with opposite leaves and angular stems. Flowers in terminal panicles, dingy in colour or yellow. Corolla swollen, almost globular, with 5 lobes of which the 2 upper are erect and form a lip and the lowest is bent down; a scale under the upper lip represents a 5th sterile stamen. Latin, scrophula, in allusion to its use for the disease scrofula.

5. MIMULUS (p. 273)

Perennials, with opposite leaves and solitary flowers in the upper leaf axils. Calyx 5-angled, with 5 short teeth. Corolla 2-lipped, the lower lip broad and 3-lobed, the upper erect, 2-lobed. Latin, mimus, a player, or Greek, mimo, an ape, from the shape of the flower.

6. DIGITALIS (p. 274)

Biennials or perennials, with alternate leaves and erect, unbranched shoots, terminating in a 1-sided raceme of drooping flowers. Sepals unequal, united at the base. Corolla narrowed just above the base, then widely and unequally bell-shaped. Capsule with many seeds, opening by valves along the partitions. Latin, digitus, a finger, from the shape of the corolla.

7. Veronica (p. 274)

Annuals or perennials with opposite or alternate leaves. Flowers solitary, in the leaf axils or in lateral or terminal racemes or spikes. Sepals 4, unequal, united near the base. Petals 4, unequal; corolla tube very short, limb flat. Stamens 2. Capsules flat, with few seeds. A Latin name of uncertain origin.

8. Euphrasia (p. 278)

Annuals, with opposite leaves and flowers in terminal, leafy spikes. Calyx with 4 lobes and a very small 5th tooth. Corolla 2-lipped, the upper lip with 2 spreading lobes. Greek, euphraino, I gladden, in allusion to curative properties.

9. Bartsia (p. 278)

Annuals or perennials, with opposite leaves and flowers in terminal and lateral, leafy spikes. Calyx with 4 lobes. Corolla 2-lipped, the upper lip slightly hooded and entire or slightly notched. Called after the German botanist Bartsch.

10. Pedicularis (p. 278)

Annuals or perennials, with alternate, much-cut leaves, and flowers in leafy spikes. Calyx with 2 lobes or 5 teeth. Corolla 2-lipped, the upper lip hooded and flattened sideways. Capsule flattened, with few seeds. Latin, pediculus, a louse, as being used against these vermin.

11. Rhinanthus (p. 278)

Annuals, with opposite leaves and yellow flowers in spikes. Calyx inflated, narrow at the tip, with 4 teeth, forming a membranous bladder in the fruit. Corolla 2-lipped, the upper hooded and flattened sideways. Capsule flattened; seeds flat, round, winged. Greek, rhinos, nose, and anthos, flower, from the shape of the corolla.

12. Melampyrum (p. 281)

Annuals, with opposite leaves and flowers solitary in the leaf axils or in spikes; bracts often coloured. Calyx 4-toothed. Corolla 2-lipped, the upper short and flattened, the lower shorter and 3-toothed, the mouth pursed up and half closed. Capsule flattened, with 2–4 seeds. Greek, melas, black, and puros, wheat, from appearance of seeds.

OROBANCHACEAE. BROOMRAPE FAMILY (p. 281)

Parasites of a brown or purplish colour, with only scale-leaves. These plants grow on the roots of the host and above ground there appears an erect, usually unbranched stem, terminating in a spike of irregular flowers. Calyx 2-, 4-, or 5-toothed or lobed. Corolla 2-lipped, with a curved tube. Stamens 4, in 2 pairs. Carpels 2, united and superior; style slender; stigma 2-lobed. Fruit a 1-chambered capsule opening by 2 valves.

A. Rhizome with fleshy scales   Lathraea, **2**
B. No rhizome   Orobanche, **1**

1. OROBANCHE (p. 281)

*Swollen base of stem in contact, through suckers, with the host root, and con-
tinued upwards into the flowering shoot. Flowers each with 3 bracts. Calyx
deeply 2-lobed, each lobe with 2 deep teeth; sometimes a small 5th tooth.
Corolla 2-lipped, the upper with 2 spreading lobes. Greek, orobos, a vetch,
and anchein, to choke, from the habit of some species.*

2. LATHRAEA (p. 281)

*A branched rhizome, beset with fleshy scales, makes contact with host roots
through its rootlets, and gives rise to the erect flowering shoots. Calyx 4-lobed.
Corolla 2-lipped, the upper arched and entire. Greek, lathraios, hidden, as
growing in concealed places.*

LENTIBULARIACEAE.   BUTTERWORT FAMILY (p. 281)

*Perennials, aquatic or of very wet situations. Leaves in a rosette and entire, or
submerged and very much divided. Flowers solitary, on leafless stalks, or in
a leafless raceme, irregular. Calyx 2- or 5-lobed. Corolla of 5, united petals,
2-lipped and spurred. Stamens 2. Carpels 2, united and superior; style
short; stigma 2-lobed. Fruit a 1-chambered capsule, opening by valves or
irregularly, with many seeds on a basal knob.*

A. Leaves entire   PINGUICULA, **2**
B. Leaves submerged, much divided   UTRICULARIA, **1**

1. UTRICULARIA (p. 281)

*Leaves submerged, much divided into hair-like segments, bearing many minute
bladders. Flowers in a leafless raceme above the surface of the water. Calyx
2-lobed. Corolla 2-lipped, the mouth very much pursed-up and closed, spurred.
Capsule opening irregularly. Latin, utriculus, a little bladder, from the leaf
bladders.*

2. PINGUICULA (p. 282)

*Perennials, with rosettes of entire, fleshy leaves. Flowers solitary on leafless
stalks. Calyx 5-lobed. Corolla 2-lipped, throat open. Capsule opening by
2–4 valves. Latin, pinguis, fat, from the slimy leaves.*

VERBENACEAE.   VERVAIN FAMILY (p. 282)

VERBENA (Only British genus)

*Herbs or shrubs, with 4-angled stem and opposite, divided leaves. Flowers in
terminal and lateral spikes, irregular. Sepals 5, united. Corolla with a flat,
unequally 5-lobed limb. Stamens 4 or 2. Ovary 4-ribbed, with a slender
terminal style; stigma forked. Fruit breaks up into 4 nutlets. Latin name of
uncertain origin.*

LABIATAE. MINT FAMILY (p. 282)

Herbs or shrubs, with square stems and opposite, usually undivided leaves, without stipules. Flowers apparently in whorls, these grouped in spikes or heads; each whorl is really a pair of opposite, compact cymes. Flowers irregular. Sepals 5, united. Petals 5, united in a corolla which is usually markedly 2-lipped. Stamens 4, in 2 pairs, or 2. Carpels 2, united and superior; the ovary is deeply cleft into 4 with the slender style rising from between the divisions; stigma forked; nectar disk below ovary. Fruit breaking up into 4 nutlets. Often aromatic.

A. Upper lip of corolla definitely hooded or arched:
   (a) Calyx unequally lobed or toothed
     1. Stamens 2   SALVIA, 4
     2. Stamens 4
        I. Bracts not like the leaves   PRUNELLA, 7
        II. Bracts like the leaves   SCUTELLARIA, 6
   (b) Calyx equally toothed or nearly so
     1. Anthers hairy   LAMIUM, 10, or GALEOPSIS, 9
     2. Anthers not hairy   STACHYS, 8, [LEONURUS, BALOTTA]
B. Upper lip of corolla flat or only slightly curved, often 2-lobed
   (a) Corolla with 4–5 nearly equal lobes
     1. Stamens 2   [LYCOPUS]
     2. Stamens 4   MENTHA, 1
   (b) Corolla 2-lipped
     1. Stamens longer than upper corolla lip
        I. Small-leaved shrub   THYMUS, 2
        II. Broad-leaved herb   ORIGANUM
     2. Stamens shorter than upper corolla lip
        I. Calyx with 5 teeth   NEPETA, 5 or STACHYS 8 or CALAMINTHA, 3
        II. Calyx of 3–5 broad lobes   [MELITTIS]
       III. Calyx with 10 teeth   [MARRUBIUM]
C. Upper lip of corolla very short, as if cut off   TEUCRIUM, 11 or AJUGA, 12

1. MENTHA (p. 282)

Perennials, spreading by suckers. Flowers in dense whorls, often collected in terminal spikes or heads. Calyx 5-toothed. Corolla small, bell-shaped, with 4, nearly equal lobes. Stamens often projecting beyond the corolla. Aromatic. The Latin name, called after the nymph Minthe.

2. THYMUS (p. 285)

Small, much branched, aromatic shrubs. Leaves small, entire. Flower-whorls in spikes or heads. Calyx 2-lipped. Corolla 2-lipped, the upper flat, notched, the lower broad, 3-lobed. Stamens protruding from the corolla. Egyptian, tham, *an aromatic plant.*

3. CALAMINTHA (p. 285)

Annuals or perennials, with the flower-whorls in leafy spikes or heads. Calyx 2-lipped, with 13 veins. Stamens 4, lving below the slightly curved, upper lip of the corolla. Greek kalos *and* minthe, *the beautiful mint.*

4. SALVIA (p. 285)

Herbs or shrubs, with flower-whorls in terminal and lateral spikes. Calyx 2-lipped, the throat hairless. Corolla with a hooded upper lip. Stamens 2. The head of each stamen is like a rocker hinged on its stalk; the upper end of the rocker lies under the hood and produces pollen, the lower end is flat and blocks the tube of the corolla. Latin, salvo, I heal, from curative properties.

5. NEPETA (p. 286)

Perennial, with flower-whorls in the leaf axils or in terminal spikes. Calyx with 15 veins and 5 teeth, equal or unequal. Corolla tube long, narrow below, wide at the throat; upper lip notched. Stamens 4, of which the 2 middle, or upper, are longest. Called after the Etrurian city Nepete.

6. SCUTELLARIA (p. 286)

Perennials of wet places, with flowers in opposite pairs in the leaf axils. Calyx of 2, unequal lips, the upper with a scale-like projection behind; closed over the fruit. Corolla tube long, upper lip hooded, lower pursed up. Latin, scutella, a dish, from the shape of the calyx.

7. PRUNELLA (p. 286)

Perennials, with flower-whorls in dense, terminal heads, the bracts differing from the leaves in shape and often coloured. Calyx 2-lipped, the lips toothed and closed over the fruit. Upper lip of corolla hooded, the tube with a hairy ring inside. Stamens with a small peg behind the head. Etymology obscure.

8. STACHYS (p. 286)

Annuals, with the flower-whorls usually in leafy spikes. Calyx with 5 equal spiny teeth. Corolla tube usually with a ring of hairs inside; upper lip curved or hooded, concealing the 2 pairs of hairless anthers. Greek, stachys, a spike, from the inflorescence.

9. GALEOPSIS (p. 289)

Annuals, with flower-whorls in the leaf axils. Calyx with 5, equal, spiny teeth. Corolla tube long, widening above; upper lip hooded, entire or slightly notched. This genus is best distinguished by the anthers which open by transverse (and not longitudinal) slits, fringed with hairs. Greek, galea, weasel, and opsis, countenance, from the appearance of the flower.

10. LAMIUM (p. 290)

Annuals or perennials, with the flower-whorls in the leaf axils or in leafy heads. Calyx with 5, equal, spiny teeth. Corolla tube widened at the top, upper lip arched. Anthers hairy all over (except in L. Galeobdolon). Greek, lamos, throat, from the shape of the corolla.

11. Teucrium (p. 293)

Perennials, with small flower-whorls in the axils of the upper leaves, or in slender spikes. Calyx with 5 unequal teeth. Upper lip of corolla very short, projecting to the sides in 2 teeth, between which the 4 stamens project. From teukrion, a Greek plant-name.

12. Ajuga (p. 293)

Annuals, with flower-whorls in the axils of the upper leaves. Calyx with 5, nearly equal teeth. Upper lip of corolla very short, notched, with the 2 pairs of stamens projecting far beyond it. Etymology obscure.

PLANTAGINACEAE (p. 293)

Annual or perennial herbs, with leaves in tufts or rosettes and leafless flowering stems terminating a close spike, or, rarely, a single flower. Flowers regular. Sepals 4, united or free. Corolla small, membranous, with 4 spreading teeth. Stamens 4, alternating with the corolla teeth, with very long slender stalks. Ovary superior, with a slender, simple style. Fruit a 1-, 2-, or 4-chambered capsule, with 1 or many seeds, opening by a lid or not opening.

A. Flowers solitary   Litorella, 2
B. Flowers in spikes   Plantago, 1

1. Plantago (p. 293)

Annual or perennial, with leaves in rosettes and flowers in close spikes. Fruit 2- or 4-chambered, opening by a lid. Latin, planta, the sole of the foot, from the leaf shape.

2. Litorella (p. 294)

Aquatic perennial with solitary, unisexual flowers; fruit a 1-seeded nutlet. Latin, litus, shore, from the place where the plant grows.

ILLECEBRACEAE. KNAWEL FAMILY (p. 294)

Small annuals or perennials, usually with opposite leaves, with or without membranous stipules. Flowers regular, minute, greenish. Sepals 5, united. Petals 5, small or absent. Stamens 5. Ovary superior, with 2-3 styles. Fruit a 1-seeded nutlet, enclosed in the persistent calyx. The 3 genera Corrigiola, Herniaria, and Illecebrum include rare species of southern England.

A. Leaves alternate   [Corrigiola]
B. Leaves opposite
    (a) Leaves ovate or oval   [Illecebrum, Herniara]
    (b) Leaves linear   Scleranthus, 1

1. Scleranthus (p. 294)

Small perennials or annuals, with narrow leaves, without stipules, and small green flowers in terminal cymes. Calyx with an ovoid tube enclosing the ovary. Petals absent. Greek, skleros, hard, and anthos, a flower, from the dried-up appearance.

CHENOPODIACEAE. GOOSEFOOT FAMILY (p. 297)

Herbs, rarely shrubs, usually with rather fleshy, alternate leaves, without stipules. Flowers regular, sometimes unisexual, small, green, in clusters often grouped in racemes or panicles. Sepals usually 5, united. Petals 0. Stamens 5 or fewer, opposite the sepals. Ovary superior; styles 2–3, short. Fruit a 1-seeded nutlet.

A. Without leaves   SALICORNIA, 3
B. With leaves
  (*a*) Leaves narrow, spiny   SALSOLA, 5
  (*b*) Leaves narrow not spiny   SUAEDA, 4
  (*c*) Leaves broad   CHENOPODIUM, 1 or ATRIPLEX, 2, [BETA]

1. CHENOPODIUM (p. 297)

Herbs, often mealy, with broad leaves, usually toothed or lobed. Flower clusters in spikes or panicles. Flowers usually hermaphrodite, with 5 sepals and stamens; styles 2–3; calyx enclosing the fruit, but not enlarging. Greek, chen, a goose, and pous, a foot, from the leaf shape.

2. ATRIPLEX (p. 297)

Herbs or shrubs, with broad, mealy leaves. Flower clusters in spikes or panicles. Flowers unisexual; the female have no sepals but are surrounded by 2 small bracts which enlarge and often become thick and warty, enclosing the fruit. The Latin name.

3. SALICORNIA (p. 297)

Succulent herbs or shrubs, of salt marshes. Stem green, jointed, without leaves. Flowers minute, sunk in the notches of the stem, usually in opposite groups of three. Calyx fleshy, 3- or 4-lobed. Stamens 2. Latin, sal, salt, and cornu, a horn, a plant with horn-like branches growing in salty places.

4. SUAEDA (p. 297)

Herbs or shrubs of the coast, with narrow, fleshy leaves. Flowers in small clusters in the axils of the upper leaves. Sepals and stamens 5. Styles 2–3. Nutlet enclosed in the calyx. From an Arabic plant-name.

5. SALSOLA (p. 298)

Herbs of the coast, with fleshy leaves ending in spines. Flowers sessile in the axils of the upper leaves, each with 2, leaf-like, bracts. Sepals and stamens 5. Style forked. The sepals enclose the fruit and become winged. Latin, sal, salt, a plant growing in salty places.

POLYGONACEAE. DOCK FAMILY (p. 298)

Herbs, with alternate, simple, usually entire leaves; stipules membranous, joined round the stem between leaf and stem. Flowers small, regular, usually in spikes, racemes or panicles. Sepals 5–6, free, green or petal-like, coloured. Petals o. Stamens 6–9. Ovary superior, often 3-angled; styles 2–3. Fruit a nutlet with 1 seed. Oxyria has 4 sepals.

A. Leaves kidney-shaped   OXYRIA, **2**
B. Leaves of other shapes
  (*a*) Sepals 6, inner larger   RUMEX, **3**
  (*b*) Sepals 5, all equal, often coloured   POLYGONUM, **1**

1. POLYGONUM (p. 298)

Annuals or perennials, often prostrate; stipules forming a tube or funnel round the stem. Flowers usually in spikes, sometimes in clusters, in the leaf axils. Sepals 5, pink, white, or greenish. Stamens 5–8. Styles 2–3. Nutlet 3-angled or flattened, enclosed by the persistent calyx. Greek, polus, many, and gonu, the knee, from the prominent nodes.

2. OXYRIA (p. 302)

Perennial, with rather fleshy leaves, distinguished from Rumex by having only 4 sepals and 2 styles, and by the winged fruit. Greek, oxus, acid, from the taste.

3. RUMEX (p. 302)

Erect perennial herbs, with a stout stock, tapering into the tap-root. Flowers hermaphrodite or unisexual, in terminal panicles. Sepals 6, the 3 inner larger and enlarging in the fruit. Stamens 6. Styles 3, with brush-like stigmas. Fruit a 3-angled nut. The Latin name for sorrel.

THYMELEACEAE. SPURGE LAUREL FAMILY (p. 305)

DAPHNE (Only British genus)

Shrubs, with stringy bark and alternate leaves, undivided and without stipules. Flowers regular. Sepals green or coloured, united, with a definite tube. Petals o. Stamens 8, on the tube of the calyx. Ovary superior, with a knob-like stigma almost sessile on the top. Fruit a berry. Called after the Greek nymph Daphne.

ELAEAGNACEAE. SEA BUCKTHORN FAMILY (p. 305)

HIPPOPHAE (Only British genus)

Small trees or shrubs, with alternate leaves, undivided and without stipules; leaves and young shoots with minute, brown or grey scales. Flowers regular, small, solitary or in small groups, unisexual. Male flowers with 2 sepals united below, o petals and 4 stamens. Female flowers with a tubular, 2-toothed calyx; ovary enclosed in the calyx tube, superior, with a slender style. Fruit a false berry, the fleshy part being the swollen calyx which encloses the true fruit, a 1-seeded nutlet. The Greek name of a shrub.

SANTALACEAE. SANDALWOOD FAMILY (p. 306)

THESIUM (Only British genus)

Herbs or shrubs, with alternate, undivided leaves, without stipules. Flowers regular, minute, with 2 bracts just below the calyx. Calyx tubular, with 4 sepal lobes. Petals 0. Stamens 4 on the calyx tube. Ovary inferior, with a short style and lobed stigma. Fruit a 1-seeded nutlet. From theseion, a Greek plant-name.

EUPHORBIACEAE. SPURGE FAMILY (p. 306)

Herbs, shrubs, or trees with opposite or alternate, undivided leaves, with or without stipules; often with milky juice. Flowers small, regular, unisexual. Sepals 0, 3, or 4, free. Petals 0. Stamens 1–12. Carpels 2 or 3, united and superior, with as many styles, often forked. The fruit breaks up into 3 portions, each with a single seed, and each splits open, sometimes explosively. In Euphorbia the male and female flowers occur in small inflorescences which look like hermaphrodite flowers.

A. Shrub   BUXUS, 2
B. Herbs
    (a) With milky juice   EUPHORBIA, 1
    (b) Without milky juice   MERCURIALIS, 3

1. EUPHORBIA (p. 306)

Herbs, usually with alternate leaves, without stipules; juice milky. The female flower consists of an ovary on a stalk; it is surrounded by a number of male flowers, each consisting of a single stamen; the whole is surrounded by a cup, formed by the fusion of 5 bracts, the edges of which bear 4 yellowish nectaries and 5 minute teeth. This little inflorescence resembles a flower. The inflorescences are usually grouped in umbels or panicles and are often associated with leafy bracts differing from the foliage leaves in shape and colouring. Called after Euphorbos, a Greek physician.

2. BUXUS (p. 309)

Shrub with opposite, evergreen leaves, without stipules. Male and female flowers together, in small clusters in the leaf axils. Sepals 4. Stamens 4. The Latin name.

3. MERCURIALIS (p. 309)

Herbs, with opposite, toothed leaves; stipules small, membranous. Male and female flowers usually on separate plants. Sepals 3. Stamens 9–12. Carpels 2; styles 2. Called after Mercury, who was said to have discovered its medicinal virtues.

ULMACEAE. ELM FAMILY (p. 309)

ULMUS (Only British genus)

Deciduous trees, with alternate, undivided leaves, with stipules which fall early. Flowers small, regular. Calyx bell-shaped, with 5 lobes. Petals 0. Stamens 5, in the throat of the calyx and opposite the sepals. Carpels 2, united and superior, with a forked stigma; ovary 2-chambered; ovules 2, only 1 maturing; fruit a 1-seeded nutlet, surrounded by a broad green wing. The Latin name.

URTICACEAE. NETTLE FAMILY (p. 309)

Herbs, sometimes climbing, with opposite or alternate, hairy leaves, usually with stipules. Flowers small, unisexual, regular. Sepals 4–5, united. Petals 0. Stamens 4–5, opposite the sepals. Ovary superior, with 1–2 styles; fruit a 1-seeded nutlet.

A. Leaves lobed   [HUMULUS, CANNABIS]
B. Leaves not lobed
   (a) Leaves opposite   URTICA, **1**
   (b) Leaves alternate   PARIETARIA, **2**

1. URTICA (p. 309)

Annuals or perennials, with opposite leaves; stipules small. Male and female flowers on the same or different plants. Sepals and stamens 4, the sepals of the female flower unequal; stigma a small brush of hairs on the top of the ovary. Latin, uro, I burn, in allusion to the stinging hairs.

2. PARIETARIA (p. 310)

Herbs, with alternate leaves, without stinging hairs. Flowers in small clusters. Sepals and stamens 4. Stigma a tuft of hairs on top of a short style; fruit a very small nutlet enclosed by the calyx tube. Latin, paries, a wall, the plant growing on walls.

MYRICACEAE. BOG-MYRTLE FAMILY (p. 310)

MYRICA (Only genus)

Shrubs, with alternate, undivided leaves, without stipules. Flowers unisexual, in catkins. Sepals and petals 0. Male flower of 4–8 stamens, united to a brown scale bract. Female flower an ovary with 2 thread-like stigmas, united to a bract and with 2 small scales at the base. Fruit a nutlet with wings derived from the small scales. Aromatic when crushed; the bracts are covered with minute resin glands. From myrike, a Greek plant-name.

BETULACEAE. BIRCH FAMILY (p. 310)

Shrubs or trees, with alternate, undivided, deciduous leaves, with stipules which fall early. Flowers unisexual, male and female on the same tree. Flowers in groups of 1, 2, or 3 in the axil of a scale-like bract, with or without scales, and gathered into catkins; these are formed in the summer before they open. Calyx usually rudimentary or 0. Corolla 0. Stamens 2–4. Ovary minute, with 2 prominent crimson styles. Fruit a nut or nutlet enclosed in the bracts which sometimes become greatly enlarged. Pollen abundant, light, and powdery, shed before the leaves are fully expanded, carried by wind.

A. Large shrub of woods and hedges   CORYLUS, 4
B. Tree of wet places with very blunt leaves   ALNUS, 2
C. Trees and shrubs with very slender twigs   BETULA, 1
D. Tree with doubly toothed leaves   CARPINUS, 3

1. BETULA (p. 310)

Shrubs and small trees, with bark stripping in sheets and very slender, often drooping twigs. Male and female catkins drooping, dense, cylindrical, expanding with the leaves in spring. Fruit a small, winged nut; fruiting bracts cross-shaped. The Latin name.

2. ALNUS (p. 310)

Trees of damp woods. Male catkins in drooping, long, cylindrical clusters; female small, ovoid, erect, stalked, in small groups, becoming woody and cone-like in the fruit. Male flowers with 4 distinct sepals and 4 stamens. Nutlets without wings. The Latin name.

3. CARPINUS (p. 313)

Tree. Male catkins, lateral, drooping; female catkins terminal, short and stiff, elongating and drooping in the fruit. Fruit a small nut with the much enlarged bract forming a wing. The Latin name.

4. CORYLUS (p. 313)

Shrubs. Male catkins long, cylindrical, drooping; female catkins like enlarged leaf-buds, with stigmas protruding from the tip. Fruit a large nut, enclosed in a husk of enlarged green bracts. The Latin name.

FAGACEAE. BEECH FAMILY (p. 313)

Trees with alternate, deciduous or evergreen leaves. Flowers unisexual, in catkins, male and female on the same tree. Male catkins conspicuous, with many flowers; male flower with calyx of 4–7 united sepals and 4–12 stamens. Female catkins small, few-flowered, inconspicuous; female flower with minute calyx or 0; ovary 3-chambered with 3 stigmas; only a single seed ripens.

Fruit a large nut; 1, 2, or 3 nuts in a warty or spiny cupule formed from fused bracts.

A. Leaves lobed (or if evergreen, lobed or entire)   QUERCUS, **1**
B. Leaves sharply toothed   [CASTANEA]
C. Leaves with shallow blunt teeth   FAGUS, **2**

1. QUERCUS (p. 313)

Trees with deciduous (or evergreen in exotic species) leaves. Buds blunt. Male catkins slender, loose, drooping, with many flowers. Sepals small. Stamens about 10. Female catkins small, stiff, with few flowers. Fruit a rounded nut, the base surrounded by a warty cup, borne singly or in groups. The Latin name.

2. FAGUS (p. 314)

Tree with deciduous leaves, chaffy stipules which fall early, and long, pointed, brown buds. Male catkins rounded, drooping; male flowers with a bell-shaped calyx and numerous stamens. Female catkins small, on stiff stalks. Fruit a 3-cornered nut, occurring in pairs, in a spiny, woody, 4-valved cupule. The Latin name.

SALICACEAE. WILLOW FAMILY (p. 314)

Shrubs or trees, with alternate, undivided leaves; stipules falling early. Flowers in catkins, unisexual, male and female on separate plants. Male flower, a scale-like bract and 2, 3, or many stamens. Female flower, a scale-like bract and an ovary of 2 united carpels with 2 forked stigmas. Fruit a small, 1-chambered capsule, opening by valves, with many seeds bearing silky hairs.

A. Catkins drooping, buds with several scales   POPULUS, **2**
B. Catkins usually erect, buds with 1 scale   SALIX, **1**

1. SALIX (p. 314)

Trees or shrubs, with entire or toothed leaves and stipules which usually fall early. Catkins usually erect, bracts entire. Stamens usually 2 or 3, on the small bract, with a scale-like nectary at their base. Ovary on the small bract, with a scale-like nectary at its base; stigmas 2, more or less forked. There are some 20 British species of Salix, many of them closely similar and crossing to give intermediate forms; only a few contrasting species can be given here. The Latin name.

2. POPULUS (p. 317)

Trees, with broad, alternate leaves; stipules falling early. Buds enclosed in several scales, often sticky. Catkins drooping. Stamens numerous on a round disk in the axil of a fringed bract. Ovary in a cup in the axil of a fringed bract; stigmas deeply cleft; nectaries o. The Latin name.

EMPETRACEAE. CROWBERRY FAMILY (p. 318)

EMPETRUM (Only British genus)

Shrub, with small, alternate leaves, without stipules. Flowers minute, in small groups in the leaf axils, unisexual, male and female on separate plants. Sepals and petals 3, similar, coloured, free. Stamens 3. Ovary superior, 6–9 chambered, with a single, short style and 6–9 small stigmas. Fruit fleshy, with several seeds enclosed in little stones. Greek, en, on, and petra, rock, the plant growing in stony places.

CERATOPHYLLACEAE. HORNWORT FAMILY (p. 318)

CERATOPHYLLUM (Only genus)

Submerged aquatics, with finely divided leaves in whorls, without stipules. Flowers minute, solitary in the leaf axils, unisexual, male and female on the same plant. A cup, with about 10 lobes representing a whorl of united bracts, surrounds the stamens or ovary. Sepals and petals 0. Stamens 12–20, without stalks. Ovary 1-chambered, with 1 seed and 1 pointed style. Fruit an achene, tipped by the persistent style, sometimes with 2 spurs near the base. Greek, keras, horn, and phullon, leaf, from the leaf shape.

HYDROCHARIDACEAE. FROG-BIT FAMILY (p. 318)

Aquatic plants, with opposite or whorled leaves, submerged, floating, or aerial. Flowers regular, unisexual, male and female usually on separate plants, the buds enclosed by 2–3 membranous bracts. Sepals 3, united. Petals 3, united. Stamens 3–12. Ovary inferior, 1–6 chambered; styles 1, 3, or 6, forked. Seeds liberated by the rotting of the small, green fruit which ripens under water.

A. Leaves small, whorled, submerged   ELODEA, **1**

B. Leaves floating, kidney-shaped   HYDROCHARIS, **2**

C. Leaves sword-shaped   [STRATIOTES]

1. ELODEA (p. 318)

Stem long, branched, with opposite or whorled, submerged leaves. Flowers small, solitary, the bud enclosed in 2 bracts. Female with calyx tube 2–3 in. long; stigmas 3, large, forked; 3 scales represent stamens and sometimes have anthers. Male flowers with 9 stamens. Greek, helos, a marsh, the plant growing in watery places.

2. Hydrocharis (p. 318)

Aquatics, with floating leaves. Flowers large. Female solitary, with 1 large, membranous bract. Male in groups of 2–3, with 2 bracts. The female flower has 6 styles, each with a forked stigma, and 6 small scales representing stamens. The male flower has 12 stamens, some of which are sterile. Greek, hudor, water, and charis, beauty.

ORCHIDACEAE. ORCHIS FAMILY (p. 321)

Perennial herbs, often with tuberous roots and with undivided, sheathing leaves (brown scales in saprophytic species). Flowers irregular, in terminal spikes or racemes (solitary in Cypripedium). Sepals 3, often coloured. Petals 3, that in front usually larger than the others, forming a lip, often spurred. The single stamen is fused with the style and forms a fleshy column in front of the upper sepal; pollen usually glued into 2 club-shaped masses. Stigma a sticky patch, at the back of the corolla throat, below the column; ovary inferior, forming the stalk of the flower. Fruit a 1-chambered capsule, opening by 3 valves, with very numerous, minute seeds.

A. Flowers solitary [Cypripedium]
B. Flowers in spikes, no green leaves   Neottia, **1**, [Corallorhiza, Epipogon]

C. Flowers in spikes, leaves green
   (a) Corolla spurred (spur sometimes very short)   Orchis, **5** or Habenaria, **9**

   (b) Corolla not spurred
     1. Flowers green or yellowish green
       I. Lip long, forked   Listera, **2**
       II. Lip long, 4-lobed   Aceras, **6**
       III. Lip short, 3-lobed   Herminium, **8**
       IV. Lip short, simple   [Liparis, Malaxis]
     2. Flowers white or creamy, small   Goodyera, **3**, [Spiranthes]
     3. Flowers rather large, brown, purple, pink, or white
       I. Lip puffed out   Ophrys, **7**
       II. Lip not puffed out, constricted at the middle   Epipactis, **4**, [Cephalanthera]

1. Neottia (p. 321)

Brown saprophyte, with only scale-leaves. Flowers shortly stalked, in a terminal raceme. Sepals and side petals curved inwards; lip rather long, forked, hanging down, not spurred; pollen powdery. Greek, neottia, a nest, from the appearance of the rhizome.

2. Listera (p. 321)

Perennials, fibrous roots, 2 nearly opposite leaves, small greenish flowers in terminal racemes. Sepals and side petals curved inwards: lip long, forked, not spurred. Pollen in 2 loose masses. Called after the botanist Lister.

3. GOODYERA (p. 321)

Perennials, with branching rhizome. Leaves shortly stalked. Flowers in a 1-sided spike, small, white. Upper sepal and side petals pointing up, side sepals bent down beside the short, broad lip. Called after the botanist Goodyer.

4. EPIPACTIS (p. 322)

Perennials, with a rhizome, leafy stem, and flowers in a terminal raceme. Sepals and side petals spreading, or somewhat bent in; lip narrowed about the middle, the upper portion hollow, the lower broad and rounded. Pollen in loose masses. A Greek plant-name.

5. ORCHIS (p. 322)

Perennials, with tuberous roots, leaves mostly near the base of the stem, and flowers in spikes. Upper sepal and side petals curved in over the column, side sepals curved in or spreading; lip large, lobed, spurred; flowers usually pink or purple. Pollen in compact masses. Greek, orchis, testicle, from the appearance of the tubers.

6. ACERAS (p. 325)

Perennials with tuberous roots. Sepals and side petals forming a hood; no spur. Greek, a, without, and keras, horn, that is without a spur.

7. OPHRYS (p. 325)

Perennials, with tuberous roots, flowers in loose spikes. Sepals large, spreading; side petals small, often greenish; lip usually very large, broad and velvety; spur 0. Greek, ophrus, eyebrow, from the brown markings.

8. HERMINIUM (p. 326)

Perennials, with root tubers and 2–3 leaves. Flowers small, green, in a slender spike. Sepals and petals curved inwards; lip 3-lobed, no larger than the sepals; spur 0. Greek, hermis, a bedpost, from some fancied likeness of the inflorescence or perhaps the tuber.

9. HABENARIA (p. 326)

Perennials, with root tubers, and often leafy stems. Bracts green. Upper sepal and side petals curved in over the column; spur short or very long. A genus botanically very similar to Orchis and distinguished only by the arrangement of the pollen masses, which lie in slits parallel or spreading below, with the sticky bases of their stalks more or less exposed; in Orchis the slits come together below, and the sticky bases are concealed in a lobed pouch. Latin, habena, a strap, from the shape of the lip.

IRIDACEAE.　IRIS FAMILY (p. 329)

Perennials with rhizomes, root tubers, or corms, and long, narrow leaves. Flowers usually regular, solitary, or in small groups, each with 2 bracts enclosing the bud. Sepals 3, united, coloured. Petals 3, united. Stamens 3. Ovary inferior, style 1, stigmas 3, often very large. Fruit a 3-chambered, 3-angled capsule, with many seeds, opening by 3 valves.

A. Flowers in a small terminal group on a stem:
  (*a*) Flowers irregular　　　　　　　　　　　　　[GLADIOLUS]
  (*b*) Flowers regular
    1. Sepals and petals similar　　　　　　　　[SISYRINCHIUM]
    2. Sepals and petals dissimilar　　　　　　　IRIS, **1**
B. Flowers solitary　　　　　　　　　　　　　　　　[CROCUS]

1. IRIS (p. 329)

Perennials, with leaves in 2 opposite rows, flattened from side to side, each ensheathing the next higher at the base. Flowers in small, terminal cymes. Sepals large, coloured, reflexed. Petals smaller, more or less erect. Stigmas large and like petals, each lying on a sepal with a stamen between. Greek, iris, a rainbow, from the flower colours.

AMARYLLIDACEAE.　DAFFODIL FAMILY (p. 329)

Perennials, with bulbs and long, narrow leaves. Flowers solitary, regular, or in small terminal groups, the bud enclosed by a membranous bract. Sepals 3, more or less like the 3 petals. Stamens 6. Ovary inferior. Fruit a capsule, opening by 3 valves.

A. Sepals and petals united　　　　　　　　　　　NARCISSUS, **1**
B. Sepals and petals free
  (*a*) Sepals and petals similar　　　　　　　　[LEUCOJUM]
  (*b*) Sepals and petals dissimilar　　　　　　　[GALANTHUS]

1. NARCISSUS (p. 329)

Flowers solitary or in small groups on a long, leafless stalk, with a large membranous bract near the top. Calyx with a tube. Sepals and petals spreading, with a crown—a tubular or ring-like outgrowth from the mouth of the throat. Called after Narcissus.

DIOSCOREACEAE.　YAM FAMILY (p. 329)

TAMUS (Only British genus)

Twining perennials, with a tuber. Leaves alternate, with netted veins. Flowers regular, small, unisexual. Sepals 3, like the 3 petals. Stamens 6. Ovary inferior, with 3 short styles. Fruit a berry. A Latin plant-name.

LILIACEAE (p. 330)

Perennials, with rhizomes or bulbs. Leaves long and narrow or broad, with parallel veins. Flowers regular, rarely unisexual. Perianth of 6 parts, rarely fewer, free or united, usually brightly coloured. Stamens 6 or 8. Ovary superior; style 1, stigmas 1 or 3. Fruit a berry or 3-chambered capsule, opening by 3 valves.

A. Flowers solitary:
  (a) Flower greenish-yellow   PARIS, 9
  (b) Flower mottled   FRITILLARIA, 5
  (c) Flower yellow   [TULIPA]
  (d) Flower white and pink   [LLOYDIA]
  (e) Flower pale purple   COLCHICUM, 6
B. Flowers in small groups in the leaf axils or apparently on the face of the leaves:
  (a) Shrub   RUSCUS, 1
  (b) Herbs   POLYGONATUM, 2, [ASPARAGUS]
C. Flowers in umbels or heads:
  (a) Flowers blue   [MUSCARI]
  (b) Flowers not blue   ALLIUM, 3
D. Flowers in racemes, panicles, corymbs, or spikes:
  (a) Flowers white or greenish-white
    1. Leaves, broad, 2   MAIANTHEMUM, CONVALLARIA
    2. Leaves narrow, several   [ORNITHOGALLUM]
  (b) Flowers blue or purplish   SCILLA, 4, [MUSCARI]
  (c) Flowers yellow   NARTHECIUM, 7, [GAGEA]
  (d) Flowers green, small   TOFIELDIA, 8

1. RUSCUS (p. 330)

Evergreen shrubs. The leaves are small scales with broad, flattened, leaf-like shoots in their axils; on the face of these are borne the small flower-groups. Flowers small. Stamens 3. Fruit a berry. The Latin name.

2. POLYGONATUM (p. 330)

Perennials, with a stout rhizome and leafy stems. Flowers in small groups in the leaf axils. Perianth narrowly bell-shaped, 6-toothed, with the stamens half-way down the tube. Fruit a berry. Greek, polus, many, and gonu, the knee, from the knotted rhizome.

3. ALLIUM (p. 330)

Bulbous perennials, with long, sheathing, radical leaves and flowers in terminal umbels, the whole umbel enclosed in the bud by 1 or 2 large, membranous bracts. Perianth segments 6, free. Stamens 6. Fruit a 3-angled, 3-chambered capsule, with 3–6 black seeds, opening by 3 valves. Latin, allium, an onion.

4. SCILLA (p. 333)

Bulbous perennials, with long, narrow, radical leaves. Flowers blue, in terminal racemes or corymbs, on leafless stems. Perianth segments 6, free or nearly so. Stamens 6, inserted near the base of the perianth segments. Fruit a capsule, opening by 3 valves; seeds black. Greek, skilla, a squill.

5. FRITILLARIA (p. 333)

Bulbous perennials, with leafy stems. Flowers large, usually solitary. Perianth segments 6, free. Stamens 6, on the base of the perianth segments. Fruit a long capsule, opening by 3 valves; seeds numerous, flattened. Latin, fritillus, a dice-box, from the shape of the flower.

6. COLCHICUM (p. 333)

Perennials, with a corm formed by the swollen, solid base of the stem. Leaves radical, large and broad. The flowers, which resemble those of the crocus, arise singly or in small groups from the corm and are carried above ground by the long, slender perianth tube. Perianth segments 6. Stamens 6, at the mouth of the perianth tube. Styles 3, thread-like. The capsule is raised to the surface of the ground by the lengthening of the flower stalk. Called after Kolchis, in Asia Minor.

7. NARTHECIUM (p. 334)

Perennials, with a rhizome and narrow, radical leaves. Flowers in a terminal raceme on a scaly stem. Perianth segments 6, free, not falling when the flower is past. Stamens 6, with hairy stalks. Style short. Capsule opening by 3 valves; seeds small, with a slender point at each end. From narthex, a Greek plant-name.

8. TOFIELDIA (p. 334)

Perennials, with a rhizome and narrow, radical leaves. Flowers in a small terminal raceme. Perianth segments 6, free, not falling when the flower is past. Stamens 6, with hairless stalks. Styles 3. Capsules opening by 3 valves; seeds minute. Called after the botanist Tofield.

9. PARIS (p. 334)

Perennial, with a rhizome. Stem with a whorl of broad, net-veined leaves, and a single, terminal flower. Sepals 4, free. Petals 4, free. Stamens 8. Ovary 4-lobed, with 4 styles. Fruit a berry. The parts of the flower are sometimes in fives. Latin, par, equal.

JUNCACEAE. RUSH FAMILY (p. 334)

Herbs, usually perennial. Leaves stiff, cylindrical, pointed or grass-like. Flowers in crowded groups or loose panicles or corymbs, small, brown or green; perianth scaly, of 6 free leaves, persisting in the fruit. Stamens 3 or 6. Ovary superior, with 3 slender styles. Fruit a capsule, with 3 or many ovules, opening by valves.

A. Capsule with many seeds, leaves usually more or less cylindrical
JUNCUS, **1**

B. Capsule with 3 seeds, leaves grass-like
LUZULA, **2**

1. JUNCUS (p. 334)

Usually perennials, with stiff, cylindrical or flattened, sometimes grass-like, leaves. Flowers in irregular false panicles, corymbs, or dense clusters, sometimes springing from the side of the stem. Capsule with many minute seeds. Of the score of British species, many of which are rare, only 4 contrasting species can be described here. The Latin name, from jungo, I join, from their use for tying.

2. LUZULA (p. 337)

Perennials, with grass-like leaves with long, fine, white hairs about the edges. Flowers in dense or loose terminal inflorescences. Capsules with 3 seeds. Etymology obscure.

TYPHACEAE. REED-MACE FAMILY (p. 338)

TYPHA (Only genus)

Perennials, of lake and river margins, with long, narrow, flat, sheathing leaves. Flowers unisexual, male and female on the same plant. Perianth represented by a number of fine hairs. Male flower with 2–5 stamens, united below. Female flowers with a minute stalked ovary. Fruit a minute nutlet, surrounded by fine hairs. Greek, tuphos, a fen, from the habitat.

SPARGANIACEAE. BUR-REED FAMILY (p. 338)

SPARGANIUM (Only genus)

Perennials of stream-sides, with soft leaves. Flowers unisexual, male and female on the same plant, in round, spiky heads. Perianth of 3–6 green, spoon-shaped scales. Male flower with 3 stamens. Ovary superior, with a slender style. Fruit a soft achene, tipped with a beak developed from the style. Greek, sparganon, a band, from the leaf shape.

ARACEAE.　ARUM FAMILY (p. 341)

Perennials, usually with broad, net-veined leaves. Flowers hermaphrodite or unisexual, massed in a thick, often fleshy, close spike, usually enclosed in a very large membranous or leafy bract. Perianth of 6 leaves or o. Stamens 1–6. Ovary superior. Fruit a berry.

A. Leaves broad　　　　　　　　　　　　　　　　　　　　ARUM, 1
B. Leaves narrow　　　　　　　　　　　　　　　　　　　ACORUS, 2

1. ARUM (p. 341)

Perennials, with a tuber and large, broad, net-veined leaves. The inflorescence terminates a naked stalk and is enclosed by a large greenish, hooded bract; at the base is a mass of female flowers, each consisting of a single ovary; above these is a ring of sterile, female flowers with spike-like styles; then a mass of male flowers, consisting of sessile stamens and, finally, a ring of stout hairs; above these the axis of the inflorescence terminates in a purple club which projects into the hood. From aron, *the Greek name.*

2. ACORUS (p. 341)

Perennial of stream-sides, with long, narrow leaves. Inflorescence a thick spike, apparently springing from the side of a stem; the part above it is really the bract. Flowers hermaphrodite, with 6 perianth leaves, 6 stamens, and a superior ovary. From akoros, *a Greek plant-name.*

LEMNACEAE.　DUCKWEED FAMILY (p. 341)

LEMNA (Only British genus)

Small, floating aquatics, consisting of green blades with or without a root hanging down into the water; there is no true stem or leaf. Flowers minute and rarely seen, in a notch of the blade, consisting of a bract and 1–2 stamens or an ovary. A Greek plant-name.

ALISMACEAE.　WATER-PLANTAIN FAMILY (p. 341)

Aquatic or marsh perennials, with broad or narrow, parallel-veined leaves. Flowers regular, coloured, often large, solitary, or in umbels, racemes, or panicles, on leafless stems. Sepals 3, petals 3, or perianth of 6 coloured leaves, free. Stamens 6, 9, or many. Carpels 3, 6, or many, free or nearly so; superior. Flowers sometimes unisexual. Fruit a collection of achenes, or of pods.

A. Leaves narrow　　　　　　　　　　　　　　　　　　BUTOMUS, 3
B. Leaves arrow-shaped　　　　　　　　　　　　　　SAGITTARIA, 2
C. Leaves more or less oval:
　　(*a*) Fruit of over 12 achenes　　　　　　　　　　ALISMA, 1
　　(*b*) Fruit of, usually, 6 pods　　　　　　　　[DAMASONIUM]

1. ALISMA (p. 341)

Aquatic perennials, with submerged and aerial leaves, sometimes with floating leaves. Flowers in a panicle or umbel. Sepals 3, petals 3, stamens 6; carpels numerous. Fruit a collection of achenes. A Greek plant-name.

2. SAGITTARIA (p. 342)

Aquatic perennial, with broad leaves. Flowers unisexual, male and female on the same plant. Sepals 3. Petals 3. Stamens 6. Fruit a collection of achenes. Latin, sagitta, an arrow, from the leaf shape.

3. BUTOMUS (p. 342)

Aquatic perennials, with narrow, erect leaves. Flowers in a terminal umbel. Perianth of 6, similar, rose-coloured leaves. Stamens 9. Carpels 6. Fruit a collection of pods. From butomos, a Greek plant-name.

JUNCAGINACEAE. ARROW-GRASS FAMILY (p. 342)

Marsh plants, with erect, linear leaves and small, green flowers in a slender spike; flowers regular. Perianth leaves 6, free. Stamens 6. Carpels 3 or 6, more or less united in the flower, but separating in the fruit into small pods.

A. Flowers without bracts   TRIGLOCHIN, 1
B. Flowers with bracts   [SCHEUCHZERIA]

1. TRIGLOCHIN (p. 342)

Flowers in a slender spike, without bracts; carpels 3 or 6, each with a feathery stigma, all united round a central axis, from which they break away in the fruit, each opening to liberate a single seed. Greek, treis, three, and glochin, point, from the form of the fruit.

NAIADACEAE. PONDWEED FAMILY (p. 345)

Aquatics, with a rhizome and long, slender, branched stems. Leaves opposite or alternate, broad or narrow, floating or submerged, sheathing at the base. Flowers unisexual or hermaphrodite, small, green. Perianth 0 or of 4 leaves. Stamens 1–4. Carpels 1–4, free, superior. Fruit of 1–4 achenes.

A. Marine plants with long grassy leaves   ZOSTERA, 2
B. Aquatics with broad or narrow leaves and flowers in small spikes
                                   POTAMOGETON, 1
C. Aquatics with narrow leaves and flowers not in spikes
                   [NAIAS, ZANNICHELLIA, RUPPIA]

1. POTAMOGETON (p. 345)

Perennials, with a rhizome rooting in the mud and floating, branching stems. Leaves broad or narrow, floating on the surface or submerged, sheathing or with a membranous sheath in the axil. Flowers hermaphrodite, small, in short spikes above the water. Perianth of 4 leaves. Stamens 4 on the perianth leaves. Carpels 4, free, superior. Fruit of 4 achenes. There are about 24 British species, of which many are common pond and river plants. Greek, potamos, river, and geiton, neighbour, from the habitat.

2. ZOSTERA (p. 345)

Perennials, of sandy and muddy shores, growing about the low-tide level. Stems creeping and rooting below, slender, branched. Leaves alternate, long, grasslike. Flowers unisexual, in a short spike, enclosed in a sheath at the base of the leaf. Male and female flowers mixed together, the former a single stamen, the latter a single ovary, with a forked style. Greek, zoster, a girdle, from the strap-shaped leaves.

CYPERACEAE. SEDGE FAMILY (p. 346)

Herbs, usually unbranched, with solid, 3-angled stems and grass-like leaves, the sheaths of which are not split down one side. Flowers minute, greenish or brownish, unisexual or hermaphrodite, each in the axil of a small bract, in small, close spikes; the spikes are solitary and terminal, or grouped in clusters or panicles, with a scaly or leafy bract at the base of the spike or of the whole inflorescence. Perianth o or a number of small scales or bristles. Stamens 3, rarely 2. Ovary superior, 1-chambered with 1 style and 2–3 feathery stigmas, or with a 2–3 forked style. Fruit a flattened or 3-angled nutlet. Characteristic of damp situations.

A. Flowers unisexual, male and female usually on separate spikes of different
               appearance on the same plant   CAREX, 4, [KOBRESIA]
B. Flowers hermaphrodite:
   (*a*) Tall plant; leaves saw-edged   [CLADIUM]
   (*b*) Not as in (*a*), fruiting head with abundant silky hairs ERIOPHORUM, 2
   (*c*) Not as in (*a*) and (*b*)
      1. Inflorescence a loose or close cluster of spikes with 1 or more leafy
         bracts at the base
        I. Flower bracts in 2 opposite rows   [CYPERUS]
        II. Flower bracts all round spike   SCIRPUS, 1
      2. Inflorescence a terminal group of small spikes and several stalked
         lateral spikes   [RHYNCHOSPORA]
      3. Inflorescence a terminal head of 2 opposite rows of spikes
                                 [BLYSMUS]
      4. Inflorescence a terminal cluster or solitary spike
        I. Flower bracts in 2 opposite rows   SCHOENUS, 3
        II. Flower bracts all round spike   SCIRPUS, 1

1. SCIRPUS (p. 346)

Perennials of wet places, with green stems and, sometimes, with the leaves reduced to sheaths. Spikes solitary and terminal, or in close clusters or irregular panicles; sometimes appearing to come from below the tip of the stem; bract at base of inflorescence green and leafy or scale-like. Flowers hermaphrodite. Perianth 0 or of 3–6 short bristles. Stamens 3. Stigmas 2–3. Fruit a 3-angled or flattened nutlet. There are about 20 British species, of which only a few contrasting types can be described here. A Latin name.

2. ERIOPHORUM (p. 349)

Perennials, of wet places, with or without leaves. Spikes solitary or few, in a terminal umbel. Flowers as in Scirpus, *except that the perianth bristles are numerous and elongate into long, silky hairs, turning the fruiting head into a conspicuous white tuft. Greek,* erion, *wool, and* pherein, *to bear, from the hairy fruits.*

3. SCHOENUS (p. 349)

Perennials of wet places, with stiff stem and leaves. Spikes small, a few gathered in a close, terminal head. In the spikes the flowers (and their bracts) are arranged in 2 opposite rows. Flowers hermaphrodite. Perianth of 1–6 bristles. From schoinos, *a Greek name for some such plant.*

4. CAREX (p. 350)

Perennials, usually of wet places, with grassy leaves. Flowers unisexual, usually in separate spikes on the same plant; male spikes higher on the stem than the female. In some species male and female flowers occur in different parts of the same spike or on different plants. Perianth 0. Stamens 3, rarely 2. Ovary, with 2–3 feathery stigmas, enclosed in a flask-shaped 'utricle' which persists and encloses the fruit. There are over 50 British species, of which only a few can be described here. The Latin name.

GRAMINEAE. GRASS FAMILY

Perennial, rarely annual, herbs. Stems branched at the base only, usually tufted or creeping and spreading by runners or suckers. Leaves alternating in two opposite rows and arising from swollen nodes on the stem. The leaf has a split sheath surrounding the stem and at its junction with the narrow blade there is a scale, the ligule. *The inflorescence is a spike or panicle composed of a large number of ears or* spikelets. *The spikelet bears at its base 2 scales, the* glumes, *within which are 1, 2, or several flowers. Each flower is enclosed by 2 scales, the* pales, *and consists of 3 stamens and an ovary with 2 stigmas. The glumes and pales frequently bear bristles called* awns. *The spikelet sometimes includes a terminal rudimentary flower. There are exceptions to the number of pales and glumes. The stamens and feathery stigmas, when mature, hang out of the spikelet for a short time and wind pollination takes place. The fruit is the* grain, *a kind of achene often enclosed by the dried pales or glumes, which form the* chaff. *The genera and species of grasses can be identified only with the help of botanical characters often of minute structures; there are about 150 British species of grass.*

A. Inflorescence a spike or close, spike-like panicle:

  (*a*) Spikelets sessile in notches of axis

    1. Spikelets on 1 side of the axis

      I. Grass of moors   NARDUS, **24**

      II. Grass of shores   [LEPTURUS]

    2. Spikelets on 2 sides of axis, edge on   LOLIUM, **22**

    3. Spikelets on 2 sides of axis, side on

      I. Spikelets 1-flowered, with long awns   HORDEUM, **25**

      II. Spikelets several-flowered

           * Spikelets solitary   AGROPYRUM, **23**

          ** Spikelets paired   ELYMUS, **26**

  (*b*) Spikelets on short, sometimes branched, stalks.

    1. Spikelets 1-flowered

      I. Lower pale awned

          * Glumes unequal   ANTHOXANTHUM, **2**

          ** Glumes equal   ALOPECURUS, **3**, [GASTRIDIUM, LAGURUS]

      II. Lower pale not awned

          * Leaves long, rigid, sharp   PSAMMA, **6**

          ** Leaves short, flat, soft   PHLEUM, **4**

    2. Spikelets with more than 1 flower

      I. Lower pale not awned   [KOELERIA]

      II. Lower pale awned

          * Spikelets all fertile   BRACHYPODIUM, **21**

          ** Sterile spikelets present   CYNOSURUS, **12**

B. Inflorescence a more or less open panicle:

  (*a*) Spikelets 1-flowered

    1. Lower pale awned and with silky tuft   [CALAMAGROSTIS]

    2. Lower pale awned, without silky tuft   AGROSTIS, **5**

    3. Lower pale not awned

      I. Silky tuft at base of flower   DIGRAPHIS, **1**

      II. No silky tuft

          * Panicle much branched, pales unequal   AGROSTIS, **5**

          ** Panicle much branched, pales equal   [MILIUM]

          *** Inflorescence of few simple spikes [SPARTINA, CYNODON]

  (*b*) Spikelets 2-flowered

    1. Lower pale with short awn   AIRA, **7** or HOLCUS, **8**

    2. Lower pale with long awn   AVENA, **9** or ARRENATHERUM, **10**

    3. Pale not awned

      Grass of woods   MELICA, **14**

      Grass of moors   MOLINIA, **13**

      Grass of ditches   [CATABROSA]

  (*c*) Spikelets several-flowered

    1. Lower pales awned

      I. Awn from back of pale   AVENA, **9**

      II. Awn from just below tip of pale   BROMUS, **20**

      III. Tip of pale prolonged into awn   FESTUCA, **19**

2. Lower pale not awned
  I. Panicles markedly 1-sided
    Spikelets with silky hairs   ARUNDO, 11
    No silky hairs   DACTYLIS, 15
  II. Panicles not markedly 1-sided
    Spikelets broad, drooping   BRIZA, 16
    Spikelets narrow, inclined, or erect
        POA, 17 or GLYCERIA, 18, or FESTUCA, 19, or [TRIODIA]

1. DIGRAPHIS (p. 354)

Inflorescence a close panicle. Spikelets with 1 flower and 1 or 2 minute rudiments. Glumes nearly equal, boat-shaped, enclosing the flower. Greek, dis, twice, and graphis, a style, from the two hairy tufts at the base of the pale.

2. ANTHOXANTHUM (p. 354)

Inflorescence a very close panicle or loose spike. The spikelet consists of 2 pointed glumes, the upper larger than the lower, 2, awned, sterile pales and 2 pales enclosing the single flower, which has only 2 stamens. Greek anthos, a flower, and xanthos, yellow, from the tint of the inflorescence.

3. ALOPECURUS (p. 354)

Inflorescence a close cylindrical spike. Spikelets 1-flowered. Glumes equal, boat-shaped, pointed; there is only 1 pale and from its back springs a long awn. The Greek name, alōpecouros, from alopex, a fox, and oura, a tail, from the form of the inflorescence.

4. PHLEUM (p. 354)

Inflorescence a close, cylindrical spike. Spikelets 1-flowered. Glumes boat-shaped, pointed or tipped with an awn; pales 2, small, without awns. Greek phleos, the name of a grass.

5. AGROSTIS (p. 356)

Inflorescence a delicate open panicle. Spikelets very small, 1-flowered. Lower glume rather larger than upper; pales smaller than the glumes, the lower with or without a slender awn. The Greek name of a grass.

6. PSAMMA (p. 356)

Inflorescence a dense, thick spike. Spikelets large, 1-flowered. Glumes nearly equal, boat-shaped, pointed; pales nearly as long as the glumes. Greek psammos, sand, as the plant grows in dunes.

7. AIRA (p. 356)

Inflorescence a loose or, sometimes, rather close panicle. Spikelets small, 2-flowered. Glumes nearly equal, as long as the pales; lower pale toothed at the tip and with a slender awn springing from the back. Greek name of a grass.

8. HOLCUS (p. 358)

Inflorescence an open panicle. Spikelets 2-flowered, the upper flower with stamens only. Glumes hairy, boat-shaped, the upper rather larger, 3-veined; lower pale of the upper flower with a short awn. Greek, holkos, the name of a grass.

9. AVENA (p. 358)

Inflorescence a very loose panicle. Spikelets large, 2–6 flowered, the upper flowers usually rudimentary. Glumes unequal, or nearly equal, pointed, nearly as long as the pales; lower pale toothed at the tip with a conspicuous, long, bent, and twisted awn on the back. Latin, avena, the oat.

10. ARRHENATHERUM (p. 358)

Characters of Avena, but the spikelets are 2-flowered; the lower flower is male and it alone has an awn. Greek arren, male, ather, a bristle.

11. ARUNDO (p. 360)

Inflorescence a dense panicle inclined to one side. Spikelets very numerous, 2–5 flowered. Glumes unequal, pointed; lower pale with a long point. Flower surrounded at the base with long silky hairs. Latin arundo, a reed.

12. CYNOSURUS (p. 360)

Inflorescence a narrow, spike-like panicle or head with the spikelets turned to one side. The spikelets are in small clusters of which the outer spikelet is flat and consists of 2 ranks of narrow, sterile pales. The inner spikelets have 2 somewhat unequal, pointed glumes and 2–5 flowers. There are no awns. Greek kuon, a dog, and oura, a tail, from the appearance of the spike.

13. MOLINIA (p. 360)

Inflorescence a narrow panicle with erect branches. Spikelets 2–3 flowered, the upper flower sterile. Glumes nearly equal, sharply pointed, 1-veined, much shorter than the spikelets; no awns. Called after the naturalist Molin.

14. MELICA (p. 360)

Inflorescence a very loose panicle with few spikelets. Spikelets 2-flowered, with a small, terminal, club-shaped, sterile flower. Glumes nearly equal; no awns. Etymology doubtful.

15. DACTYLIS (p. 362)

Inflorescence a dense, ovoid or triangular panicle. Spikelets in clusters, pointing to one side, 2–3 flowered. Glumes hairy, sharply pointed, shorter than the spikelets; pales with short terminal bristles. Greek, dactylos, a finger, from the shape of the inflorescence.

16. BRIZA (p. 362)

Inflorescence a very open panicle, with solitary spikelets hanging on slender stalks. Spikelets 7–9 flowered. Glumes boat-shaped, blunt, membranous, much shorter than the spikelets. Greek, brizein, to nod.

17. POA (p. 362)

Inflorescence an open panicle. Spikelets numerous, small, 3–9 flowered. Glumes unequal, pointed, shorter than the lowest pales; lower pale pointed, 5–7 veined; upper pale with a blunt, toothed tip, 2-veined; no awns. Greek poa, fodder grass.

18. GLYCERIA (p. 362)

Characters of Poa, but the spikelets are very long and narrow, usually with more than 9 flowers; lower pale blunt; grasses of wet places. Greek, glykeros, *sweet.*

19. FESTUCA (p. 364)

Inflorescence a panicle, sometimes spike-like, sometimes open, usually little-branched, sometimes 1-sided. Spikelets with 3 or more flowers. Glumes unequal, keeled; pointed; lower pale tipped by a bristle or awn, upper pale toothed at the tip. The Latin name for straw.

20. BROMUS (p. 364)

Inflorescence usually a rather close panicle. Spikelets very large, 5–10 flowered. Glumes unequal, pointed, shorter than the lowest pale; lower pale with a long awn; upper pale toothed at the tip. Greek, bromos, *a kind of grass.*

21. BRACHYPODIUM (p. 364)

Inflorescence a loose spike of very long, almost sessile, spikelets. Spikelets 6–10 flowered. Lower pales awned at the tip. Greek, brachys, *short, and* podion, *a foot, from the short stalks of the spikelets.*

22. LOLIUM (p. 364)

Inflorescence a flattened spike. Spikelets flattened, sessile, edge-on in notches of the stem. There is only 1 glume which stands outside the spikelet. Latin, lolium, *the darnel.*

23. AGROPYRUM (p. 366)

Characters of Lolium, but with 2 glumes which are sometimes awned. Greek, agros, *a field, and* puros, *wheat.*

24. NARDUS (p. 366)

Inflorescence a very thin spike with the spikelets all on one side. There are no glumes. Lower pale larger than upper, and ending in a bristle. Greek, nardos, *spikenard.*

25. HORDEUM (p. 366)

Inflorescence a dense spike; spikelets flattened, set side-on to the stem. The spikelets occur in groups of 3; the 2 outer are generally sterile and consist of narrow, awn-like glumes; the central spikelet has 2, awned glumes and a single flower with an awned pale; the spike has a very bristly appearance. The Latin name for barley.

26. ELYMUS (p. 366)

Inflorescence a dense spike. Spikelets 3–5 flowered, flattened, set broad-side on in notches of the stem. Glumes large, ending in points or bristles. Greek, elumos, *a sheath, the grain being covered by the pale.*

INDEX OF BOTANICAL TERMS

NOTE

In the descriptions in this book the duration and habit are placed first; e.g. shrub, annual, perennial, &c. It should be noted that shrubs and trees are always perennial and that the word 'perennial' means 'herbaceous perennial'. Then comes an indication of size. The figure given is the average range of height, or, for prostrate plants, of spread. This is followed by the sort of situation in which the plant grows and its distribution. It should be understood that in a brief phrase only a rough indication of the distribution can be given. Thus 'throughout Britain' means from north to south, but does not mean that the plant is found everywhere in the island. The letter 'I.' means that it is found in Ireland. The description of the plant follows. To this may be added short references to other species. These are grouped, as far as possible, under the illustrated species which they most resemble. There are also notes on points of biological interest, such as pollination and dispersal of seeds. It may be assumed that when the pollination of only one species in a genus is described, the pollination of the other species is similar.

PRONUNCIATION

Pronunciation of the Latin names is indicated in the text by an accent, thus: HELLE′BORUS. The syllable immediately preceding the accent is to be stressed.

The pronunciation of the generic name is given once only, on the first appearance of the name in the text, and is not repeated under each species.

CONIFERAE. PINE FAMILY

JUNI'PERUS

1. *Juniperus commu'nis.* **Juniper.**

Bushy shrub, 2–5 ft., sometimes growing into a small tree, local through-out Britain on dry soils in hilly regions; I. Leaves in threes, awl-shaped, sharply-pointed, leathery, bluish-green, evergreen. Female cone at first green, ripening in the 2nd year to a hard, bluish-black 'berry' which is used in flavouring gin.

TA'XUS

2. *Taxus bacca'ta.* **Yew.**

Tree up to 50 ft. high, common on chalk and limestone hills in England, planted throughout Britain; I. Leaves linear, pointed, leathery, dark green above, paler below, evergreen. The single ovule stands on a green disk which ripens into a scarlet cup half-enclosing the seed. This 'berry' is eaten by birds; the foliage is poisonous to stock. The yew stands clipping well and is much used for hedges and topiary work. The *Irish Yew* is a variety with upright branches.

PI'NUS

3. *Pinus sylve'stris.* **Scots Pine.**

Tree, up to 100 ft. high, native in northern Scotland and extensively planted throughout Britain; I. Mature tree with rounded crown and rough, ruddy bark. Leaves needle-shaped, bluish-green, in pairs. Male cones in dense clusters, shedding abundant pollen in June. Young female cones the size of a small pea, in groups of 2 to 3; they ripen and become woody in their 2nd or 3rd year when the scales gape and liberate the winged seeds, which are scattered by wind. An important timber tree.

LA'RIX EUROPAE'A, the *Larch*, A'BIES PECTINA'TA, the *Silver Fir*, PI'CEA EXCE'LSA, the *Spruce*, PSEU'DOTSU'GA DOUGLA'SII, the *Douglas Fir*, CE'DRUS LI'BANI, the *Cedar*, and many other conifers are much planted in forests and for ornament.

1. Juniper

3. Scots Pine

2. Yew

7 Wood Anemone.

4.
Old Man's Beard

6. Pasque-flower

5. Meadow Rue

DICOTYLEDONS

RANUNCULACEAE. BUTTERCUP FAMILY

CLE'MATIS

4. *Clematis Vita'lba.*   Old Man's Beard, Traveller's Joy.

Shrubby climber, common in hedges and thickets on calcareous soil in southern England; I. Flowers greenish-white, late summer. Leaves opposite, pinnately compound; leaflets ovate, few coarse teeth; leaf stalks twine, acting as tendrils. Flowers in small corymbs, scented but without nectar, and pollinated by bees and flies which collect pollen; stigmas mature before stamens. Styles elongate into long, feathery floats which assist the dispersal of the fruits by wind.

THALI'CTRUM

5. *Thalictrum fla'vum.*   Meadow Rue.

Perennial, 3 ft., not uncommon in damp places in England, rare in southern Scotland; I. Flowers yellowish, summer. Stem stout, furrowed, erect from a stock which gives off suckers. Leaves 2-pinnate; leaflets large, lance-shaped, or ovate, often notched. Flowers in a feathery panicle, pollinated by wind. T. MI'NUS is a smaller plant not uncommon in rocky places and sand dunes. T. ALPI'NUM is an alpine species, 4–6 in. high, found in damp spots on mountains in northern England, Wales, and Scotland.

ANEMO'NE

6. *Anemone Pulsati'lla.*   Pasque-flower.

Perennial, about 6 in., locally common on calcareous pastures in mid-England. Flowers purple, spring. Leaves and flowering stem from a stout stock. Leaves and bracts cut into narrow segments. Flowers large, appearing while the leaves are small. Leaves and sepals with silky hairs. The outer stamens are sterile and secrete nectar for which the flowers are visited by bees and flies. Styles become long and silky after flowering and aid in dispersal of the fruits by wind.

7. *Anemone nemoro'sa.*   Wood Anemone.

Perennial, 6 in., common in woods throughout Britain; I. Flowers white or pale purple, spring. Leaves and flowering stems from a rhizome which branches and spreads in loose soil so that the plant grows in extensive colonies. Leaves with 3 leaflets, which are cut or notched. Flowers with about 6 white sepals, and with 3 leafy bracts. There is no nectar; the flower is pollinated by bees and pollen-eating flies. The anemone tolerates shade by coming up early, before the trees are in foliage.

RANU'NCULUS

8. *Ranunculus Droue'tii.*   Water-fennel.

Perennial aquatic, rooting in the mud and floating in masses near the surface
of ponds and ditches, common throughout Britain; I. Flowers white,
summer. Leaves all submerged, divided into very fine segments which col-
lapse into a tassel when removed from the water. Flowers solitary, opposite
the leaves, rising above the surface. Petals narrow. Achenes glabrous,
ripening below water. Detached fragments root easily and multiply the
plant, and such fragments pass the winter in the mud.

9. *Ranunculus pelta'tus.*   Water Crowfoot.

Perennial aquatic, common in ponds and ditches throughout Britain; I.
Flowers white, summer. Submerged leaves divided into fine, stiff segments;
floating leaves kidney-shaped with 3–5 broad, notched lobes, shining green.
The white flowers, larger than those of the last species, often star the water
over extensive patches. Petals broad. Achenes hairy.

10. *Ranunculus hedera'ceus.*   Ivy-leaved Crowfoot.

Perennial, common in the mud of ditches throughout Britain; I. Flowers
white, summer. Stems creeping on the mud, rooting at the nodes; sometimes
submerged. Leaves kidney-shaped, with 3–5 shallow lobes. Flowers small
with narrow petals.

There are several other species of *Water Crowfoot*, differing in details
from the 3 common and contrasting species here described. The flowers
are visited by small flies and beetles, but sometimes remain under water and
are self-pollinated.

11. *Ranunculus Fla'mmula.*   Lesser Spearwort.

Perennial, about 1 ft., common in wet places throughout Britain; I. Flowers
yellow, summer. Stem often prostrate and rooting below, hollow. Upper
leaves sessile and narrowly lance-shaped, lower leaves stalked and broader,
slightly toothed, glabrous. Flowers $\frac{1}{2}$ in. across. The juice is very irritating
and was formerly used for blistering. R. LI'NGUA, the *Greater Spearwort*,
a plant up to 3 ft. high with flowers $1\frac{1}{2}$ in. across, is much less common.
R. SCELERA'TUS, the *Celery-leaved Crowfoot*, not uncommon in muddy places,
has a hollow, furrowed stem, leaves divided into 3 segments, and small
flowers with petals no longer than the sepals.

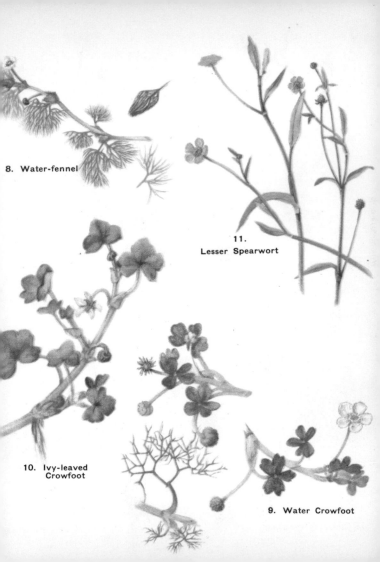

8. Water-fennel

11.
Lesser Spearwort

10. Ivy-leaved
Crowfoot

9. Water Crowfoot

13. Meadow Buttercup

12. Goldilocks

14. Creeping Crowfoot

15.
Bulbous Buttercup

12. *Ranunculus auri'comus*.   **Goldilocks.**

Perennial, 1 ft., not uncommon in shady moist places in England and southern Scotland; I. Flowers yellow, spring. Lower leaves long-stalked, kidney-shaped, with 3 shallow, toothed lobes, glabrous; upper leaves deeply cut. Some of the petals are often small or absent.

13. *Ranunculus a'cris*.   **Meadow Buttercup.**

Perennial, 2 ft., common in meadows throughout Britain; I. Flowers golden yellow, summer. Stems tall, erect, branched, from a short stock. Leaves deeply cut into 3–5 lobes which divide into narrow, toothed segments, hairy. Flowers 1 in. across. Sepals spreading. Flower-stalks round. Like the following species of this genus (and no. 11) the nectary at the base of the petals is covered by a small scale; the flowers are visited by small bees, hoverflies, and other insects; slight differences in the time of ripening of stamens and stigmas favour cross-pollination.

14. *Ranunculus re'pens*.   **Creeping Crowfoot.**

Perennial, ½–1 ft., common in waste places and as a weed throughout Britain; I. Flowers golden yellow, summer. Leaves with 3 leaflets, each with 3 broad, toothed lobes, stalked, hairy. Flower-stalks furrowed. The short stock gives off runners which root and form new plants, thus multiplying and spreading the weed.

15. *Ranunculus bulbo'sus*.   **Bulbous Buttercup.**

Perennial, 1 ft., common in meadows and pastures throughout Britain; I. Flowers golden yellow, early summer. Leaves stalked, hairy, with 3 leaflets, each divided into broad, lobed segments. Flower-stalks furrowed. Sepals bent sharply back. Base of stem swollen into a small corm.

16. *Ranunculus arve'nsis*.   **Corn Crowfoot.**

Annual, 1–1½ ft., not uncommon as a cornfield weed from mid-Scotland southwards; I. Flowers pale yellow, summer. Leaves stalked, hairy, divided into narrow segments. Easily distinguished by the prominent hooked spines which cover the achenes and may aid fruit-dispersal by catching on passing animals.

17. *Ranunculus Fica'ria*.   **Lesser Celandine, Pilewort.**

Perennial, 6 in., common in moist woods and hedgerows throughout Britain; I. Flowers yellow, spring. Leaves mostly radical, stalked, bluntly heart-shaped, somewhat notched, shining green. Flowers 1–2 on a stalk, 1 in. across. Sepals 3. Petals 6–8. The plant is propagated by tuberous roots which become detached with a small bud. It tolerates shade by appearing early, before the foliage of the trees. The flowers close in cold weather and open in the sun.

CA'LTHA

18. *Caltha palu'stris*.   **Marsh-marigold, King-cup.**

Perennial, 1–2 ft., common in damp meadows and marshes throughout Britain; I. Flowers golden yellow, spring. Stems erect or prostrate, and rooting at the base, hollow. Radical leaves long-stalked, stem-leaves short-stalked, round or kidney-shaped, round-toothed, with large membranous stipules, glabrous and shining. The flowers, which are few and large, are visited by beetles, flies, and bees for the abundant nectar secreted by two nectaries at the base of each pod.

TRO'LLIUS

19. *Trollius europae'us*.   **Globe-flower.**

Perennial, 1 ft., not uncommon in wet mountain meadows in northern England, Wales, and Scotland; I. Leaves stalked, glabrous, palmately 5-lobed, lobes divided into 3 sharply-toothed segments. The petals are small and strap-shaped with a nectar gland at the base, and the flowers are visited by flies and small bees. Sepals large, yellow, petal-like.

16. Corn Crowfoot

17. Lesser Celandine

18. Marsh-marigold

19. Globe-flower

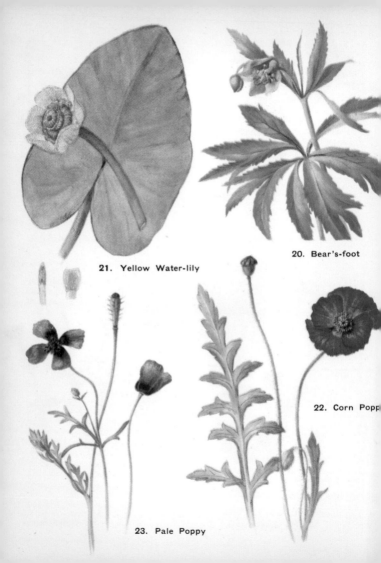

20. Bear's-foot

21. Yellow Water-lily

22. Corn Poppy

23. Pale Poppy

HELLE'BORUS

20. Helleborus vi'ridis.   **Bear's-foot, Green Hellebore.**

Perennial, 1 ft., of shady places on calcareous soils, native in southern England only. Flowers green, spring. Leaves and flowering stem spring from a stout stock. Leaves stalked, palmately divided into 5–7 toothed lobes; stem-leaves sessile. Flowers few, large, drooping. Sepals green, spreading. The petals are small pouches secreting nectar for which bees visit the flowers; in the young flower the stigmas project beyond the stamens and are grasped and pollinated by visiting insects; later the stigmas wither and the stamens elongate and shed pollen on visitors. H. FOE'TIDUS, the *Stinking Hellebore* or *Setterwort*, is a similar but larger plant, the sepals of which are edged with purple and do not spread apart. H. NI'GER, which is not native, is the *Christmas Rose.*

NYMPHAEACEAE. WATER-LILY FAMILY
NU'PHAR

21. Nuphar lu'tem.   **Yellow Water-lily, Brandy-bottle.**

Perennial aquatic, common in quiet waters throughout Britain, except in northern Scotland; I. Flowers yellow, summer. A stout rhizome, in the mud, sends leaves and flowers on long stalks to the surface. Leaves heart-shaped, or nearly round, thick, leathery, and waxy; there are also membranous submerged leaves. Flowers 2 in. across, with a scent supposed to be spirituous. Nectar is secreted by the backs of the petals and the flowers are visited by beetles and flies; the stigmas are ripe before the stamens. NYMPHAE'A A'LBA, the *White Water-lily*, has flowers 4 in. across; there is a series of transition forms between the stamens and the petals.

PAPAVERACEAE. POPPY FAMILY
PAPA'VER

22. Papaver Rhoe'as.   **Corn Poppy, Corn-rose.**

Annual, 2 ft., common in cornfields, except in northern Scotland; I. Flowers scarlet, summer. Stem branched, with bristly hairs. Leaves long, deeply divided into many, notched segments. Flowers 3 in. across, one pair of petals much larger than the other. Petals scarlet, often with black blotch at base. Capsule broadly ovoid, smooth. The fruit stalks are stiff and the seeds are jerked out through the pores to a little distance when the heads are swung by the wind or by passing animals. Like other members of the family the flowers of the poppy have no nectar and are visited by bees and many other insects for pollen.

23. Papaver Arge'mone.   **Pale Poppy.**

Annual, 1 ft., of cornfields and waste places throughout Britain; I. Flowers pale scarlet, summer. A slighter plant than the last. Leaves deeply divided into narrow, deeply notched segments. Petals narrow, with purple blotch. Capsules club-shaped, with rough bristles. P. DU'BIUM has larger flowers, and a smooth club-shaped capsule. P. SOMNI'FERUM, the *Opium Poppy*, sometimes found as a weed, has glaucous leaves and large, white flowers, tinged with bluish-purple.

GLAU'CIUM

24. Glaucium fla'vum.   **Horned Poppy, Sea-poppy.**

Biennial, 1–2 ft., of sandy and shingle beaches from mid-Scotland southwards; I. Flowers yellow, summer and autumn. Stem stout and branched,
sometimes prostrate. Leaves deeply cut; segments notched, with pointed,
twisted lobes; blue-green. Pods up to 1 ft. long, narrow, curved.

CHELIDO'NIUM

25. Chelidonium ma'jus   **Greater Celandine.**

Perennial, 2 ft., of shady places throughout Britain; I. Flowers yellow,
summer. Leaves deeply cut into segments which are lobed or notched;
apical segments larger; deep green and bluish below. Flowers in small
umbels. The seeds have a small fleshy outgrowth sought for by ants, and
these, carrying the seeds about, disperse them.

FUMARIACEAE. FUMITORY FAMILY

CORYDA'LIS

26. Corydalis clavicula'ta.   **Climbing Fumitory.**

Annual climber, local in hedges and thickets throughout Britain; I.
Flowers small, white or cream, summer and autumn. Stem long, branched,
weak, and rambling. Leaves pinnately compound; the stalked leaflets are
again compound with 3–5 leaflets; apical portion of the leaf a branched
tendril. Flowers in small racemes opposite the leaves, visited by bees for
the nectar in the petal spur. C. LU'TEA, common naturalized on old walls,
is an erect, tufted plant with large terminal racemes of yellow flowers.

FUMA'RIA

27. Fumaria officina'lis.   **Fumitory.**

Annual, up to 1 ft., common in waste places and as a weed of cultivated
ground throughout Britain; I. Flowers rosy purple, late summer and
autumn. Stem weak with spreading branches. Leaves pinnately compound,
the leaflets cut into notched lobes; glabrous. Fruit an ovoid nutlet. There
are some 10 closely related species of fumitory, differing chiefly in the shape
of sepals, fruits, &c., and often difficult to distinguish.

26.
Climbing Fumitory

24.
Horned Poppy

27. Fumitory

25. Greater Celandine

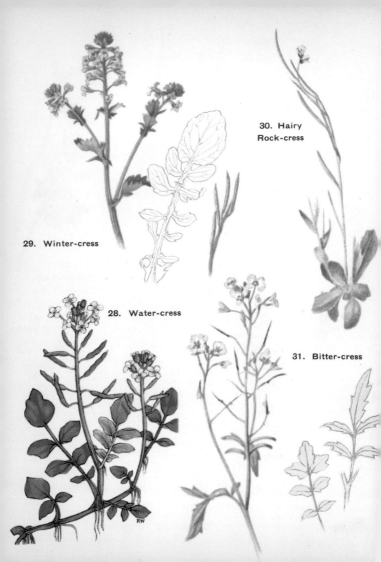

30. Hairy Rock-cress

29. Winter-cress

28. Water-cress

31. Bitter-cress

RW

CRUCIFERAE. WALLFLOWER FAMILY
NASTUR'TIUM

28. *Nasturtium officina'le*. **Water-cress.**

Perennial, $\frac{1}{2}$–2 ft., common in slow streams and ditches throughout Britain and cultivated in cress-beds; I. Flowers white, summer. Stem hollow, prostrate and rooting below, then ascending or floating. Leaves pinnately compound, terminal leaflet rounded, bluntly angled, larger than the oval side leaflets; deep green. Flowers in terminal racemes, small. Stalks of pods spreading, pods bent. N. PALU'STRE, not uncommon in wet places, has yellow flowers, as have the less common N. SYLVE'STRE, with a creeping stem and the larger N. AMPHI'BIUM.

BARBARE'A

29. *Barbarea vulga'ris*. **Winter-cress, Yellow Rocket.**

Biennial, 1–2 ft., common in damp places from mid-Scotland southwards. Flowers small sulphur-yellow, summer. Stem erect, little branched. Lower leaves pinnately lobed or compound; upper leaves less deeply lobed, half-clasping the stem; terminal lobe largest, rounded, bluntly toothed; glabrous. Flowers in racemes. Pods slender, erect. A similar species, B. PRAECOX, is grown as a winter salad.

A'RABIS

30. *Arabis hirsu'ta*. **Hairy Rock-cress.**

Biennial, up to 1 ft., rather uncommon on dry banks and walls throughout Britain; I. Flowers white, summer. Rosette leaves oval, narrowing into a stalk; stem leaves lance-shaped sessile; whole plant rough with short hairs. Flowers small in a stiff raceme which lengthens into a long spike of narrow erect pods. There are several other uncommon species including A. PETRAE'A, the *Alpine Rock-cress*, a small plant of mountains in Wales and Scotland.

CARDAMI'NE

31. *Cardamine ama'ra*. **Bitter-cress.**

Perennial, about $1\frac{1}{2}$ ft., much less common than the next species in meadows and along streams, from mid-Scotland southwards; I. Flowers white, early summer. Stem erect from a short stock which gives off suckers. Leaves pinnately compound; leaflets oval, bluntly toothed, those of the upper leaves narrower; glabrous. Flowers in a terminal raceme, rather large, with conspicuous purple stamens.

32. *Cardamine prate'nsis*.   Cuckoo-flower, Lady's Smock.

Perennial, about 1½ ft., common in marshes and wet meadows throughout Britain; I. Flowers lilac, early summer. Stem erect from a rather thick stock. Leaves pinnately compound; leaflets of lower leaves almost round, of upper leaves narrow, oblong or oval, entire; glabrous. Flowers large in a showy raceme; stamens yellow. Nectar is secreted by 2 nectaries at the base of the short stamens and collects in pouches at the base of the sepals opposite these. The petals and sepals form a short tube which can be probed by insects with moderate tongues. The flower is visited rather sparingly by bees, flies, and butterflies. The insect rubs the stigma and stamens with opposite sides of its head so that cross-pollination is often effected. This type of mechanism is common throughout the Cruciferae, though there are great variations in detail. The cuckoo-flower is self-sterile. C. BULBI'FERA, the *Coralwort*, a rare species of woods in southern England, has a scaly rhizome, large lilac flowers, and forms small bulbils in the leaf axils.

33. *Cardamine hirsu'ta*.   Hairy Bitter-cress.

Annual, up to 1 ft., common in waste places, especially if moist, throughout Britain; I. Flowers white, summer. Leaves pinnately compound; slightly hairy; leaflets of lower leaves round or oval, of upper narrow, somewhat toothed. Flowers small; exceptional in having only 4 stamens. Pods long and slender; if touched when ripe the valves roll up explosively and throw out the seeds. There are two varieties (sometimes described as separate species) of this plant; that figured is the variety *flexuo'sa*, which differs from the type in being perennial, having 6 stamens, rather wavy stems, and in growing in shady places.

DRA'BA

34. *Draba ve'rna*.   Spring Whitlow-grass.

Annual, 1–5 in., common on dry banks throughout Britain; I. Flowers white, spring. Leaves in a rosette, lance-shaped, toothed, hairy. From the rosette spring several wiry flowering stems each terminating in a small raceme of small, white flowers with spreading sepals and deeply cleft petals. The seeds come up in autumn and the plant passes the winter as a leaf rosette, flowers early and withers in summer, thus surviving in dry places by avoiding the dry period. Often self-pollinated. The species is a very variable one and many varieties (sometimes called species) are described. D. INCA'NA, the *Hoary Whitlow-grass*, a mountain plant of northern England, Wales, and Scotland, has slightly notched petals, and leaves grey with hairs.

COCHLEA'RIA

35. *Cochlearia officina'lis*.   Scurvy-grass.

Perennial, about 8 in., common along the coast throughout Britain, especially in Scotland; I. Flowers white, summer. Many stems spread out from the stout stock, prostrate and then rising. Radical leaves long-stalked, kidney-shaped; stem-leaves shortly stalked or sessile, bluntly angled or notched; glabrous. Flowers small, in dense showy racemes. Pods nearly globular, the style forming a sharp tip. The plant is widely spread in the arctic circle, and the English name refers to its former use by navigators for

33. Hairy Bitter-cress

32. Cuckoo-flower

35. Scurvy-grass

34. Spring Whitlow-grass

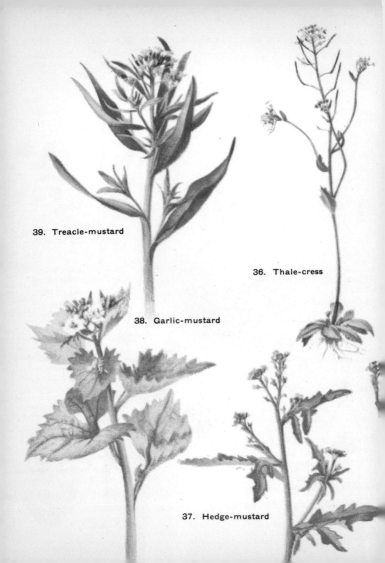

39. Treacle-mustard

36. Thale-cress

38. Garlic-mustard

37. Hedge-mustard

curing scurvy. There are several smaller species, of which the commonest is C. ALPI'NA, the *Alpine Scurvy-grass*, found in damp places on mountains in Scotland, Wales, and northern England. C. ARMORA'CIA, the *Horse Radish*, is sometimes found as an escape.

SISY'MBRIUM

36. Sisymbrium Thalia'na.   **Thale-cress.**

Annual, about 8 in., common on dry banks and waste places throughout Britain; I. Flowers white, summer. A slender rather bluish-green plant. Rosette leaves short-stalked, elliptical, toothed, slightly hairy; stem leaves few. Pods small, 4-angled, erect on spreading stalks.

37. Sisymbrium officina'le.   **Hedge-mustard.**

Biennial, 1–2 ft., common in dry waste places throughout Britain; I. Flowers yellow, summer. Radical leaves large, deeply cut into triangular lobes with coarse teeth; upper leaves small, halbert-shaped; hairy. The narrow, tapering pods are closely pressed to the stem. S. SOPHI'A, the *Flixweed*, occasionally found in waste places, has leaves twice cut pinnately into narrow segments; yellow flowers; the pods not pressed to the stem.

38. Sisymbrium Allia'ria.   **Garlic-mustard, Jack-by-the-Hedge, Sauce Alone.**

Biennial, up to 3 ft., common on shady banks throughout Britain; I. Flowers white, spring. A coarse, erect, leafy plant. Leaves large, stalked, heart-shaped, the lower more rounded than the upper; smelling of garlic when crushed. Flowers in showy corymbs. Pods about 2 in. long, rather stout; valves with a prominent rib.

ERY'SIMUM

39. Erysimum cheiranthoi'des.   **Treacle-mustard.**

Annual, 1–1½ ft., occasional as a weed in southern England; I. Flowers yellow, summer. Leaves on the little-branched stem, lance-shaped or elliptical, hardly stalked, greyish with short adpressed hairs. Pods erect, on slender, spreading stalks.

SUBULA'RIA

40. Subulata aqua'tica. **Awlwort.**

Submerged aquatic perennial, about 3 in., occasionally found near the margins of upland lakes in the Lake District, Wales, and Scotland. Leaves in radical tufts, awl-shaped, olive-green. Flowers few, on leafless stems. This little plant is very exceptional in producing its flowers under water where they are self-pollinated.

BRA'SSICA

41. Brassica Sina'pis. **Charlock.**

Annual, up to 2 ft., a common weed of cultivation throughout Britain. Flowers yellow, summer. Stem erect branched. Lower leaves large, oblong, with irregular lobes, the terminal the largest; upper leaves oval, short-stalked, irregularly notched and toothed; roughly hairy. Flowers ½ in. across, sepals spreading. Pods spreading, with a beak about half the length of the pod; valves with 3 veins. The flowers are visited by flies, bees, and butterflies, but if insect pollination fails the stigmas grow up against the long stamens and are self-pollinated. The genus includes the *White* and *Black Mustard* which are sometimes found as weeds; also the *Cabbage* and *Turnip* and the wild species from which they are derived, rare plants of the coast.

DIPLOTA'XIS

42. Diplotaxis tenuifo'lia. **Wall-rocket.**

Perennial, 1–2 ft., not uncommon in waste places in England and southern Scotland; I. Flowers pale yellow, summer. Stem branched and rather bushy. Leaves pinnately cut into narrow segments, glabrous and bluish-green. Pods long, erect on long stalks. D. MURA'LIS, the *Sand-rocket*, a smaller weed of southern England, has an unbranched, hairy stem and notched, glabrous leaves.

CAPSE'LLA

43. Capsella Bu'rsa pasto'ris. **Shepherd's Purse.**

Annual, up to 1 ft., a common weed throughout Britain; I. Flowers white, almost throughout the year. Rosette leaves elliptical, very variable, entire, coarsely toothed, notched or deeply divided into narrow segments; stem leaves arrow-shaped, clasping the stem. Flowers in small corymbs lengthening in fruit to long racemes. Pods conspicuous, reverse heart-shaped, on slender stalks.

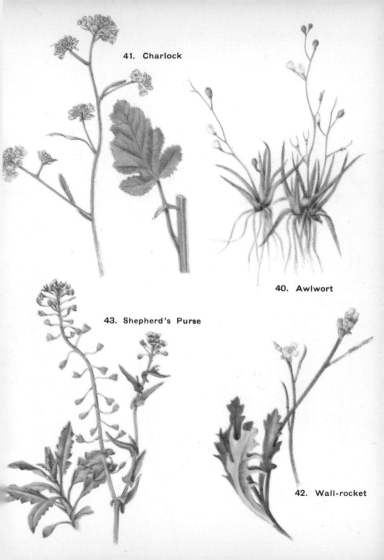

41. Charlock

40. Awlwort

43. Shepherd's Purse

42. Wall-rocket

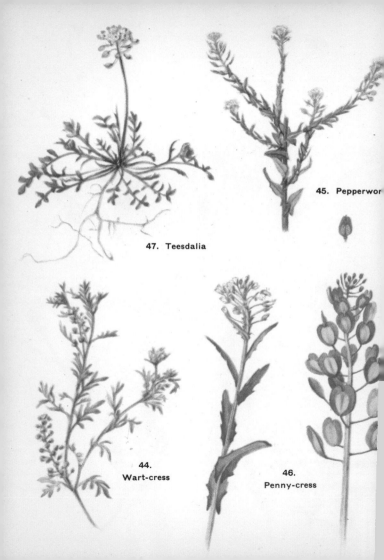

45. Pepperwor[t]

47. Teesdalia

44.
Wart-cress

46.
Penny-cress

CORONO'PUS

44. Coronopus di'dymus. **Wart-cress.**

Annual weed, prostrate, an occasional weed from mid-Scotland southwards. Flowers white, summer. Stem branched at the base, branches spreading on the ground. Leaves deeply pinnately cut, lobes deeply notched; glabrous. Pods less than $\frac{1}{12}$ in. across, wrinkled. C. RUE'LLII, *Swine's Cress*, is a similar and somewhat commoner weed; the leaves are less cut and the fruits twice as broad and deeply wrinkled.

LEPI'DIUM

45. Lepidium Smi'thii. **Pepperwort, Smith's Cress.**

Perennial, up to 1 ft., common in waste places from mid-Scotland southwards; I. Flowers white, summer. Stem branched from the base. Leaves arrow-shaped, clasping, hairy. Anthers violet. Pods ovoid, with an apical wing and the style protruding from the apical notch. L. CAMPE'STRE, the *Field Cress*, is a similar plant branching above; anthers yellow; style shorter than the notch of the pod. L. LATIFO'LIUM, the *Dittander*, is a rare plant of salt marshes with large radical leaves oval, stalked, and toothed; pods oval without notch.

THLA'SPI

46. Thlaspi arve'nse. **Penny-cress, Mithridate Mustard**

Annual, up to 1 ft., not uncommon as a field weed, especially in England; I. Flowers small, white, summer. Lower leaves tapering to the base; upper leaves arrow-shaped, clasping, slightly toothed, glabrous. Pods large, round, flat, with a broad wing and a deep apical notch. T. ALPE'STRE, the *Alpine Penny-cress*, a smaller alpine plant of northern England, Wales, and Scotland, has oval, stalked, radical leaves, glabrous and bluish-green.

TEESDA'LIA

47. Teesdalia nudicau'lis. **Teesdalia.**

Annual, 4–6 in., rather scarce in dry places and on walls from mid-Scotland southwards. Flowers small, white, early summer. Leaves in a flat rosette, deeply cut into spreading lobes. From the rosette rise several *naked* stems terminating in short racemes of small white flowers. HUTCHI'NSIA PETRAE'A is a rare plant of limestone rocks in the west resembling Teesdalia but smaller and with leaves on the flowering stems.

CRA'MBE

48. *Crambe mari'tima.*   **Sea-kale.**

Perennial, up to 2 ft., a rare plant of sand and shingle beaches from mid-Scotland southwards; I. Flowers white, summer. The thick stock gives rise to spreading branches. Leaves large, oval, divided into deep lobes with coarse teeth, glabrous, bluish-green, rather fleshy. Inflorescence a showy corymb; flowers fragrant. Apical joint of pod ovoid. The parent of the cultivated plant.

CAKI'LE

49. *Cakile mari'tima.*   **Sea-rocket.**

Annual, up to 1 ft., common on sandy shores throughout Britain; I. Flowers lilac, summer. Leaves oblong, with blunt lobes, glabrous. Flowers rather large, fragrant.

RA'PHANUS

50. *Raphanus mari'timus.*   **Sea Radish.**

Biennial, 2–3 ft., occasionally found on the coast from southern Scotland southwards; I. Flowers yellow, summer. Leaves deeply pinnately cut into toothed lobes, the terminal the largest. Pods usually with 2 joints and a terminal beak. R. RAPHANI'STRUM, the *Wild Radish*, is a field weed with usually white flowers and a pod with several joints.

RESEDACEAE. MIGNONETTE FAMILY

RESE'DA

51. *Reseda lu'tea.*   **Wild Mignonette.**

Biennial, 1–2 ft., rather uncommon in waste places especially on calcareous soil in England and the east of Scotland; I. Flowers pale yellow, summer. A rosette of leaves is formed in the 1st year, and the erect flowering stem in the 2nd. Leaves pinnately cut into narrow segments which are sometimes again cut; glabrous. Flowers in long dense racemes, scentless; visited by bees for nectar. R. LU'TEOLA, the *Dyer's Weed* or *Weld*, is a commoner plant of waste places with dark green, undivided leaves and greenish flowers; formerly used as a source of yellow dye.

**49.
Sea-rocket**

48. Sea-kale

**51.
Wild Mignonette**

50. Sea Radish

54. Marsh Violet

52. Rock-rose

53. Sweet Violet

55. Wood Dog-vio[let]

CISTACEAE. ROCK-ROSE FAMILY
HELIA'NTHEMUM

52. *Helianthemum Chamaeci'stus*   **Rock-rose.**
A small prostrate shrub with branches extending to 6–12 in., common in dry pastures and rocky places throughout Britain; I. Flowers yellow, summer. Leaves oval, blunt, grey with short hairs below; stipules small, pointed. Flowers 1 in. across, in terminal racemes; buds drooping. No nectar; pollinated by pollen-collecting bees. The stamens are sensitive to touch and move outwards when rubbed. H. CA'NUM is a rare plant of limestone rocks, with hoary leaves. H. POLIFO'LIUM is a rare plant of western England with white flowers and hoary leaves.

VIOLACEAE. VIOLET FAMILY
VI'OLA

53. *Viola odora'ta*.   **Sweet Violet.**
Perennial, 3–4 in., common in hedgerows in southern England. Flowers white with purple veins or purple, spring. Leaves and shoots from a woody stock, spreading by runners. Leaves stalked, heart-shaped, with rounded apex and teeth, enlarging after flowering. Style hooked. The fragrant flowers are visited principally by bees which push against the stigma before they touch the stamens and cross-pollinate the flowers. Visits are infrequent and most of the ripe fruits are produced from small bud-like flowers hidden among the leaves in summer; these do not open and are self-pollinated. VIOLA HI'RTA, the *Hairy Violet* with heart-shaped, hairy leaves, is not uncommon in thickets and pastures on calcareous soils.

54. *Viola palu'stris*.   **Marsh Violet.**
Perennial, 3–4 in., local in bogs throughout Britain. Flowers lilac, early summer. A creeping, branching rhizome gives rise to tufts of leaves, long-stalked, kidney-shaped, with rounded teeth, glabrous. Flowers small; sepals blunt; style straight; spur short.

55. *Viola Rivinia'na*.   **Wood Dog-violet.**
Perennial, 3–6 in., common in dry hedge banks throughout Britain; I. Flowers violet with a paler spur, early summer. The short stock bears a tuft of leaves surrounded by leafy, flowering branches. Leaves long-stalked, broadly heart-shaped with blunt teeth; stipules with long, narrow teeth. Style bent, club-headed. The seeds of this and other species are sought for and carried about by ants.

56. *Viola cani'na.*   **Heath Dog-violet.**

Perennial, 3–4 in., common on heaths and pastures throughout Britain; I.
Flowers blue-violet, with a yellow spur, early summer. The short stock
gives rise to leafy and flowering branches without a central leaf tuft. Leaves
narrowly heart-shaped with blunt teeth; slightly hairy. Stipules scarcely
toothed. There are several other species of dog-violet closely similar to the
last two.

57. *Viola tri'color.*   **Heartsease.**

Annual, up to 1 ft., common in dry fields throughout Britain; I. Flowers
purple and yellow, summer. Stem branched, straggling, angled. Leaves
stalked, ovate, with deep blunt teeth; stipules large and leafy, cut into
segments. Petals longer than the sepals. Style straight, round-headed; the
stigma has a flap which is closed over it as an insect leaves the flower, thus
preventing self-pollination.

58. *Viola arve'nsis.*   **Field Heartsease.**

Annual, 6–12 in., common in fields and waste places throughout Britain; I.
Flowers yellowish, summer and autumn. Stem, leaves, and stipules like those
of the last species, but the leaves narrower. Petals shorter than the sepals.

59. *Viola lu'tea.*   **Mountain Pansy.**

Perennial, 4–5 in., not uncommon in upland pastures in northern England,
Wales, and Scotland. Flowers large, yellow, sometimes purple, summer. A
slender underground rhizome sends up simple stems at intervals. Leaves
lance-shaped, toothed; stipules large with narrow segments.

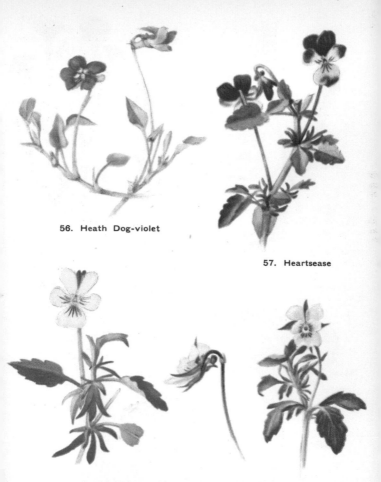

56. Heath Dog-violet

57. Heartsease

59. Mountain Pansy

58. Field Heartsease

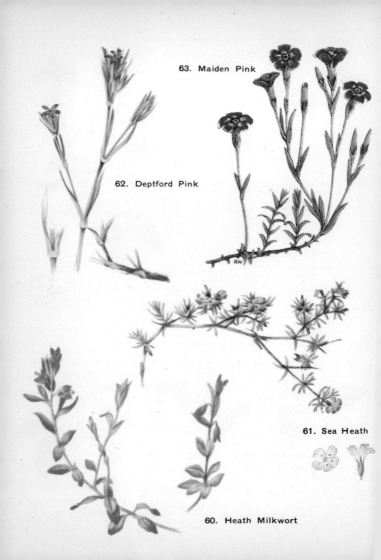

63. Maiden Pink

62. Deptford Pink

Rw

61. Sea Heath

60. Heath Milkwort

POLYGALACEAE. MILKWORT FAMILY
POLY'GALA

60. *Polygala serpylla'cea*.　　　　　　　　　　　**Heath Milkwort.**

Perennial, 2–6 in., common on heaths and pastures throughout Britain; I. Flowers dark blue, pale blue, pink, or white, summer. Stem simple or branched, spreading, slender. Leaves mostly opposite, elliptical, entire, glabrous. P. VULGA'RIS, the *Common Milkwort*, is another common plant of pastures with lance-shaped, alternate leaves. Pollinated chiefly by bees.

FRANKENIACEAE. SEA-HEATH FAMILY
FRANKE'NIA

61. *Frankenia lae'vis*.　　　　　　　　　　　　　**Sea-heath.**

A small, prostrate shrub, ½–1 ft., not uncommon on the south-east coast of England. Flowers small, pink, summer. Stems prostrate and much branched. Leaves $\frac{1}{10}$ in. long, narrow, with backward rolled margins. Petals notched; sepals reddish.

CARYOPHYLLACEAE. CAMPION FAMILY
DIA'NTHUS

62. *Dianthus Arme'ria*.　　　　　　　　　　　　**Deptford Pink.**

Annual, about 1 ft., an uncommon plant of dry places in southern and eastern England and Scotland. Flowers rose, late summer. Stems erect, little branched. Leaves narrow, pointed, each pair joined at the base. Flowers in close clusters; bracts lance-shaped, long-pointed, as long as the calyx; petals small.

63. *Dianthus deltoi'des*.　　　　　　　　　　　　**Maiden Pink.**

Perennial, about 8 in., common locally in dry pastures except in northern Scotland. Flowers rose, summer. Stem much branched from the base, branches erect. Leaves small, narrowly lance-shaped, pointed. Flowers solitary, about ½ in. across; bracts ovate, with a long narrow point, half as long as the calyx; petals toothed. The claws of the petals, confined by the calyx-tube, form a narrow tube ½ in. long at the bottom of which nectar is produced. The 5 outer stamens first grow out of the tube and shed their pollen, to be followed by the 5 inner stamens; finally the 2 styles grow out of the tube and the stigmas become receptive. The flowers are visited by butterflies whose long probosces probe the tube; they cross-pollinate the flowers. The other pinks show similar pollination mechanisms. D. CAE'SIUS, the *Cheddar Pink*, a rare plant of the Cheddar Gorge, has pale rose, sweetly scented flowers 1 in. across, with fringed petals; foliage glaucous.

SILE'NE

64. *Silene mari'tima*.   **Sea Campion.**

Perennial, about 6 in., common on rocky shores and river shingle throughout Britain; I. Flowers white, summer. Stem much branched from the base, branches spreading and forming tufts. Leaves oval or ovate, tapering to the base, bluish-green. Petals notched, with a large scale. S. CUCU'BALUS, the *Bladder Campion* or *White Bottle*, is a similar plant but taller, more erect and with broader leaves, commonly found on roadsides and fields.

65. *Silene co'nica*.   **Pink Catchfly.**

Annual, up to 1 ft., a rare plant of sandy places near the sea in south-eastern England. Flowers rose, summer. Stem erect, little branched. Leaves narrowly lance-shaped, hairy. Calyx ovoid; petals small.

66. *Silene acau'lis*.   **Moss Campion.**

Perennial alpine, about 2 in., abundant at high levels on mountains in northern England and Scotland; I. Flowers rose, summer. The much branched stems form dense cushions. Leaves small, narrow, pointed. Flowers solitary, $\frac{1}{2}$ in. across. One of the most characteristic and abundant of British alpine plants.

67. *Silene nu'tans*.   **Nottingham Catchfly.**

Perennial, about $1\frac{1}{2}$ ft., a rare plant of dry, stony places from mid-Scotland southwards. Flowers white, summer. Stem erect, branched from the base, with sticky glandular hairs. Leaves oval or lance-shaped, with soft hairs. Flowers numerous, drooping, in loose, terminal panicles, petals deeply cleft. The petals curl up by day and expand at night when the flowers are scented; they are visited by night-flying moths. On the first night of opening the outer stamens shed their pollen, on the second the inner, and on the third the stigmas are exposed. Flowers devoid of stamens and others with stamens only also occur. S. A'NGLICA, the *English Catchfly*, is an annual weed of sandy fields with small, white flowers, solitary in the leaf axils. S. OTI'TES, the *Spanish Catchfly*, is a perennial of sandy places in eastern England with numerous small, greenish-yellow flowers.

64. Sea Campion

66. Moss Campion

67.
Nottingham Catchfly

65. Pink Catchfly

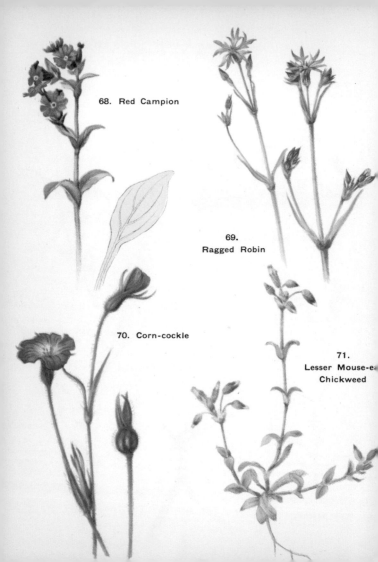

68. Red Campion

69. Ragged Robin

70. Corn-cockle

71. Lesser Mouse-eared Chickweed

LY'CHNIS

68. Lychnis dioi'ca. **Red Campion.**

Perennial, up to 2 ft., common in shady hedges and copses throughout Britain; I. Flowers deep rose, summer. Stems erect from the stock. Radical leaves long-stalked, broadly oval; stem leaves narrower, more pointed, short-stalked; softly hairy. Flowers in loose cymes, 1 in. across, unisexual, the male and female on separate plants. Teeth of capsule bent back. Pollinated by butterflies. L. ALB'A, the *White Campion*, is a very similar plant distinguished by its straight capsule teeth and the white flowers, which open in the evening and are pollinated by moths. SILENE NOCTIFLO'RA, the *Night-flowering Catchfly*, resembles this plant but may be distinguished by the 3 styles and the very pale, livid-pink flowers; an annual field weed.

69. Lychnis Flos-cucu'li. **Ragged Robin.**

Perennial, 1–2 ft., common in marshes and wet meadows throughout Britain; I. Flowers rose, early summer. Stems several, erect, rather sticky above. Leaves narrowly lance-shaped, those on the stem sessile, glabrous. Flowers nearly 2 in. across, in loose terminal cymes; petals cut into 4 narrow segments. Pollinated by bees and butterflies.

70. Lychnis Githa'go. **Corn-cockle.**

Annual, about 2 ft., not a native but occasionally abundant as a weed in cornfields throughout Britain; I. Flowers purple-red, late summer. Stems erect. Leaves long, narrow, pointed, softly hairy. Calyx with narrow, pointed teeth longer than the ovoid tube and longer than the petals.

CERA'STIUM

71. Cerastium semideca'ndrum. **Lesser Mouse-ear Chickweed.**

Annual, 2–4 in., common in dry sandy places throughout Britain; I. Flowers white, early summer. Stem branched from the base. Leaves oval, the lower narrowing to a stalk; softly hairy. Flowers small in rather crowded cymes; bracts and sepals with prominent membranous tips; petals slightly notched, shorter than the sepals; capsule just longer than the calyx, slightly curved. The fruit stalk is at first recurved and later erect. Flowers pollinated by flies, or self-pollinated.

72. *Cerastium visco'sum*.   Common Mouse-ear Chickweed.

Annual, about 6 in., common in fields and waste places throughout Britain; I. Flowers white, summer. Stem branched from the base, with sticky hairs. Leaves oval, softly hairy. Petals deeply notched, nearly as long as the sepals; bracts without membranous tips. Capsule nearly twice as long as the calyx, bent. Fruit stalks erect.

There are several other common species closely similar to these two.

73. *Cerastium arve'nse*.   Field Mouse-ear Chickweed.

Perennial, about 8 in., rather uncommon in dry fields from mid-Scotland southwards; I. Flowers white, summer. Tufts of branches rise from a slender rhizome. Leaves narrowly lance-shaped, softly hairy. Flowers few, in loose terminal cymes, ½ in. across; petals much longer than the sepals. C. ALPI'NUM, the *Alpine Mouse-ear Chickweed*, is a smaller plant of high mountains in northern England, Wales, and Scotland with large, white flowers.

STELLA'RIA

74. *Stellaria Holo'stea*.   Greater Stitchwort.

Perennial, 1–2 ft., common in hedgerows throughout Britain; I. Flowers white, early summer. Stem very slender and weak at the base, but thickening and becoming 4-angled above; plant half rambling. Leaves lance-shaped, tapering to a long point, rough, rich green. Flowers large and showy; petals much longer than the sepals, deeply notched. The flowers are visited chiefly by hover-flies for nectar secreted by 5 green nectaries at the base of the stamens. The stamens shed their pollen before the stigmas are ripe. First the stamens and later the stigmas are so spread over the mouth of the flower that the insect must touch them. If cross-pollination fails the stigmas bend over and are selfed by the inner stamens.

75. *Stellaria grami'nea*.   Lesser Stitchwort.

Perennial, 1–2 ft., common in hedges and pastures throughout Britain; I. Flowers white, summer. Stems weak, spreading. Leaves narrowly lance-shaped, rough, yellowish-green. Flowers in much-branched cymes; petals about as long as the sepals, deeply cleft into 2 narrow segments.

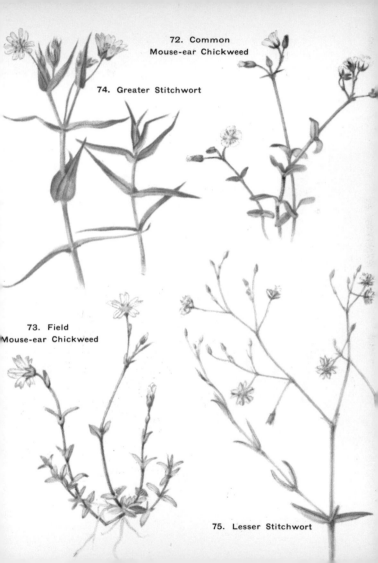

72. Common
Mouse-ear Chickweed

74. Greater Stitchwort

73. Field
Mouse-ear Chickweed

75. Lesser Stitchwort

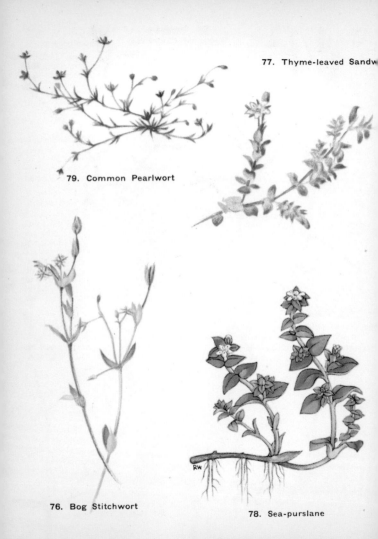

77. Thyme-leaved Sandw

79. Common Pearlwort

76. Bog Stitchwort

78. Sea-purslane

76. *Stellaria uligino'sa.* Bog Stitchwort.

Perennial, about ½ ft., of bogs and ditches throughout Britain; I. Flowers white, summer. Stems weak, spreading. Leaves oval or lance-shaped, pointed. Flowers small; petals deeply cleft, shorter than the sepals. S. ME'DIA, the *Chickweed*, the common garden weed, has spreading stems with a line of hairs running down one side, ovate leaves and petals shorter than the sepals. S. AQUA'TICA, the *Great Chickweed*, is a larger, coarser, hairier plant of wet places; styles 5.

ARENA'RIA

77. *Arenaria serpyllifo'lia.* Thyme-leaved Sandwort.

Annual, 2–12 in., common in dry places throughout Britain; I. Flowers white, summer. Stem branched from the base, branches short and erect or long and spreading. Leaves small, sessile, ovate, pointed, fringed with fine hairs. Flowers small; petals oval, just shorter than the pointed sepals; pod ovoid, with 6 teeth. A variable plant.

78. *Arenaria peploi'des.* Sea-purslane.

Perennial, 3–12 in., common on sand and shingle of the coast throughout Britain; I. Flowers greenish-white, summer. A slender white rhizome branches through the sand and sends up numerous branching, prostrate shoots. Leaves oval or ovate, pointed, glabrous, fleshy, yellowish-green. Flowers small, few about the tips of the shoots, male and female on separate plants; petals about the length of the sepals. Capsules large, globular, with few large seeds. A. TRINE'RVIA, the *Three-nerved Sandwort*, is a plant of shady places, very like the *Chickweed* from which it may be distinguished by its entire petals, and the 3 prominent veins of the leaf. There are several uncommon species; A. SEDOI'DES, the *Cyphel*, is a small tufted plant with greenish flowers of high mountains in Scotland.

SAGI'NA

79. *Sagina procu'mbens.* Common Pearlwort.

Annual, 2–4 in., common as a garden weed and in stony places throughout Britain; I. Flowers greenish, summer. Branches spreading from a central rosette of leaves, rooting. Leaves awl-shaped, with fine points. Sepals and petals 4 or 5, the latter smaller than the sepals or missing. Several closely similar species have been described of which S. APE'TALA is another common plant of similar places distinguished by the erect branches which do not root; petals always absent.

80. *Sagina nodo'sa*.   **Knotted Pearlwort.**

Perennial, about 4 in., not uncommon on moist heaths throughout Britain; I.
Branches spreading from the stock and then rising, slender. Leaves awl-
shaped, dark green, with short leafy shoots in their axils so that they appear
tufted. Flowers few, ¼ in. across, with petals much larger than the sepals;
sepals and petals 5. S. SUBULA'TA, a much scarcer plant, 2 in. high, of heaths,
has slightly hairy leaves terminating in a bristle point and petals about
as long as the sepals.

SPE'RGULA

81. *Spergula arve'nsis*.   **Corn Spurrey.**

Annual, about 1 ft., common as a weed of cornfields on light soil throughout
Britain; I. Flowers white, summer. Branched from the base, the branches
bending up. Leaves in pairs, with short leafy shoots in the axils so that they
appear whorled, narrow, almost cylindrical, pointed, fleshy, and dark green;
the whole covered with slightly sticky hairs, with an unpleasant odour when
damp. Flowers ¼ in. across, in loose, terminal cymes.

SPERGULA'RIA

82. *Spergularia ru'bra*.   **Red Spurrey.**

Annual or biennial, about 6 in., common on sandy roadsides and waste
places throughout Britain; I. Flowers pink, summer. Stem branched from
the base; branches spreading and prostrate. Leaves appearing tufted from
the short leafy shoots in their axils; flat, narrow, with fine bristle points;
stipules papery, large, ovate. Flowers ¼ in. across, the petals and the capsules
just shorter than the sepals; seeds not winged.

83. *Spergularia margina'ta*.   **Sea Spurrey.**

Perennial, up to 1 ft., common in muddy salt marshes throughout Britain.
Flowers pink, summer. Stem branched from the base; branches prostrate
and rooting. Leaves narrow, rather fleshy, pointed, appearing whorled;
stipules triangular. Flowers nearly ½ in. across in small cymes; petals as
long as, and capsules twice as long as, the sepals; seeds with a broad wing.

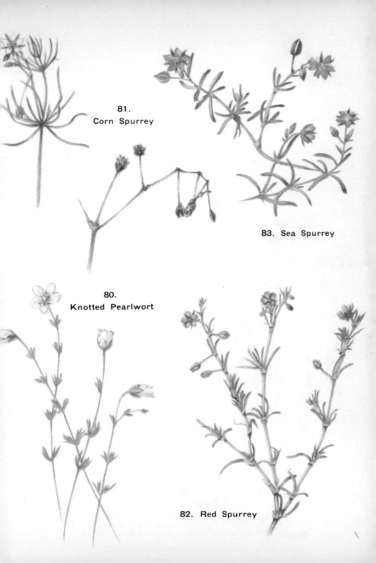

81.
Corn Spurrey

83. Sea Spurrey

80.
Knotted Pearlwort

82. Red Spurrey

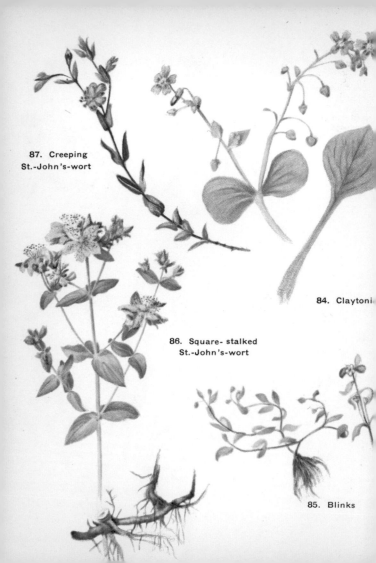

87. Creeping
St.-John's-wort

84. Claytoni

86. Square- stalked
St.-John's-wort

85. Blinks

PORTULACACEAE. BLINKS FAMILY
CLAYTO'NIA

84. *Claytonia sibi'rica*. Claytonia.

Annual, about 1 ft.; a North American plant frequently found naturalized in shrubberies. Flowers pink, summer. Radical leaves long-stalked, ovate; stem leaves opposite, sessile. Flowers in terminal racemes; petals much longer than the sepals, deeply notched. C. PERFOLIA'TA, also frequently found naturalized, is a smaller plant with small, white flowers; leaves united round the stem by their broad bases.

MO'NTIA

85. *Montia fonta'na*. Blinks.

Annual, 2–3 in., common in brooks and damp heaths throughout Britain; I. Flowers greenish-white; summer. The branching stems form dense tufts in the water or are tufted on mud. Leaves opposite, spoon-shaped, glabrous, pale green. Flowers very small, stalked; petals white, 2 larger than the others.

HYPERICACEAE. ST.-JOHN'S-WORT FAMILY
HYPE'RICUM

86. *Hypericum quadra'ngulum*. Square-stalked St.-John's-wort.

Perennial, about 2 ft., common in wet places from mid-Scotland southwards; I. Flowers pale yellow, late summer. Stems erect from a woody rhizome, 4-angled. Leaves sessile, oval, blunt, with few clear dots or none. Flowers about 1 in. across, in rather close panicles; petals with black glandular dots; stamens in 3 bundles. Capsule 3-chambered. H. PERFORA'-TUM, the *Common St.-John's-wort*, is a plant of similar habit, common in dry places; stem with 2 ridges; leaves narrowly oval with many clear dots. Pollinated by bees and flies visiting the flowers for pollen.

87. *Hypericum humifu'sum*. Creeping St.-John's-wort.

Perennial, 6–8 in., local on dry pastures throughout Britain; I. Flowers yellow, late summer. Branches from the rhizome spreading and prostrate, with 2 ridges. Leaves sessile, elliptical, glabrous, rather leathery, with margins slightly rolled back, clear dots and marginal black glands. Flowers about $\frac{1}{2}$ in. across, in small terminal cymes; stamens in 3 bundles. Capsule with 3 chambers. H. ELO'DES, the *Bog St.-John's-wort*, is a small creeping plant of bogs in southern England and western Scotland with oval or rounded hairy leaves and small, pale yellow flowers; stamens in 3 bundles, the filaments united nearly to the top.

88. Hypericum pu'lchrum.   Slender St.-John's-wort.

Perennial, about 1½ ft., common in dry thickets and heaths throughout Britain; I. Flowers yellow, tinged red in the bud, summer. Stems round, slender, erect, from a woody rhizome. Leaves sessile, heart-shaped or ovate, blunt, with clear dots, glabrous. Flowers over ½ in., in a slender panicle. Petals fringed with black dots; stamens in 3 bundles. Capsule with 3 chambers. H. HIRSU'TUM, the *Hairy St.-John's-wort*, is a common plant of thickets with shortly stalked, ovate, hairy leaves and pale yellow flowers, about ¾ in., in a dense panicle. H. ANDROSAE'MUM, *Tutsan*, a shrubby species not uncommon in woods, has large, blunt, ovate, leathery leaves; stamens in 5 bundles and a black berry. H. CALYCI'NUM, the *Rose of Sharon*, a south European species often naturalized in shrubberies, has flowers about 3 in.; stamens in 5 bundles; styles 5.

MALVACEAE.   MALLOW FAMILY
ALTHAE'A

89. Althaea officina'lis.   Marsh-mallow, Guimauve.

Perennial, about 3 ft., occasionally found in marshes near the sea in England, Wales, and southern Scotland; I. Flowers pale rose, late summer. Stems unbranched, erect from a woody stock. Leaves stalked, ovate or heart-shaped, with 3–5 shallow lobes, bluntly toothed, softly hairy. Flowers over 1 in., in small clusters in the axils of the upper leaves.

LAVATE'RA

90. Lavatera arbo'rea.   Tree-mallow.

Perennial, up to 6 ft., occasionally found in rocky places near the sea in England, Wales, and southern Scotland; I. Flowers purple with dark veins, late summer. Stem stout, erect. Leaves large, round in outline, with 5–7 lobes, rounded teeth, softly hairy. Flowers 1–2 in., crowded in long terminal spikes.

MA'LVA

91. Malva rotundifo'lia.   Dwarf Mallow.

Perennial, about 1 ft., not uncommon in waste places from mid-Scotland southwards; I. Flowers pink with purple veins, summer. Stem branching from the base, branches spreading. Leaves stalked, kidney-shaped, with very shallow lobes and prominent teeth, downy. Flowers 1 in., in small racemes in the leaf axils. In the young flower the anthers form a cone over the stigmas and shed their pollen; later the filaments bend back and the stigmas are exposed and become receptive. The flowers are visited chiefly by bees for nectar secreted between the bases of the petals, but, as the flowers of this species are rather inconspicuous and tend to be hidden in the leaves, visits are few and self-pollination often takes place by the stigmas bending among the stamens. In other members of the family insect visits are frequent and self-pollination rare. M. SYLVE'STRIS, the *Common Mallow*, a common plant of waste places, has erect stems, ivy-shaped leaves and purple flowers about 1½ in. M. MOSCHA'TA, the *Musk Mallow*, is distinguished by the deeply cut leaves, hairy fruits, and large, pale rose flowers.

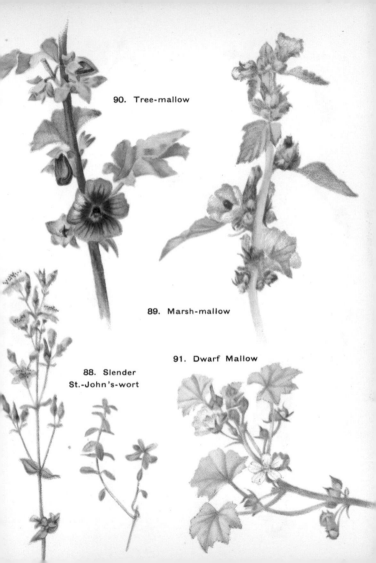

90. Tree-mallow

89. Marsh-mallow

91. Dwarf Mallow

88. Slender
St.-John's-wort

93.
Perennial Flax

94. Bloody Crane's-bill

92. Purging Flax

95.
Meadow Crane's-b[ill]

LINACEAE. FLAX FAMILY
LI'NUM

92. *Linum catha'rticum*.   **Purging Flax.**

Annual, 2 in. to 1 ft., usually about 4 in., common in pastures throughout Britain; I. Flowers white, summer. Stem simple or branched, erect. Leaves opposite, elliptical, sessile, bluish green. Flowers small, in loose terminal cymes.

93. *Linum pere'nne*.   **Perennial Flax.**

Perennial, 1–2 ft., a rare plant of calcareous pastures in eastern England, often grown in rockeries. Flowers bright blue, summer. Stems many from the woody stock, stiff and wiry. Leaves alternate, narrowly lance-shaped, glabrous. Flowers 1 in., in terminal cymes, lasting only 1 day. Flowers of 2 sorts on different plants (*a*) with long stamens and short styles, and (*b*) with short stamens and long styles; pollen is transferred from the one sort to the other by bees and flies and cross-pollination is certain. L. ANGUSTIFO'LIUM is a less rare plant of similar appearance but with smaller, paler flowers and pointed sepals. L. USITATI'SSIMUM, the *Cultivated Flax* or *Linseed*, is occasionally found as an escape or weed; it has unbranched stems and large blue flowers.

GERANIACEAE. CRANE'S-BILL FAMILY
GERA'NIUM

94. *Geranium sangui'neum*.   **Bloody Crane's-bill.**

Perennial, about 1 ft., locally found in rocky places throughout Britain; I. Flower crimson purple, summer. The stout woody stock gives rise to several branches, bent at the base, then erect. Leaves stalked, round in outline, deeply cut into 5–7 deeply notched, narrow segments; hairy. Flowers 1 in., solitary in the leaf axils.

95. *Geranium prate'nse*.   **Meadow Crane's-bill.**

Perennial, 2–3 ft., common in meadows and along roadsides from mid-Scotland southwards; I. Flowers bright purple-blue, summer. Stems erect from a stout stock, branched above. Radical leaves long-stalked, stem leaves sessile; round in outline, deeply cut into 7–9 elliptical lobes which are deeply notched and irregularly toothed; hairy. Flowers over 1 in., in pairs grouped in showy corymbs; filaments of stamens broad below.

96. *Geranium sylva'ticum.*   Wood Crane's-bill.

Perennial, 1–2 ft., locally common in moist and shady meadows in northern England and Scotland; I. Flowers rich blue-purple, summer. Stems erect from a stout stock. Radical leaves stalked, stem leaves sessile; deeply cut into 7–9 rather broad lobes; these are notched but not so deeply as in the last species. Flower less than 1 in., in pairs grouped in showy corymbs; filaments narrow. The flower is visited by bees, butterflies, and other insects for the nectar produced by the glands at the base of the stamens; this is protected from rain, and from small insects, by hairs near the base of the petals. The inner stamens become erect and shed their pollen first, then bend back while their place is taken by the outer stamens; later the stigmas spread out, become receptive and cross-pollination is certain; the pollination mechanism is similar in other species, but in some self-pollination may take place by the stigmas bending out amongst the stamens. G. PHAE'UM, the *Dusky Crane's-bill*, is a similar species naturalized in shady places, with smaller, deep purple-black flowers. G. PYRENA'ICUM, the *Mountain Crane's-bill*, is a more slender plant of hedgerows in England, with lobed, kidney-shaped leaves, and smaller flowers of a fine red purple.

97. *Geranium mo'lle.*   Dove's-foot Crane's-bill.

Annual, up to 1 ft., common in waste and cultivated ground throughout Britain; I. Flowers pink, summer. Stem branched, straggling. Leaves stalked, round in outline, with 5–7 broad, wedge-shaped, notched lobes, softly hairy. Flowers ½ in., in pairs in the leaf axils; petals notched, rather longer than the hairy sepals; carpels glabrous. G. DISSE'CTUM, the *Jagged-leaved Crane's-bill*, another common weed, has leaves deeply cut into narrow lobes which are again deeply cut and notched; flowers deep pink on stalks as long as the leaves; carpels hairy. G. COLUMBI'NUM, a less common weed, has leaves like those of the last with narrower segments; flower-stalks much longer than the leaves; carpels glabrous. G. PUSI'LLUM, another less common weed, has leaves like those of G. MOLLE, from which it is distinguished by its smaller flowers and hairy fruits.

98. *Geranium Robertia'num.*   Herb Robert.

Annual, about 1 ft., common on shady walls and stony places throughout Britain; I. Flowers rose, summer. Stems and leaves with sparse hairs, glistening and tinged with red. Leaves stalked, with 3–5 leaflets, deeply cut and notched. Sepals erect, closely applied to the petals, and closing over the fruit. G. LU'CIDUM, the *Shining Crane's-bill*, is a rarer plant of similar habit and station; markedly glistening; leaves kidney-shaped, with 5 broad, toothed lobes.

ERO'DIUM

99. *Erodium cicuta'rium.*   Stork's-bill.

Biennial, 3–12 in., common in sandy places especially near the sea throughout Britain; I. Flowers pink, summer. Leaves pinnately compound, leaflets cut and toothed, softly hairy; aromatic. Flower-stalks with 2 or more flowers, flowers ½ in. There are two other rare species, E. MOSCHA'TUM, the *Musky Stork's-bill*, a coarse plant about 2 ft. long with a strong musky smell, and E. MARI'TIMUM, the *Sea Stork's-bill*, a small plant with simple, toothed leaves.

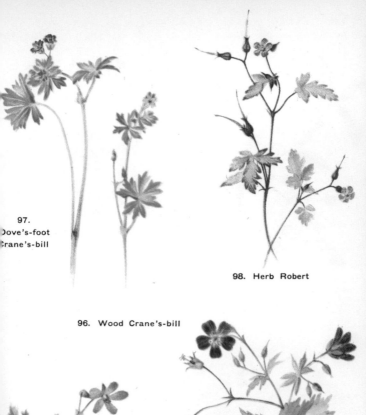

97.
Dove's-foot
Crane's-bill

98. Herb Robert

96. Wood Crane's-bill

99. Stork's-bill

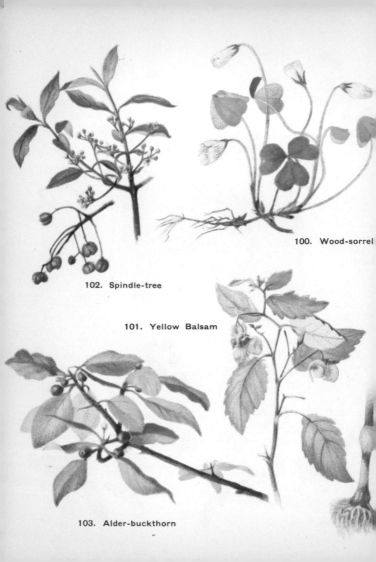

100. Wood-sorrel

102. Spindle-tree

101. Yellow Balsam

103. Alder-buckthorn

OXALIDA'CEAE. WOOD-SORREL FAMILY

O'XALIS

100. *Oxalis Acetose'lla*.   **Wood-sorrel.**

Perennial, 3–5 in., common in woods throughout Britain; I. Flowers white tinged lilac, late spring. Stem a branching rhizome partly covered with the fleshy bases of old leaves which act as food stores. Leaves all radical, long-stalked, trifoliate; leaflets reverse heart-shaped, finely hairy; stipules membranous. Flowers solitary on slender stalks with 2 small bracts, inclined, closing at night. Seed enclosed in an elastic coat, which, when ripe, squirts it out to some distance. Flowers only rarely visited by small flies; bud-like flowers which do not open and are self-pollinated are also formed.

BALSAMINACEAE. BALSAM FAMILY

IMPA'TIENS

101. *Impatiens No'li-me-ta'ngere*. Yellow Balsam, Touch-me-not.

Annual, about 2 ft., occasionally found in rough, shady places in England, usually an escape; I. Flowers yellow spotted with red, autumn. Stems hollow, succulent with thick nodes. Leaves alternate, stalked, oval, sharply toothed, glabrous. Flowers in stalked groups of 2–3 in the leaf axils. Pollinated by bees; the stigmas are exposed by the stamens separating after they have shed their pollen. If the ripe pod is touched the 5 valves roll up violently inwards and throw the seeds to some distance.

CELASTRACEAE. SPINDLE-TREE FAMILY

EUO'NYMUS

102. *Euonymus europae'us*.   **Spindle-tree.**

Shrub or small tree, about 10 ft., common in hedges and thickets on calcareous soil in southern Scotland and England; I. Flowers greenish-white, early summer. Young twigs ridged, green; older branches with smooth grey bark. Leaves stalked, opposite, elliptical, finely toothed. Flowers in small cymes. Ripe capsule coral-red, when open contrasting beautifully with the seeds, which have an extra, fleshy, orange coat; sought after and distributed by thrushes and other birds. There are hermaphrodite, male and female flowers on the same or different trees, visited chiefly by small flies.

RHAMNACEAE. BUCKTHORN FAMILY

RHA'MNUS

103. *Rhamnus Fra'ngula*. Alder-buckthorn, Berry-bearing Alder.

Large shrub, about 10 ft., local in woods and thickets in England, rare in Scotland; I. Flowers greenish-white, summer. Leaves stalked, reverse ovate, pointed, entire. Parts of flower in fives. Fruit red, black when ripe. R. CATHA'RTICUS, the *Buckthorn*, is a rather uncommon shrub in England; leaves ovate, toothed; twigs sometimes ending in a thorn; parts of flower in fours; male and female flowers on separate shrubs.

ACERACEAE. MAPLE FAMILY
A'CER

104. *Acer campe'stre*.   **Hedge Maple.**

A small tree, up to 20 ft., or shrub, common in hedgerows in England, especially in the south; I. Flowers green, early summer. Leaves palmately divided into 5 blunt, notched lobes, hairy on the veins. Flowers in small erect corymbs. The 2 wings of the fruit stand almost in a straight line. The flowers may be male, female, or hermaphrodite; much nectar is produced and they are visited and pollinated by bees. A. PSEUDOPLA'TANUS, the *Sycamore Maple*, is completely naturalized throughout the country; a tall tree with large, 5-lobed, toothed leaves; flowers in dense, pendulous racemes, appearing after the leaves; wings of fruit at an angle. A. PLATANOI'DES, the *Norway Maple*, is frequently planted, as are several other exotic species; it has erect inflorescences appearing before the sharply lobed leaves.

LEGUMINOSAE. PEA FAMILY
GENI'STA

105. *Genista a'nglica*.   **Petty Whin.**

Shrub, 1–2 ft., common on heaths and heather moors throughout Britain. Flowers yellow, early summer. A woody rhizome gives rise to many, straggling, woody branches; more or less spiny. Leaves small, glabrous, oval or ovate, without stipules. Flowers in short racemes. Pod glabrous, dark brown, and inflated. G. PILO'SA, *Hairy Greenweed*, is a rare shrub of heaths in southern Wales and England, without spines and with hairy pods.

106. *Genista tincto'ria*.   **Dyer's Greenweed.**

Shrub, 1–2 ft., not uncommon in rough pastures in England and southern Scotland. Flowers yellow, late summer. Much branched, branches stiff, erect, without spines. Leaves lance-shaped, glabrous or slightly hairy, with very small stipules. Flowers in long terminal racemes. Pod long, narrow, glabrous. Formerly used for a yellow dye.

U'LEX

107. *Ulex europae'us*.   **Gorse, Furze, Whin.**

Shrub up to 6 ft., common on heaths and pastures throughout Britain; I. Flowers yellow, most abundant in early summer. Much branched and often forming close cushions when nibbled by sheep. Leaves awl-shaped, with sharp points. Flowers solitary, or in small groups, on the spines; calyx with spreading hairs; wings longer than keel. Like other members of the family with 10 stamens united the gorse has no nectar; insects alighting on the wings press down the keel which opens suddenly so that first the stigma and then the stamens are pressed against the under surface of the insect's body, the stigma receiving pollen and the stamens dusting the body with pollen; bees are the chief visitors. The pod when dry explodes, the valves curling in and throwing out the seeds; the seeds are sought for and carried about by ants which eat the little orange outgrowth at the base of the stalk.

106.
Dyer's Greenweed

104. Hedge Maple

107. Gorse

105.
Petty Whin

108. Welsh G

111. Black Medick

110. Rest-harrow

109. Broom

RW

108. *Ulex Ga'llii.*   **Welsh Gorse.**

Small shrub, 1–3 ft., common on heaths in western England and Wales; I. Flowers orange-yellow, late summer and autumn. Spines strong. Hairs of calyx appressed; wings longer than keel. U. NA'NUS, the *Dwarf Gorse*, is a very similar plant of heaths in south-eastern England, distinguished by its more prostrate growth, lighter yellow flowers; wings of the corolla shorter than the keel.

CY'TISUS

109. *Cytisus scopa'rius.*   **Broom.**

Shrub, up to 6 ft., common along roadside, especially on gravelly soils, throughout Britain; I. Flowers yellow, summer. Much branched, with erect, prominently ribbed, switch branches. Leaves small, shortly stalked, with 1 or 3 small, oval, pointed, silky leaflets; stipules minute. Flowers large, in terminal racemes. The flower is pollinated by honey and humble bees, which alone are heavy enough to burst open the keel and liberate the stamens and style; 5 short stamens dust the under-side of the body and the stigma and 5 long stamens strike the insect on the back, the stigma first; the style then curls round so that the stigma touches the under side of the body of insects visiting the flower later; there is no nectar. The pod explodes violently, the valves twisting into a spiral and throwing out the seed.

ONO'NIS

110. *Ononis re'pens.*   **Rest-harrow.**

Shrub, 1–2 ft., common throughout Britain in sandy pastures, especially near the sea; I. Flowers rose-pink, summer. The woody rhizome spreads by underground suckers and gives rise to many low, spreading branches, sometimes with a few spines. Leaflets oval, blunt, with small, sharp teeth; whole plant with rather sticky soft hairs and with a somewhat unpleasant odour. Pods ovoid, pale brown, hairy. The weight of a visiting bee forces the style out of a small opening at the tip of the keel, and this is followed by pollen pumped out by the pressure of the stamens, from which it has been shed. O. SPINO'SA, *Upright Rest-harrow*, is an upright shrub with many spines, of barren pastures.

MEDICA'GO

111. *Medicago lupuli'na.*   **Black Medick, Nonsuch**

Annual, 6–12 in., common in dry grassy places throughout Britain; I. Flowers yellow, summer. Branching from the base and spreading on the ground. Leaflets reverse-ovate, finely toothed; stipules with long points. Flowers small, in small, round heads on slender stalks which are longer than the leaves. Pods curled, black when ripe.

112. *Medicago ara'bica*.   **Spotted Medick.**

Annual, 1–2 ft., not uncommon in dry places in southern England; I. Flowers yellow, summer. Stem branching and spreading on the ground. Leaflets reverse wedge-shaped, finely toothed, often spotted with purple or brown; stipules toothed, pointed. Flowers in heads of 2–5 on slender stalks which are shorter than the leaves. Pods coiled, grooved, with curved spines. M. SATI'VA, the *Lucerne*, is an important fodder plant sometimes found as an escape; erect, with purplish flowers and smooth, coiled pods.

TRIFO'LIUM

113. *Trifolium me'dium*.   **Zigzag Clover.**

Perennial, 1–2 ft., common on rough pastures and roadsides throughout Britain; I. Flowers bright red-purple, summer. Stem straggling, zigzag. Leaflets oval, finely hairy; stipules long, narrow, pointed. Flowers in round, stalked heads. T. PRATE'NSE, the *Red Clover*, is a similar plant; leaflets broader, reverse-ovate; flower heads very shortly stalked, dull purple.

114. *Trifolium arve'nse*.   **Hare's-foot Trefoil.**

Annual, ½–1 ft., not uncommon in sandy places, except in northern Scotland; I. Flowers pink, late summer. Stems branched from the base, more or less erect. Leaflets very narrow, oblong, with a blunt finely toothed apex, softly hairy. Flowers in numerous, cylindrical, brownish-pink heads; calyx with narrow teeth longer than the corolla, covered with silky hairs and giving the head a downy appearance.

115. *Trifolium re'pens*.   **White Clover, Dutch Clover.**

Perennial, ½–1 ft., common in pastures throughout Britain; I. Flowers white, summer. Stems creeping and rooting. Leaflets reverse-ovate, finely toothed. Flower-heads broadly rounded on very long stalks; flowers on short stalks, fragrant; corolla much longer than calyx. In the fruiting head the flowers turn down and the corolla becomes brown. Nectar is abundant (as in all species of clover and medick) and the flowers are pollinated chiefly by bees which burst the keel and cause the stigma and stamens to strike the lower surface of their bodies. In the red clover the corolla is so long that nectar can be reached only by the humble bee. T. HY'BRIDUM, the *Alsike Clover*, is a similar larger plant; stems not rooting, flowers tinged pink.

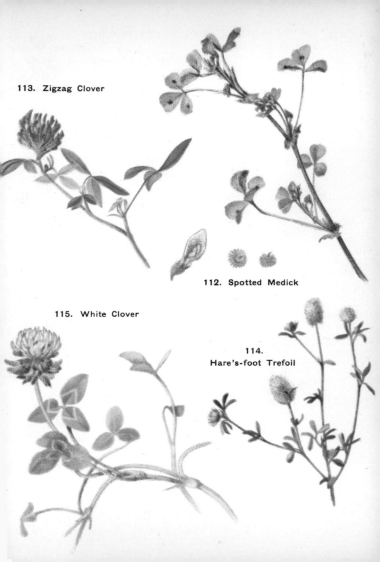

113. Zigzag Clover

112. Spotted Medick

115. White Clover

**114.
Hare's-foot Trefoil**

117. Hop Trefoil

118. Yellow Trefoil

116. Strawberry Trefoil

116. *Trifolium fragi'ferum.* Strawberry Trefoil.

Perennial, up to 1 ft., not uncommon in pastures in southern Scotland and England; I. Flowers pink, late summer. Resembles the last species in habit and foliage. Flower-head globular on a long stalk; flowers sessile; there is a ring of bracts just below the flower head. The calyx becomes very large and inflated in the fruit. T. STRIA'TUM, the *Knotted Trefoil*, a not uncommon plant of sandy pastures in southern Scotland and England, is an annual, about 6 in., with small heads of rosy flowers sessile in the leaf axils; calyx swollen in fruit with straight teeth. T. SCA'BRUM is a stiffer, and less common, plant with white or pinkish flowers and calyx teeth recurved in fruit. T. SUB-TERRA'NEUM, of sandy pastures in southern England, is a small plant with reverse heart-shaped leaflets and heads of 2–5 flowers the stalks of which bend and carry the fruiting head down to the soil. There are several other rarer species.

117. *Trifolium procu'mbens.* Hop Trefoil.

Annual, ½–1½ ft., common in pastures and waste places throughout Britain; I. Flowers yellow, summer. Stem much branched from the base, spreading and rising at the tips. Leaflets reverse-ovate, finely toothed. Flower heads of 20–40 flowers, round, on slender stalks which are longer than the leaves. The persistent brown corollas make the fruiting head like a small hop.

118. *Trifolium du'bium.* Yellow Trefoil.

Annual, up to 1 ft., common in dry pastures and waste places throughout Britain; I. Flowers yellow, summer. Stem branched, straggling or creeping. Leaflets oval or reverse-ovate. Flowers in heads of about 12 flowers, on stalks longer than the leaves. T. FILIFO'RME is a smaller and less common species, with only 2–3 flowers in the head.

ANTHY'LLIS

119. *Anthyllis Vulnera'ria.*   Lady's Fingers, Kidney Vetch.

Perennial, 1 ft., not uncommon on dry pastures and railway banks throughout Britain; I. Flowers cream, yellow or tinged red, summer. Stems nearly
erect from a woody stock. Leaflets elliptical, hairy, the largest at the apex.
Flowers in dense, terminal, paired heads.

LO'TUS

120. *Lotus cornicula'tus.*   Bird's-foot Trefoil.

Perennial, $\frac{1}{2}$–$1\frac{1}{2}$ ft., common in pastures and heaths throughout Britain; I.
Flowers orange-yellow, summer. The woody rhizome gives rise to branching
stems spreading out on the ground. Leaflets reverse-ovate, or oval. Flowers
in heads on long, erect stalks. Pods long, dark brown, spreading out like
the claws of a bird's foot.

121. *Lotus uligino'sus.*   Marsh Bird's-foot Trefoil.

Perennial, up to 2 ft., common in marshes and ditches except in northern
Scotland; I. Flowers bright yellow, late summer. Stems branching and
rambling. Leaflets oval or reverse-ovate. A coarser plant than the last. As
in the last species the flowers are visited by many insects and pollinated by
bees; the pollen is shed inside the tip of the keel and, when this is depressed,
is pumped out by the pressure of the swollen filaments of 5 of the stamens;
the stigma protrudes first. L. HI'SPIDUS is a rare seaside plant of south-
western England with only 3–5 flowers in the head and very hairy leaves.

119. Lady's Fingers

121. Marsh Bird's-
foot Trefoil

120. Bird's-foot Trefoil

122. Purple Milk-vetch

124. Bird's-foot

125.
Horseshoe-vetch

123. Sweet Milk-vetch

ASTRA'GALUS

122. Astragalus da'nicus. **Purple Milk-vetch.**

Perennial, about 6 in., locally common in dry pastures, especially near the sea in eastern England and Scotland; I. Flowers bright purple, summer. Stems slender, more or less erect, from a rhizome. Leaves with many pairs of small, lance-shaped or elliptical leaflets. Flowers in heads, on long stalks in the leaf axils, but appearing terminal. A. ALPI'NUS, the *Alpine Milk-vetch*, is a rare plant of Scottish mountains with racemes of cream-coloured blue-tipped flowers.

123. Astragalus glycyphy'llos. **Sweet Milk-vetch, Wild Licorice.**

Perennial, 2–3 ft., rather uncommon in bushy places and copses throughout most of Britain. Flowers pale yellow, summer. Stems branched, straggling, rather woody. Leaves with about 6 pairs of oval or ovate, glabrous, light green leaflets. Flowers in stalked racemes in the leaf axils.

ORNI'THOPUS

124. Ornithopus perpusi'llus. **Bird's-foot.**

Annual, 6–18 in., not uncommon in waste places, except in northern Scotland; I. Flowers white, veined red, early summer. Stem much branched, slender, straggling. Leaves with many pairs of small, oval, or elliptical leaflets. Flowers in stalked heads of 3–5; pods ¾ in., curved and beaded.

HIPPOCRE'PIS

125. Hippocrepis como'sa. **Horseshoe-vetch.**

Perennial, ½–1 ft., a typical plant of pastures on calcareous soils in southern England, rarer in the north. Flowers yellow, summer. The woody rhizome gives rise to more or less erect branches. Leaves with 4–5 pairs of small, elliptical, glabrous leaflets. Flowers few, in long-stalked heads. Pods about 1 in., brown, much flattened.

VI'CIA

126. *Vicia hirsu'ta.*   **Hairy Vetch.**

Annual, 1–2 ft., common in waste places throughout Britain; I. Flowers pale blue, or lilac, summer. Stems branched and rambling. Leaves with many pairs of narrow, oblong, blunt leaflets, ending in a branched tendril. Flowers 3–6 in stalked racemes, very small. Pods fat, 2-seeded, hairy. V. TETRASPE'RMA, the *Slender Vetch*, is a similar less common plant; flowers in pairs; leaflets fewer; pods glabrous with 4 seeds.

127. *Vicia Cra'cca.*   **Tufted Vetch.**

Perennial, 2–5 ft., common in hedgerows throughout Britain; I. Flowers bright blue-purple, summer. Stems branched, angled, weak and climbing. Leaflets in many pairs, narrowly oblong or lance-shaped, with small sharp points; leaf ending in a branched tendril. Flowers many, in showy racemes. Pods dark brown, narrow. V. SYLVA'TICA, the *Wood Vetch*, occasionally found in woods in hilly districts, has tendrils and long, loose racemes of large white, blue-veined flowers.

128. *Vicia se'pium.*   **Bush Vetch.**

Perennial, 1–3 ft., common in hedgerows throughout Britain; I. Flowers purple, summer. Stem branched, weak, rambling. Leaves with about 6 pairs of ovate leaflets indented at the tip and with a short sharp point; slightly hairy; ending in tendrils. Pods narrow, black. Spreads by suckers from the rhizome. The pollen is shed into a brush of hairs near the tip of the style and, when the keel is burst open by a visiting bee, the insect is dusted with pollen by this brush; the stigma only becomes receptive when it has been bruised by rubbing against the insect. The pollination mechanism is similar in other vetches.

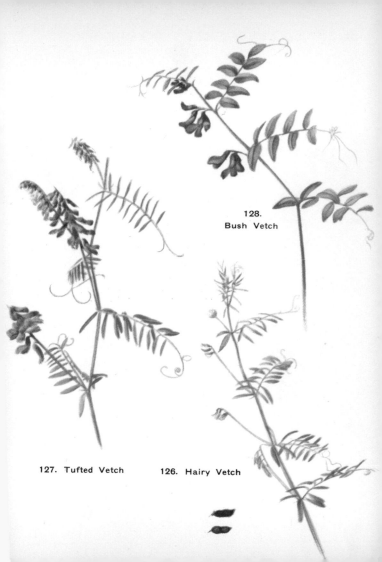

128.
Bush Vetch

127. Tufted Vetch   126. Hairy Vetch

129. Narrow-leaved Vetch

132.
Crimson Vetchling

131.
Yellow Vetchling

130. Spring Vetch

129. *Vicia angustifo'lia.*   **Narrow-leaved Vetch.**

Annual, about 1 ft., occasionally found in waste and grassy places throughout Britain; I. Flowers bright red-purple, summer. Branches spreading or climbing. Leaves ending in branched tendrils; leaflets elliptical, with fine points. Flowers rather large, 1 or 2 together on very short stalks in the leaf axils. V. SATI'VA, the cultivated *Tare*, is probably derived from this species; a coarser plant with broad leaflets.

130. *Vicia lathyroi'des.*   **Spring Vetch.**

Annual, 3–6 in., locally common in sandy places throughout Britain; I. Flowers lilac, spring. Stem branched from the base, branches spreading. Leaves ending in a point, with few pairs of reverse lance-shaped leaflets. Flowers solitary in the leaf axils. An ephemeral, passing through its life in a few weeks and surviving the driest season as seed.

LA'THYRUS

131. *Lathyrus A'phaca.*   **Yellow Vetchling.**

Annual, 1–2 ft., a rare field weed of southern England. Flowers yellow, summer. Stems branched, trailing or climbing. The leaves consist of a branched tendril and 2 large, leafy, broadly halbert-shaped stipules. Flowers solitary on long stalks in the leaf axils.

132. *Lathyrus Nisso'lia.*   **Crimson Vetchling, Grass Vetchling.**

Annual, about 1½ ft., a rare plant of grassy places in southern England. Flowers bright crimson, early summer. Stem more or less erect. The leaves are reduced to the long, narrow, flattened, grass-like stalks and have neither tendrils nor leaflets. Flowers solitary or in pairs on long stalks in the leaf axils.

133. *Lathyrus prate'nsis*.   **Meadow Vetchling.**

Perennial, about 2 ft., common in hedgerows and grassy places throughout Britain; I. Flowers bright yellow, summer. Stem angled, branched, rambling. Leaves with 1 pair of elliptical, pointed leaflets and terminal, branched tendrils; stipules leafy, arrow-shaped. Flowers in showy racemes, on long stalks in the leaf axils. Pollination takes place in a way similar to that in *Vicia*.

134. *Lathyrus mari'timus*.   **Sea-pea.**

Perennial, 1–2 ft., locally abundant on shingle beaches in southern and eastern England; I. Flowers purplish, late summer. Prostrate stems spread out from the woody rhizome. Leaves with 4 or 5 pairs of large, oval leaflets, glabrous, bluish-green, with small terminal tendrils. Racemes with few, rather large flowers on stalks not so long as the leaves. Pods long, dark brown. L. PALU'STRIS, the *Marsh-pea*, is an uncommon plant of wet meadows with a winged stem, few pairs of narrow lance-shaped leaflets and blue-purple flowers. L. LATIFO'LIUS, the *Everlasting Pea*, occasionally found as an escape, has 1 pair of large oval leaflets, winged stems and leaf-stalks, and large, pink-purple flowers.

135. *Lathyrus monta'nus*.   **Bitter-vetch.**

Perennial, ½–1 ft., common on heaths and open copses throughout Britain; I. Flowers red-purple, summer. The rhizome forms small tubers and sends up straggling, winged stems. Leaves with 2–4 pairs of narrow, elliptical or lance-shaped leaflets, ending in a simple point without tendrils. Flowers few, in loose racemes on stalks about the length of the leaves. Pods long, black.

ROSACEAE.   ROSE FAMILY
PRU'NUS

136. *Prunus spino'sa*.   **Blackthorn, Sloe.**

Shrub, about 8 ft., common in hedges and copses throughout Britain; I. Flowers white, spring. Much branched; branches crooked and very spiny. Leaves elliptical, toothed. Flowers, ½ in., in small clusters, before the leaves. Fruits, ½ in., on short stiff stalks, blue-black, astringent.

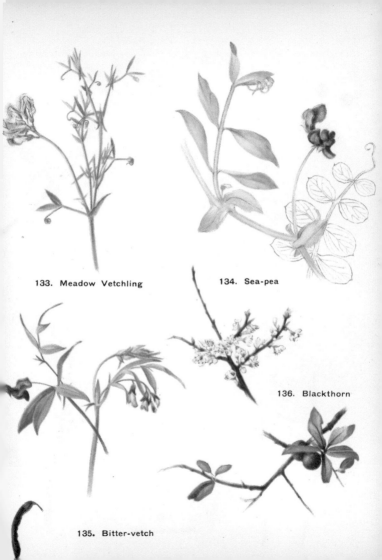

133. Meadow Vetchling

134. Sea-pea

136. Blackthorn

135. Bitter-vetch

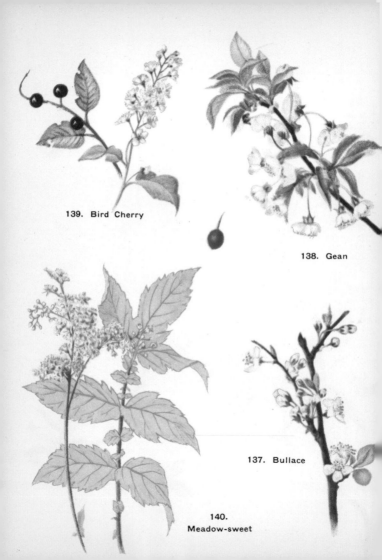

139. Bird Cherry

138. Gean

137. Bullace

140.
Meadow-sweet

137. *Prunus insti'tia*.   **Bullace.**

Shrub, about 12 ft., not uncommon in copses in England and southern Scotland. Flowers white, spring. Much branched; branches straight, with few spines. Leaves elliptical or reverse-ovate, toothed. Flowers about ⅜ in., in small clusters, before the leaves. Fruit up to 1 in., drooping, blue-black, rarely yellow.

138. *Prunus A'vium*.   **Gean.**

Tree, 20–30 ft., common in woods and copses throughout Britain; I. Flowers white, early summer. Trunk straight, branched above, with smooth, brown bark. Leaves oval or reverse-ovate, sharply toothed, pointed, on drooping stalks, downy beneath. Petals spreading. Fruit round, red, or sometimes black, with juice which stains, bitter-sweet. P. CE'RASUS, the *Wild Cherry*, is an uncommon tree of copses in England; leaves with blunt teeth and stiffer stalks, glabrous; corolla cup-shaped; fruit red, acid, with juice which does not stain. The flowers are visited chiefly by bees for nectar; the stamens stand away from the stigma and self-pollination is infrequent.

139. *Prunus Pa'dus*.   **Bird Cherry.**

Tree, 20–30 ft., not uncommon in woods and copses except in southern England; I. Flowers white, early summer. Leaves oval or reverse-ovate, coming to a point, finely and sharply toothed. Flowers in erect racemes. Fruit small, round, purple-black, bitter.

SPIRAE'A

140. *Spiraea Ulma'ria*.   **Meadow-sweet, Queen of the Meadows.**

Perennial, about 3 ft., common in damp meadows and marshes throughout Britain; I. Flowers cream, summer. Stiff, furrowed, reddish stems rise from the stock. Leaves large, pinnately compound, with small leaflets between the large; leaflets ovate, lobed or notched, and sharply toothed, downy below. Flowers small, in a showy, much branched corymb; fragrant, without nectar. S. FILIPE'NDULA, the *Dropwort*, is a smaller less common plant of pastures; leaves mostly radical with narrow, deeply notched leaflets; corymbs smaller and less dense. S. SALICIFO'LIA, a shrub with simple, toothed leaves, is often planted in hedges and shrubberies.

RU'BUS

141. Rubus frutico'sus.   **Blackberry, Bramble.**

Shrub, 4–10 ft., common in hedges and thickets throughout Britain; I.
Flowers white, often tinged with pink or purple, summer. Stem slender,
branched, arching and rambling, with curved prickles. Leaflets 3 or 5,
more or less oval or reverse ovate, toothed, usually with prickles on the
lower surface of the veins, often whitish below. Flowers rather large, in
terminal corymbs. Fruits deep purple or black. The tips of the shoots may
root and start new plants. Visited for the easily accessible nectar by a great
variety of insects. The blackberry is an extremely variable plant and a large
number of closely related species have been distinguished by specialists.
R. CAE'SIUS, the *Dewberry*, not uncommon in stony places, has prostrate
stems; leaves green on both sides; carpels few; fruits with a bluish bloom.
R. IDAE'US, the *Raspberry*, spreads by suckers, has erect stems and red or
yellow fruit.

142. Rubus saxa'tilis.   **Stone Bramble.**

Herb, ½–1 ft., not uncommon in stony woods, especially in northern England
and in Scotland; I. Flowers white, late summer. Herbaceous, rambling
stems rise from a woody rhizome; prickles few and small. Leaves 3-foliate,
leaflets thin, broadly oval or ovate, toothed. Flowers few. Carpels 2–3;
fruits deep red.

143. Rubus Chamaemo'rus.   **Cloudberry, Avrons.**

Herb, ½–1 ft., locally common on damp upland moors in Wales, northern
England, and Scotland; I. Flowers white in summer. Rhizome woody,
creeping and branching extensively. Stems erect, without prickles. Leaves
round in outline, with 5–7 rounded, toothed lobes. Flowers large, solitary,
male and female on separate plants. Fruits large, orange or red and very
fresh in flavour.

DRY'AS

144. Dryas octope'tala.   **Mountain Avens.**

Perennial, 2–3 in., an uncommon plant of mountains in northern England
and Scotland, especially on limestone; I. Flowers white, summer. Stem
woody, prostrate and much branched. Leaves stalked, ovate-oblong, with
rounded teeth, wrinkled and leathery, white with fine hairs below. Flowers
1 in., solitary on erect stalks. The feathery awns aid in wind dispersal.

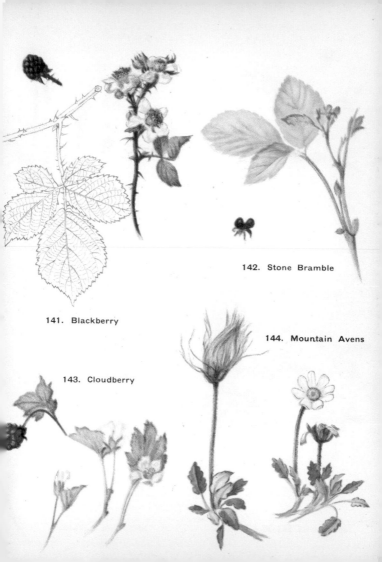

141. Blackberry

142. Stone Bramble

143. Cloudberry

144. Mountain Avens

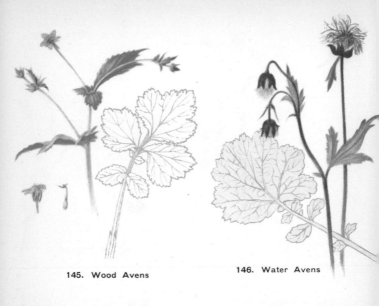

145. Wood Avens   146. Water Avens

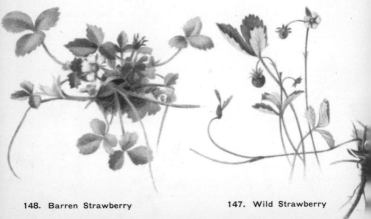

148. Barren Strawberry   147. Wild Strawberry

GE'UM

145. *Geum urba'num*.   **Wood Avens, Herb Bennet.**

Perennial, 1–3 ft., common in shady places throughout Britain; I. Flowers yellow, summer. Stems erect from a woody stock. Radical leaves with 3 large, and several smaller, leaflets, on long stalks, finely hairy; leaflets broad, rounded, notched, and toothed; stem leaves short-stalked, compound or deeply lobed and toothed; stipules large and leafy. Flowers, ½ in., solitary or in small cymes, erect. The hooked awn, catching on animals, aids in seed dispersal.

146. *Geum riva'le*.   **Water Avens.**

Perennial, 1–2 ft., common in moist shady places throughout Britain; I. Flowers pinkish-brown, summer. Stems erect from a woody stock. Radical leaves stalked, with a large terminal, and several pairs of smaller leaflets, hairy; leaflets rounded, lobed and toothed; stem leaves short-stalked, usually with 3 elliptical, toothed leaflets. Flowers few, drooping; petals dull yellow, sepals reddish. The achenes are grouped on a stalked knob.

There is a not uncommon hybrid between these two species having intermediate characters.

FRAGA'RIA

147. *Fragaria ve'sca*.   **Wild Strawberry.**

Perennial, 3–6 in., common in shady places throughout Britain; I. Flowers white, early summer. The woody rhizome produces a tuft of leaves and long runners which root and start new plants. Leaves stalked, 3-foliate; leaflets oval, sharply toothed, with silky hairs. Flowers few, inclined, on slender erect stalks. Fruit nodding, scarlet.

POTENTI'LLA

148. *Potentilla ste'rilis*.   **Barren Strawberry.**

Perennial, 3–5 in., common in shady places throughout Britain; I. Flowers white, spring. Rhizome woody and branching, giving rise to tufts of leaves but without runners. Leaves and flowers much like those of the Wild Strawberry, but the fruit consists of larger achenes on a dry knob.

149. *Potentilla ere'cta.*   Tormentil.

Perennial, 6–9 in., common in open woods and heaths throughout Britain; I.
Flowers yellow, summer. Rhizome thick, woody; stems more or less erect.
Stem leaves sessile, with 3 wedge-shaped, deeply toothed leaflets and toothed,
leafy stipules. Flowers solitary in the leaf axils; petals 4. P. PROCU'MBENS,
the *Creeping Tormentil*, is a closely related plant of heaths with a more
creeping stem, rooting at the nodes; all leaves stalked; petals often 5.
P. ARGE'NTEA, the *Hoary Cinquefoil*, is a rather uncommon plant of roadsides
in eastern Scotland and England; leaves very deeply cut into 5 wedge-
shaped, deeply toothed lobes, white with hairs beneath; flowers yellow in
terminal cymes.

150. *Potentilla re'ptans.*   Creeping Cinquefoil.

Perennial, 1–2 ft., common in waste places and as a garden weed in England
and southern Scotland; I. Flowers yellow, summer. The rhizome gives
rise to long, slender, reddish stems, creeping and rooting at the nodes; the
plant thus spreads rapidly and is a difficult weed to eradicate. Leaves long-
stalked, with 4, reverse-ovate, toothed leaflets; stipules small. Flowers
solitary, on long stalks, $\frac{3}{4}$ in.; petals 5. In shady places the plant frequently
fails to flower.

151. *Potentilla Anseri'na.*   Silver-weed.

Perennial, up to 1 ft., common in waste places, roadsides, and shingle beaches
throughout Britain; I. Flowers bright yellow, summer. The rhizome gives
rise to a tuft of leaves and long runners which root and form new plants.
Leaves pinnately compound, with small leaflets between the large; leaflets
oblong or oval, deeply toothed, silvery with hairs beneath. Flowers, $\frac{3}{4}$ in.,
solitary on long stalks. The flowers, as with other species, are visited by
a variety of insects for the easily reached nectar. In cold weather they remain
closed and are self-pollinated.

152. *Potentilla palu'stris.*   Marsh Cinquefoil.

Perennial, 1–2 ft., common in marshes and peat-bogs throughout Britain; I.
Flowers red-brown, summer. The branching rhizome gives rise to tufts of
leaves and more or less erect, flowering shoots. Leaves pinnate, with 5–7
oblong, sharply toothed, slightly hairy leaflets; stipules large, membranous,
united to the leaf-stalk. Flowers in small cymes, large, with reddish-brown
sepals and small, purplish petals. P. SIBBA'LDI is a small tufted plant, locally
abundant on high mountains in Scotland; flowers very small, yellowish-
green. There are several other rare mountain species with large white or
yellow flowers.

149. Tormentil

150. Creeping Cinquefoil

151. Silver-weed

152. Marsh Cinquefoil

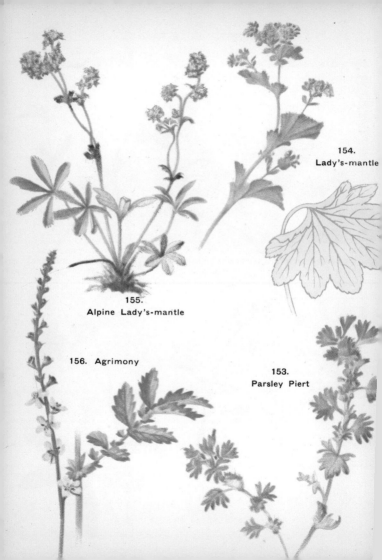

154.
Lady's-mantle

155.
Alpine Lady's-mantle

156. Agrimony

153.
Parsley Piert

ALCHEMI'LLA

153. Alchemilla arve'nsis. **Parsley Piert.**

Annual, 2–5 in., common as a weed of arable land throughout Britain; I. Flowers green, summer. Stem branching from the base; branches spreading. Leaves small, fan-shaped, deeply divided into 3 lobes which are in turn lobed; stipules leafy. Flowers minute, in inconspicuous groups in the leaf-axils.

154. Alchemilla vulga'ris. **Lady's-mantle.**

Perennial, ½–1 ft., common in meadows and waste places throughout Britain; I. Flowers yellow-green, summer. The stout woody stock gives rise to radical leaves and erect flowering stems. Leaves large, long-stalked, kidney-shaped, palmately lobed, sharply toothed, sparingly hairy. Flowers small, in rather close, conspicuous panicles. Nectar easily reached and the flowers visited by a variety of insects, though not frequently; sexes often in different flowers.

155. Alchemilla alpi'na. **Alpine Lady's-mantle.**

Perennial, about 4 in., abundant on mountains and river shingle in northern England and Scotland; I. Flowers greenish, summer. Leaves and flowering stems from a branched, woody rhizome. Leaves stalked, so deeply cut into 5–7 lobes as to be almost compound; lobes elliptical, toothed at the tip, white with silky hairs below. Flowers minute in small dense groups arranged in corymbs.

AGRIMO'NIA

156. Agrimonia Eupato'ria. **Agrimony.**

Perennial, 1½–2 ft., common along roadsides and in pastures, except in northern Scotland; I. Flowers yellow, summer. Stems erect from a stout stock. Leaves stalked, pinnately compound, with small leaflets between the larger, hairy; leaflets elliptical, with large teeth; stipules large. Flowers on short stalks in long, spike-like racemes. The cup enclosing the achenes turns downwards when ripe; its rim is beset with hooked spines which catch on passing animals and aid dispersal. A. ODORATA is a similar but rarer plant of coarser habit with an aromatic odour.

POTE'RIUM

157. Poterium officina'le.   **Greater Burnet.**

Perennial, about 2–3 ft., not uncommon in damp meadows in southern
Scotland and England; I. Flowers dark red, summer. Stems erect from a
woody stock. Leaves pinnately compound; leaflets stalked, oblong-heart-
shaped, toothed; stipules large, leafy. Flowers in dense oblong heads,
hermaphrodite; stamens 4. The flowers are visited by flies for nectar at
the mouth of the tube. P. SANGUISO'RBA, the *Salad Burnet*, is a commoner
plant of pastures, 1–2 ft.; leaflets small, ovate or oval, toothed, on short
stalks. Flower heads round, greenish red; upper flowers female, with long
styles and feathery stigmas; lower flowers male, with many stamens hanging
out on long filaments; pollinated by wind.

RO'SA

158. Rosa cani'na.   **Dog Rose.**

Shrub, 5–6 ft., common in hedgerows throughout Britain; I. Flowers pink
or white, summer. A large, much branched bush, with recurved spines on
the stems and backs of the leaves. Leaves pinnately compound; glabrous;
leaflets oval, toothed, pointed. Flowers large in small terminal corymbs;
3 of the sepals lobed. Fruit an ovoid, scarlet hip enclosing the achenes.
The flowers are visited by bees and other insects for pollen. R. ARVE'NSIS,
the *Field Rose*, common in England, has trailing branches and white, scentless flowers. R. RUBIGINO'SA, the *Sweetbriar*, has sticky, fragrant, reddish
glands on the lower side of the leaves. There are several other species and
many varieties of Rosa often difficult to distinguish.

159. Rosa spinosi'ssima.   **Burnet Rose, Scots Rose.**

Shrub, 1–2 ft., local in pastures especially near the sea, commoner in
Scotland; I. Flowers white, summer. Erect, much branched, with very
numerous, straight prickles. Leaflets oval, toothed. The stamens form a
golden boss in the centre of the flower. Hip globular, dark red or black.

PY'RUS

160. Pyrus tormina'lis.   **Service-tree.**

Tree, about 40 ft., rather uncommon in woods and copses in mid- and
southern England. Flowers cream, early summer. Young shoots and leaves
downy. Leaves broadly ovate in outline, rather irregularly and sharply
lobed, toothed. Flowers $\frac{1}{2}$ in., in corymbs. Fruit with 2 compartments,
ovoid, brown, tinged with red and green. P. A'RIA, the *Whitebeam*, is a
common tree with broad, oval, doubly toothed leaves, white below, and
scarlet fruits. P. AUCUPA'RIA, the *Rowan* or *Mountain Ash*, a common shrub
or small tree of mountain districts, has pinnately compound leaves and
small, bright scarlet berries.

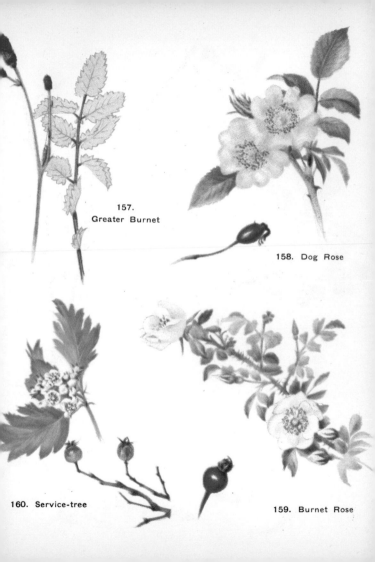

157.
Greater Burnet

158. Dog Rose

160. Service-tree

159. Burnet Rose

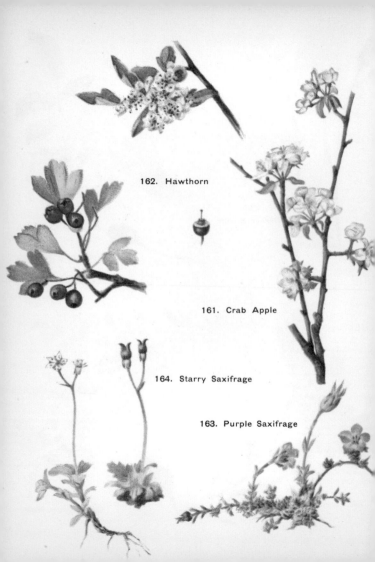

162. Hawthorn

161. Crab Apple

164. Starry Saxifrage

163. Purple Saxifrage

161. _Pyrus Ma'lus_.   **Crab Apple.**

Tree, up to 20 ft., not uncommon in thickets in England and southern Scotland, often an escape; I. Flowers pink and white, early summer. Leaves oval or round, coming to a point, toothed, downy beneath when young. Flowers 1 in., in small umbels, usually on spur shoots. Fruit about 1 in., round, red or yellow. P. COMMU'NIS, the _Pear_, with white flowers, is probably never native.

CRATAE'GUS

162. _Crataegus Oxyaca'ntha_.   **Hawthorn, Whitethorn, May.**

Large shrub or tree, up to 20 ft., common in pastures, hedges, and thickets throughout Britain; I. Flowers white, early summer. Much branched, many of the twigs terminating in spines. Leaves rhomboid-shaped in outline, lobed and toothed, glabrous, dark green, shining; stipules falling early. Flowers in dense corymbs, white with carmine anthers and very fragrant. Fruits small, ovoid, crimson. Two varieties (or species) are recognized, of which that figured is C. MONO'GYNA, with deeply cut leaves and 1 style; C. OXYACANTHOI'DES, which is less common, has less deeply lobed leaves and 2-3 styles.

SAXIFRAGACEAE. SAXIFRAGE FAMILY

SAXI'FRAGA

163. _Saxifraga oppo'sitifo'lia_.   **Purple Saxifrage.**

Perennial, 3-4 in., locally common in stony places of high mountains, especially in Scotland; I. Flowers purple, early summer. Stems prostrate, much branched, forming cushions. Leaves small, opposite, crowded usually in 4 rows, rather thick, oval. Flowers solitary, ½ in.

164. _Saxifraga stella'ris_.   **Starry Saxifrage.**

Perennial, 3-5 in., not uncommon in damp places in mountains in Wales, northern England, and Scotland; I. Rhizome branching and producing tufts of leaves. Leaves wedge-shaped or oval, toothed. Flowering stems leafless; flowers in a loose cluster, petals with 2 purple dots; anthers red. S. NIVA'LIS, the _Alpine Saxifrage_, is a rare mountain plant distinguished by the crowded flowers and the pure white petals. There are several other rare alpine species.

165. *Saxifraga aizoi'des.*   **Yellow Saxifrage.**

Perennial, 3–5 in., locally common in wet, stony places in mountains in
northern England and Scotland; I. Flowers yellow, summer. Stems creeping
and branching, sending up erect barren and flowering shoots. Leaves
alternate, narrow, pointed. Flowers few, in terminal groups. Petals yellow
with orange dots.

166. *Saxifraga tridactyli'tes.*   **Rue-leaved Saxifrage.**

Annual, 2–4 in., not uncommon on dry walls in England and eastern Scotland; I. Flowers white, early summer. Stems erect from a rosette of leaves,
branched, or simple in small specimens. Lower leaves narrowing to a stalk,
3–5 lobed, upper leaves sessile; with glandular hairs. Flowers small, in
open cymes.

167. *Saxifraga gra'nula'ta.*   **Meadow Saxifrage.**

Perennial, 6–9 in., not uncommon in dry, grassy places in England and
southern Scotland; I. The rhizome produces scaly bulbs which multiply
the plant, and erect flowering stems. Leaves stalked, alternate, lower kidney-
shaped with many shallow lobes, upper with deeper sharper lobes. Flowers
in loose terminal cymes, ½ in.

CHRYSOSPLE'NIUM

168. *Chrysosplenium oppo'sitifo'lium.*   **Golden Saxifrage.**

Perennial, 2–4 in., common in damp shady places throughout Britain; I.
Flowers greenish-yellow, late spring. Stem creeping and rooting below,
with erect leafy and flowering shoots. Leaves opposite, stalked, round, with
many shallow, rounded lobes, hairy. Flowers in leafy corymbs. C. ALTERNI-
FO'LIUM is a less common plant with alternate, kidney-shaped leaves and
brighter flowers. The flowers are visited by small insects for the easily
reached nectar; it has also been suggested that they are pollinated by small
snails.

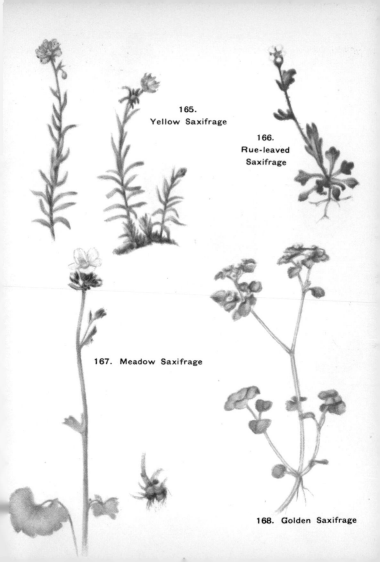

165.
Yellow Saxifrage

166.
Rue-leaved
Saxifrage

167. Meadow Saxifrage

168. Golden Saxifrage

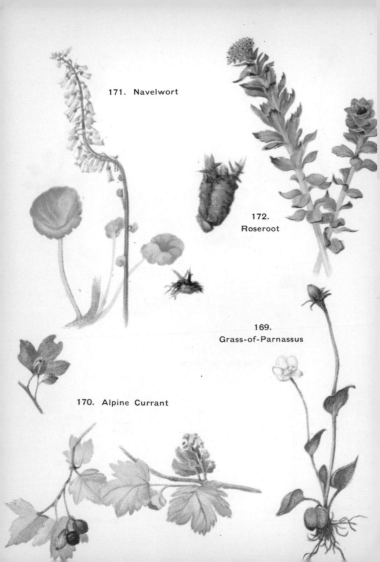

171. Navelwort

172.
Roseroot

169.
Grass-of-Parnassus

170. Alpine Currant

PARNA'SSIA

169. Parnassia palu'stris.   **Grass-of-Parnassus.**

Perennial, 6–9 in., local in bogs through most of Britain; I. Flowers white, late summer. The stock gives rise to a tuft of long-stalked, heart-shaped, glabrous leaves, and to erect flowering stems, each with 1 sessile, heart-shaped leaf. Flowers large, solitary, terminal. The flowers are visited by many insects for nectar; the branched glands seem to make the flower more conspicuous. 1 stamen sheds its pollen each day for 5 days, and, finally, the stigma becomes receptive.

RIBESACEAE. CURRANT FAMILY

RI'BES

170. Ribes alpi'num.   **Alpine Currant.**

Shrub, 3–4 ft., uncommon in woods and thickets of northern England; flowers greenish-yellow, early summer. Leaves palmate, with 3–5 deep, notched and toothed lobes, slightly hairy. Flowers small, in erect racemes, male and female on separate plants. Berries round, scarlet. R. GROSSULA'-RIA, the *Gooseberry*, R. RU'BRUM, the *Red Currant*, and R. NI'GRUM, the *Black Currant*, are not infrequently found in thickets, probably nearly always as escapes; R. SANGUI'NEUM, the *Flowering Currant*, an American species, is naturalized in many places.

CRASSULACEAE. STONECROP FAMILY

COTYLE'DON

171. Cotyledon Umbi'licus.   **Navelwort, Pennywort.**

Perennial, 4–12 in., common in stone walls and banks in southern Scotland and England; I. Flowers cream, tinged green, summer. The leaves and stems rise from a round corm buried deeply in the wall. Leaves round, with rounded indentations, the stalk inserted in the middle of the back. Stems terminating in a long raceme or panicle of drooping flowers.

SE'DUM

172. Sedum ro'seum.   **Roseroot.**

Perennial, about 1 ft., common in wet, rocky places on high mountains in northern England, Wales, and Scotland, and on the coast in Scotland; I. Flowers yellow, sometimes purple, summer. Rhizome thick and woody, with a smell of roses when dry. Stems stout, erect. Leaves sessile, alternate, reverse ovate, usually toothed, fleshy, and bluish-green. Flowers in small terminal corymbs; male and female on separate plants; petals 4.

173. Sedum Tele'phium.   Orpine, Livelong.

Perennial, about 1 ft., occasional on roadsides and rough banks through-out Britain, often an escape; I. Flowers pinkish-purple, late summer. Rhizome woody, roots fleshy. Stems erect, stout. Leaves oval or oblong, toothed, fleshy. Flowers with 5 petals in dense terminal corymbs.

174. Sedum a'nglicum.   English Stonecrop.

Perennial, 3–4 in., not uncommon in rocky places and walls, especially near the sea in western Britain; I. Flowers white, summer. Stem much branched, producing mats of barren shoots with crowded leaves, and more erect flowering shoots with fewer leaves. Leaves alternate, fleshy, glabrous, ovoid, produced backwards into a little rounded knob, bluish-green or tinged with red. Flowers in small, terminal groups; petals sharply pointed. S. A'LBUM, White Stonecrop, often found as an escape on old walls, is a similar plant with flowers in rather large groups, blunter petals, and leaves narrower and almost cylindrical. S. DASYPHY'LLUM is another similar plant found as an escape, distinguished by its finely hairy, very thick, broad leaves.

175. Sedum a'cre.   Biting Stonecrop, Wall-pepper.

Perennial, 3–4 in., common on dry walls, rocks, and sand-dunes throughout Britain; I. Flowers yellow, summer. Stems much branched, forming dense mats of leafy shoots with erect flowering stems. Leaves close set, thick and fleshy, ovoid, flat above. Flowers in small terminal groups. Pollen is shed first by the 5 outer and then by the inner stamens; usually a little later the stigmas become receptive so that self-pollination does not take place; the flowers are visited for nectar chiefly by flies and small bees. S. RUPE'STRE, Rock Stonecrop, is a rare yellow-flowered species, with flowering shoots about 8 in. high. There are several other large, yellow-flowered species found as escapes.

176. Sedum villo'sum.   Bog Stonecrop.

Biennial, 3–4 in., common in wet places in upland districts of northern England and Scotland. Flowers pink, summer. In the 1st year the slender stem bears an apical tuft of close-set leaves, and, in the 2nd, this lengthens into the flowering shoot, with scattered leaves and a few flowers at the tip. Leaves narrow; whole plant tinged with red and covered with fine glandular hairs.

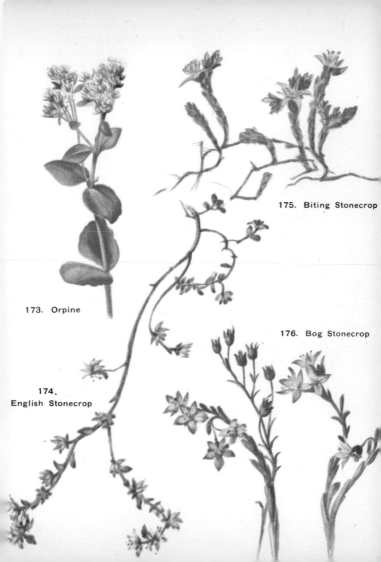

173. Orpine

174.
English Stonecrop

175. Biting Stonecrop

176. Bog Stonecrop

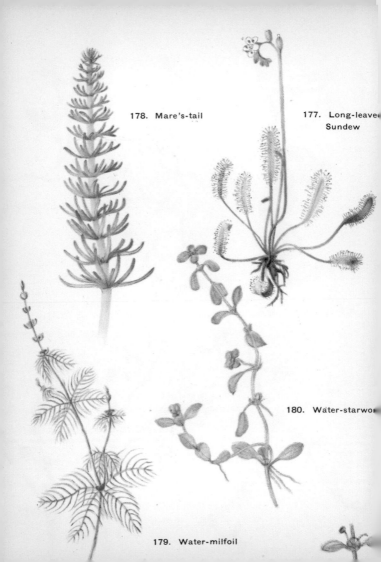

178. Mare's-tail

177. Long-leaved
Sundew

180. Water-starwort

179. Water-milfoil

DROSERACEAE. SUNDEW FAMILY
DRO'SERA

177. Drosera a'nglica.   **Long-leaved Sundew.**

Perennial, 5–6 in., rather uncommon on peaty moors throughout Britain; I. Flowers white, summer. Leaves in a rosette, long-stalked, narrowly spoon-shaped, beset with red, glandular hairs, with a glistening, sticky secretion. Flowering stems erect, leafless, with a terminal raceme of small, white flowers, which frequently do not open and are self-pollinated. D. INTER-ME'DIA is a very similar plant with broader leaves. D. ROTUNDIFO'LIA, the *Round-leaved Sundew*, is a common plant, 3–4 in., readily distinguished by its round leaves. All are insectivorous, catching and digesting small flies.

HALORAGACEAE. MARE'S-TAIL FAMILY
HIPPU'RIS

178. Hippuris vulga'ris.   **Mare's-tail.**

Perennial aquatic, 1–2 ft., frequent near the margins of ponds and back-waters throughout Britain; I. Flowers green, summer. The rhizome creeping in the mud sends erect stems above the surface of the water. Leaves pointed, small, narrow, in whorls of 6–10; submerged leaves may be 2–3 in. long. Flowers pollinated by wind.

MYRIOPHY'LLUM

179. Myriophyllum spica'tum.   **Water-milfoil.**

Perennial aquatic, common in still water throughout Britain; I. Flowers brownish, summer. The rhizome in the mud gives rise to long, flaccid stems, floating near the surface, bearing many leaves in whorls of 4. Leaves pinnately divided into very narrow segments, brownish. Flowers in terminal spikes, rising above the surface of the water, minute, upper male, lower female; bracts smaller than the flowers. M. VERTICILLA'TUM is a rarer plant with the flowers in the axils of the upper leaves and often remaining submerged. Flowers wind-pollinated; it is doubtful whether the submerged flowers are self- or water-pollinated.

CALLI'TRICHE

180. Callitriche aqua'tica.   **Water-starwort.**

Perennial (sometimes annual) aquatic, 3–9 in., common in ditches and ponds throughout Britain; I. Flowers greenish, summer. Branched stems rooting and prostrate on the mud, or floating. Leaves opposite, reverse ovate, or oval; when growing in water the submerged leaves are narrow and the upper leaves form floating rosettes. The male and female flowers are often in the axils of opposite leaves. The plant is very variable and specialists recognize about 6 distinct species.

LYTHRACEAE. LOOSESTRIFE FAMILY
PE'PLIS

181 Peplis Po'rtula.   **Water Purslane.**

Annual, 2–4 in., frequent in ditches and muddy places throughout Britain; I. Flowers green or tinged with purple, late summer. Stems branching and creeping on the surface of the mud, forming mats. Leaves opposite, stalked, reverse-ovate or rounded, glabrous, entire. Flowers solitary in the leaf axils; the petals are absent or minute and falling early. The flowers produce nectar but seem to be little visited by insects; they are regularly self-pollinated by the stamens bending over the stigmas.

LY'THRUM

182. Lythrum Salica'ria.   **Purple Loosestrife.**

Perennial, 2–3 ft., common in wet places in England and southern Scotland; I. Flowers purple, late summer. Stems erect from a rhizome. Leaves opposite, or 3 together, sessile, lance-shaped, with a heart-shaped base, entire, slightly hairy. Flowers sessile in groups in the axils of the small upper leaves, forming showy terminal spikes. The flowers are of 3 sorts on separate plants: (a) with half the stamens longer than the style and half shorter, (b) with long and medium sets of stamens and the style shorter than both, (c) with short and medium-length stamens and the style longer than both. Pollen is transferred, principally by bees, to a stigma from anthers set at the same level, that is from a different plant. Only cross-pollination yields a full crop of seed. L. HYSSOPIFO'LIUM, the *Hyssop-leaved Loosestrife*, is a rare plant, about 8 in., stem often prostrate at base, leaves opposite or alternate, elliptical, flowers small, solitary in the axils of the upper leaves.

ONAGRACEAE. WILLOW-HERB FAMILY
EPILO'BIUM

183. Epilobium angustifo'lium.   **Rosebay, French Willow, Fireweed.**

Perennial, 3–5 ft., common in open woods and copses, often invading in great numbers ground where trees have been felled, throughout Britain; I. Flowers rosy purple, late summer. The plant spreads by suckers, which grow into flowering stems the season after they have been formed. Leaves alternate, sessile, lance-shaped, long-pointed, bluish beneath, glabrous. Flowers 1 in., in showy terminal racemes; petals unequal; sepals purplish. The flowers are visited for nectar chiefly by bees which light on the stamens in young flowers, receiving the sticky pollen; in older flowers the stamens wither away and the 4-armed stigma becomes exposed.

184. Epilobium hirsu'tum.   **Hairy Willow-herb, Codlins-and-Cream.**

Perennial, 3–4 ft., common along ditches and streams in England, rarer in Scotland; I. Flowers rose and white, summer. Suckers thick, fleshy. Leaves opposite, at least below, sessile, lance-shaped, fine-toothed, hairy. Flowers in terminal, leafy racemes; corolla bell-shaped, $\frac{3}{4}$ in., deep rose

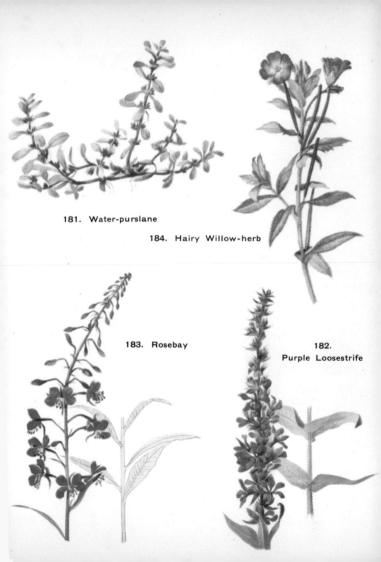

181. Water-purslane

184. Hairy Willow-herb

183. Rosebay

182.
Purple Loosestrife

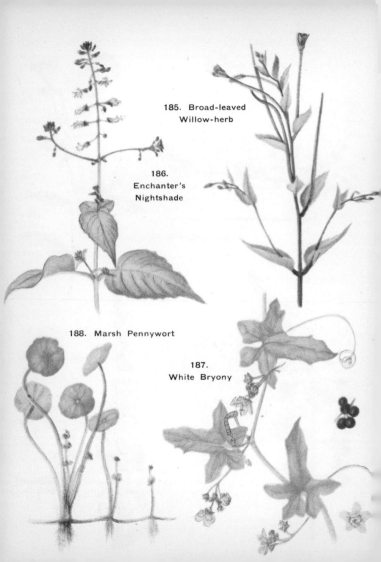

185. Broad-leaved
Willow-herb

186.
Enchanter's
Nightshade

188. Marsh Pennywort

187.
White Bryony

contrasting with a pale base and white stigmas. The seeds germinate much better in light than dark. E. PARVIFLO′RUM, the *Small Hairy Willow-herb*, is a smaller plant with alternate leaves and smaller flowers.

185. *Epilobium monta′num*. **Broad-leaved Willow-herb.**
Perennial, ½–1½ ft., common in shady places throughout Britain; I. Flowers pale purple, summer. Spreads by suckers and runners; stems erect, slender. Leaves nearly sessile, opposite, ovate, toothed, glabrous. Flowers small; stigma 4-lobed. E. RO′SEUM, the *Pale Willow-herb*, a similar plant of moist places, has stalked leaves and a club-shaped stigma. E. TETRAGO′NUM, the *Square-stalked Willow-herb*, a common plant of ditches, has 4-ribbed stems, sessile, lance-shaped, toothed leaves and a club-shaped stigma. E. PALU′STRE, the *Marsh Willow-herb*, another common plant of swamps, has nearly sessile, narrow, lance-shaped leaves with a wedge-shaped base, and round stem. There are also many hybrids and several rare species.

CIRCAE′A
186. *Circaea lutetia′na*. **Enchanter's Nightshade.**
Perennial, 1–1½ ft., common in damp woods from mid-Scotland southwards; I. Flowers pinkish-white, summer. Spreads by suckers; stem erect, square. Leaves opposite, stalked, ovate, coming to a point, toothed, almost glabrous. Flowers in slender racemes. Fruit stalks bent down and the fruit covered with hooked spines which catch in passing animals and aid in dispersal; the fruit does not open. C. ALPI′NA, a rarer plant of upland woods, is distinguished by its smaller size and more heart-shaped, shining leaves.

CUCURBITACEAE. MARROW FAMILY
BRYO′NIA
187. *Bryonia dioi′ca*. **White Bryony.**
Climber, common in hedgerows from mid-England southwards. Flowers greenish-yellow, summer. The long, branching stems come up every year from a large subterranean tuber. Leaves stalked, alternate, round in outline, palmate, with 5 pointed, toothed lobes, hairy. The unbranched tendrils arise opposite the leaves; after encircling some twig, they coil into a spiral giving elastic support. Flowers in small axillary cymes, male and female on separate plants. Berries scarlet.

UMBELLIFERAE. PARSLEY FAMILY
HYDROCO′TYLE
188. *Hydrocotyle vulga′ris*. **Marsh Pennywort.**
Perennial, creeping plant, common in marshes and wet places throughout Britain; I. Flowers greenish-lilac, summer. Stem creeping and rooting at the nodes. Leaves round, stalk affixed at centre of blade, with about 7 shallow, rounded lobes. Flowers in small clusters on stalks in the leaf axils. Carpels round, with 2 prominent ribs.

ERY'NGIUM

189. *Eryngium mari'timum*.   **Sea-holly.**

Perennial, 1–2 ft., not uncommon on sandy shores from mid-Scotland southwards; I. Flowers bluish, late summer. Spreads by suckers. Stems stout, erect. Radical leaves stalked, stem leaves sessile, all rounded in outline with deep, palmate, wavy lobes and spiny teeth, bluish green. Flowers in dense heads, each flower with a spiny bract; fruits crowned by the spiny calyx teeth.

SANI'CULA

190. *Sanicula europae'a*.   **Wood Sanicle.**

Perennial, 1–1½ ft., common in woods throughout Britain; I. Flowers white, summer. Stem erect unbranched from a stout stock. Leaves mostly radical, long-stalked, round in outline, deeply divided palmately into about 5 lobes, each notched and toothed, glabrous. Flowers in small round heads, about 9 of these grouped in a very open umbel. Fruits ovoid, covered with hooked prickles which aid in dispersal.

CONI'UM

191. *Conium macula'tum*.   **Hemlock.**

Biennial, 3–4 ft., rather common in hedges and waste places throughout Britain; I. Flowers white, summer. Stem erect from a tap root, branched, leafy, furrowed, with purplish spots. Leaves large, twice, or thrice pinnately compound, the leaflets further divided and toothed. Umbels large, with small bracts. Calyx teeth o. Fruit ⅛ in. long, ovoid, greenish brown, with 5 ridges on each half. Odour unpleasant; poisonous.

SMY'RNIUM

192. *Smyrnium Olusa'trum*.   **Alexanders.**

Biennial, 2–3 ft., not uncommon in waste places, especially near the sea in southern England and Scotland; I. Flowers greenish-yellow, early summer. Stem stout, erect, branched from a tap root. Lower leaves twice 3-foliate; upper leaves 3-foliate; base of petiole broad, membranous, sheathing; leaflets rounded, ovate or oval, notched and toothed, glabrous, rich green. Flowers in large, rounded umbels. Fruit dark brown, hard.

189. Sea-holly

190
Wood Sanicle

191. Hemlock

192. Alexanders

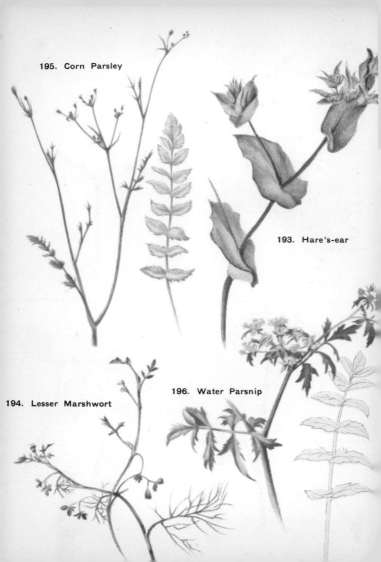

195. Corn Parsley

193. Hare's-ear

194. Lesser Marshwort

196. Water Parsnip

BUPLEU'RUM

193. *Bupleurum rotundifo'lium*.   Hare's-ear, Thorow-wax.

Annual, 1–1½ ft., a weed of cultivated ground, commonest on calcareous soils in south-eastern England. Flowers yellow, summer. Stem slender, erect, hollow, branched. Leaves oval, ovate, or nearly round, entire, pointed, encircling the stem, bluish-green. The partial umbels are surrounded by a ring of large, oval, leafy bracts. There are 3 other rare species.

A'PIUM

194. *Apium inunda'tum*.   Lesser Marshwort.

Perennial, occasionally found half-floating in pools or creeping in the mud of their margins, throughout Britain; I. Flowers white, summer. Submerged leaves very finely divided into hair-like segments, floating or aerial leaves pinnately compound, with few, notched, wedge-shaped leaflets. Flowers in small umbels opposite the leaves. A. NODIFLO'RUM, the *Marshwort*, is a creeping plant of marshy places with more or less erect flowering stems; leaves pinnately compound with ovate, toothed leaflets. A. GRA'VEO-LENS, the *Wild Celery*, of wet places near the sea, has a stout erect stem, pinnate or 3-foliate leaves, and greenish-white flowers.

CA'RUM

195. *Carum se'getum*.   Corn Parsley.

Annual, 1–2 ft., not uncommon in waste places and roadsides from mid-England southwards. Flowers white, late summer. Stem erect, branched, striate. Leaves stalked, pinnately compound; leaflets many, ovate, toothed, those of the upper leaves few and narrow. Umbels few-flowered, irregular, open; bracts narrow, pointed. C. VERTICILLA'TUM, an uncommon plant of western England and Scotland, has very finely cut leaves with the segments apparently in whorls. C. PETROSELI'NUM, the *Parsley*, with yellowish flowers, occasionally occurs as an escape.

SI'UM

196. *Sium ere'ctum*.   Water Parsnip.

Perennial, 1–2 ft., not uncommon in ditches and marshes in England, rare in southern Scotland; I. Flowers white, summer. The rhizome gives off suckers and erect, branched, leafy, furrowed stems. Leaves pinnately compound; leaflets ovate or almost lance-shaped, those of the lower leaves toothed, of the upper notched. Umbels terminal and lateral. Bracts and bracteoles leafy, notched. S. LATIFO'LIUM, the *Great Water Parsnip*, is a rarer, coarser plant with terminal umbels.

AEGOPO'DIUM

197. *Aegopodium Podagra'ria*.   **Goutweed, Bishopweed, Herb Gerard.**

Perennial, common in waste places near houses throughout Britain; I. Flowers white, summer. The branching rhizome makes the plant a troublesome weed. Stems erect, branched, furrowed. Radical leaves long-stalked, twice 3-foliate, with ovate, sharply and doubly toothed leaflets; stem leaves with sheathing bases, 3-foliate, with lance-shaped leaflets. Fruit narrowly ovoid, brown.

PIMPINE'LLA

198. *Pimpinella Saxi'fraga*.   **Burnet-saxifrage.**

Perennial, 1–2 ft., common in pastures and dry banks throughout Britain; I. Flowers white, often tinged pink, summer. Stem erect, branched above, furrowed. Leaves pinnately compound; leaflets of lower leaves oval, toothed or notched, of upper leaves narrow, deeply notched. P. MA'JOR is a less common, coarser plant, with large, ovate, coarsely toothed leaflets. Fruit ovoid, brown.

CONOPO'DIUM

199. *Conopodium denuda'tum*.   **Earthnut, Pignut.**

Perennial, 1–2 ft., common in woods and pastures throughout Britain; I. Flowers white, summer. A subterranean tuber gives rise to the erect forked stems. Radical leaves stalked, thrice 3-foliate, stem leaves with sheathing base; leaflets of lower leaves notched, of upper very narrow. Fruit narrowly ovoid, brown.

MY'RRHIS

200. *Myrrhis odora'ta*.   **Sweet Cicely.**

Perennial, 2–3 ft., common in pastures and hedge-banks in Scotland and northern England; I. Flowers white, early summer. Root fleshy. Stem erect, branched above. Leaves large with sheathing base, twice or thrice pinnate, the ovate leaflets divided or notched and toothed, softly hairy. Flowers in prominent umbels; bracteoles small, thin, pointed. Fruits, 1 in. long, narrow, with prominent ridges. Whole plant aromatic.

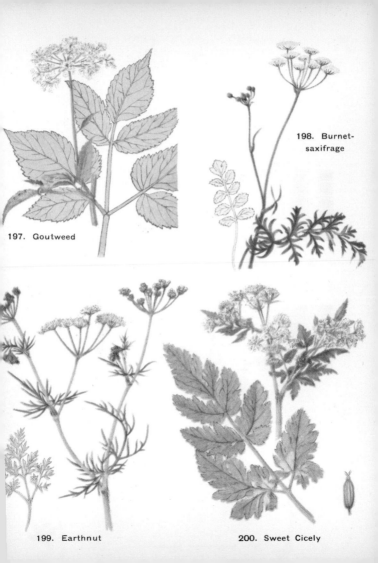

197. Goutweed

198. Burnet-saxifrage

199. Earthnut

200. Sweet Cicely

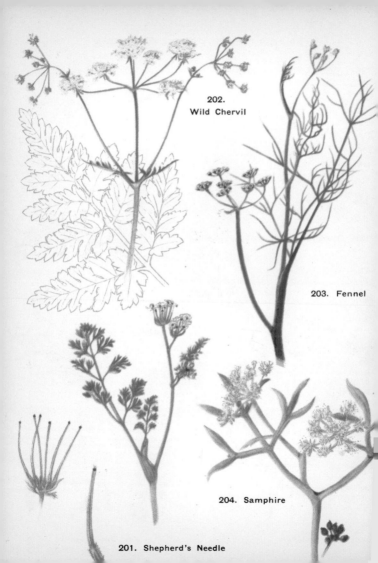

202.
Wild Chervil

203. Fennel

204. Samphire

201. Shepherd's Needle

SCA'NDIX

201. Scandix Pe'cten-Ve'neris.   **Shepherd's Needle.**

Annual, about 1 ft., a cornfield weed common in England, less so in Scotland; I. Flowers white, summer. Stem erect, branched from the base. Leaves with sheathing stalk, twice pinnately compound with finely divided leaflets, slightly hairy. Bracteoles toothed. The slender, beaked fruit may be about 2 in. long; striped light and dark brown.

CHAEROPHY'LLUM

202. Chaerophyllum sylve'stre.   **Wild Chervil, Cow-parsley.**

Perennial, 2–3 ft., common in hedge-banks throughout Britain; I. Flowers white, early summer. Stem erect, branched, furrowed, leafy. Leaves stalked with sheathing base, twice pinnately compound; leaflets ovate or lance-shaped, very coarsely toothed or notched, slightly hairy. Umbels open, bracts pointed. Fruits narrowly flask-shaped, smooth, without ridges. C. ANTHRI'SCUS, the *Beaked Parsley* or *Burr Chervil*, is a smaller plant with finer leaves, easily distinguished by the fruit which is covered with short bristles and has a short beak. CHAERORPHYLLUM TE'MULUM, the *Rough Chervil*, is a coarser plant with hairy, purple-spotted stem; fruit ridged.

FOENI'CULUM

203. Foeniculum vulga're.   **Fennel.**

Perennial, about 3 ft., of sea-cliffs and waste places inland, probably seldom native. Flowers yellow, late summer. Stem erect, shining, finely striate, almost solid. Leaves with sheathing stalks, pinnately compound, the leaflets cut several times into very fine segments; very aromatic when crushed. Umbels open. Fruit oval, slightly flattened, brown.

CRI'THMUM

204. Crithmum mari'timum.   **Samphire.**

Perennial, ½–1 ft., of sea-cliffs on the south and west coasts of England and south-west of Scotland; I. Flowers greenish-white, summer. Numerous branches spread from a woody stock. Leaves with sheathing stalk, twice pinnate, with narrow, strap-shaped leaflets, fleshy, glabrous, aromatic when crushed. Umbels small; bracts ovate, pointed. Fruits oval, ridged.

OENA'NTHE

205. Oenanthe Lachena'lii.   **Parsley Water Dropwort.**

Perennial, 2–3 ft., not uncommon in marshes, especially in brackish water, in England and southern Scotland; I. Flowers white, summer. Stock woody; roots fibrous; stem erect, branched, hollow, furrowed. Leaves twice pinnate, the leaflets of the lower leaves cut into narrowly oval, blunt segments, of the upper strap-shaped, more pointed. Bracteoles narrow, pointed. Fruits oval, crowned by the pointed calyx teeth. There are several other species of which OE. CROCA'TA, the *Hemlock Water Dropwort*, is common by ditches. It has broadly ovate, notched leaflets and tuberous roots. OE. FISTULO'SA has very hollow stems. OE. PHELLA'NDRIUM has finely cut submerged and aerial leaves. All are poisonous.

AETHU'SA

206. Aethusa Cyna'pium.   **Fool's-parsley.**

Annual, 1–1½ ft., a common garden and field weed of England and southern Scotland; I. Flowers white, summer. Stem erect and branched. Leaves twice pinnate, with ovate, deeply notched and toothed leaflets. Umbels open; bracteoles usually 3, pointing down and outwards. Fruit ovoid, ridged, brown. Highly poisonous.

ME'UM

207. Meum athama'nticum.   **Baldmoney, Spignel.**

Perennial, about 1 ft., locally common in upland pastures of northern England and Scotland. Flowers yellowish-white, summer. Apex of stock covered with fibrous remains of old leaves. Stem erect, little branched. Leaves pinnately compound, the leaflets repeatedly cut into short, tufted, hair-like segments. Fruit oval. Whole plant aromatic.

LIGU'STICUM

208. Ligusticum sco'ticum.   **Lovage.**

Perennial, 1–3 ft., not uncommon on rocky coasts of Scotland; I. Flowers white with pink tinge, late summer. Stems erect, from a thick, branched stock, furrowed, little branched. Leaves stalked with sheathing bases, 3-foliate; leaflets oval, 3-foliate or deeply 3-lobed or notched, toothed, glabrous, dark shining green. Flowers in close umbels with narrow bracts and bracteoles. Fruit long, oval, with sharp ridges. Aromatic.

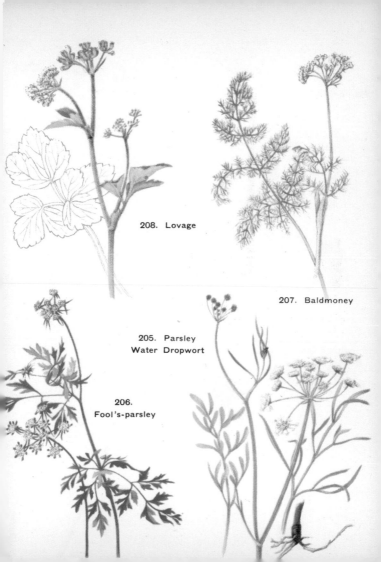

208. Lovage

207. Baldmoney

205. Parsley
Water Dropwort

206.
Fool's-parsley

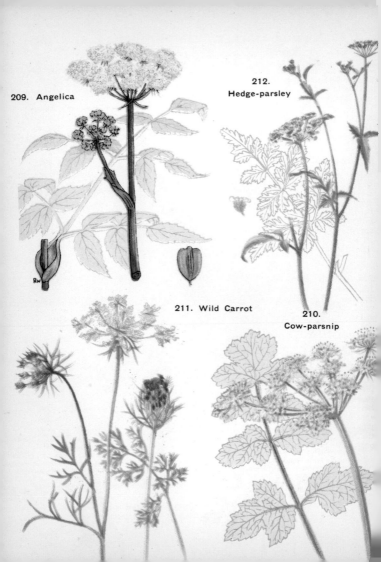

209. Angelica

212. Hedge-parsley

Rw

211. Wild Carrot

210. Cow-parsnip

ANGE'LICA

209. *Angelica sylve'stris*.   Angelica.

Perennial, 2–5 ft., common along streams and in moist shady places through-out Britain; I. Flowers white or purplish, late summer. Stem erect, stout, branched above, finely ribbed, tinged with purple. Leaves large, with large inflated sheathing bases, twice pinnate or 3-foliate; leaflets ovate, notched, and coarsely toothed. Umbels large and close. Fruit oval, winged. ARCH-ANGELICA OFFICINALIS, the *Garden Angelica*, sometimes found as an escape, has greenish flowers.

HERA'CLEUM

210. *Heracleum Sphondy'lium*.   Cow-parsnip, Hogweed.

Perennial, 3–5 ft., common in meadows and waste places throughout Britain; I. Flowers white, summer. Stem erect, stout, grooved, branched. Leaves very large, pinnately compound, with sheathing stalks; leaflets deeply divided, segments lance-shaped, notched and toothed, hairy. Umbels broad and close. Fruit flat with prominent wings. As in many other Umbelliferae, the outer petals of the outside flowers are much larger than the others, and so add to the showiness of the umbel; the flowers are visited by many short-tongued bees and flies, which suck the nectar exposed on the disk on the top of the ovary and pollinate the flowers.

DAU'CUS

211. *Daucus Caro'ta*.   Wild Carrot.

Biennial, 1–2 ft., common in fields and pastures throughout Britain; I. Flowers white, tinged with purple, summer. Stem erect, branched. Leaves twice or thrice pinnately compound, the oval or ovate leaflets finely notched and toothed. Young umbels nodding at night; bracts large and pinnately cut. In the fruiting stage the outer branches of the umbel arch in and close over the inner; fruit oval, spiny.

CAU'CALIS

212. *Caucalis Anthri'scus*.   Hedge-parsley.

Annual 1½–2 ft., common along waysides throughout Britain; I. Flowers pinkish-white, summer. Stem erect, branched, solid. Leaves pinnate or twice pinnate; leaflets oval or lance-shaped, deeply notched and toothed, hairy. Umbels loose and open. Fruits oval, spiny. There are several other species of which C. NODO'SA, the *Knotted Hedge-parsley*, is a rather common plant in the south with more or less prostrate stems and hooked bristles on the fruit. C. ARVE'NSIS, the *Field Hedge-parsley*, has also hooked bristles and only 1 bract.

CORNACEAE. DOGWOOD FAMILY
CO'RNUS

213. *Cornus sue'cica.*   **Dwarf Cornel.**

Perennial, about 6 in., locally abundant on alpine moors in northern England and the Scottish highlands. Flowers white, summer. A branching, woody, rhizome gives off erect, simple stems. Leaves opposite, sessile, ovate or oval, pointed, glabrous. The crimson flowers are very small in a terminal umbel, surrounded by 4 large, white bracts, with the appearance of a single white flower. Fruit small, red, and fleshy. C. SANGUI'NEA, the *Dogwood*, is a common shrub, about 6 ft., of England and Wales; young branches blood-red. CORNUS MAS, the *Cornelian Cherry*, is occasionally planted and has conspicuous yellow umbels in spring, before the leaves.

CAPRIFOLIACEAE. HONEYSUCKLE FAMILY
ADO'XA

214. *Adoxa Moschatelli'na.*   **Moschatel.**

Perennial, 4–6 in., locally common in moist shady places from mid-Scotland southwards; I. Flowers green, early summer. Rhizome branching, covered with white, fleshy, storage scales, the remains of the leaf-bases. Radical leaves long-stalked, 3-foliate, the very broad leaflets 3-lobed, the lobes notched. Stems erect, with a pair of 3-foliate leaves and a terminal head of small flowers. The stalks of the fruiting heads curl down under the leaves. The flowers are visited by small beetles which suck the nectar exposed on a ring at the base of the stamens; a musky smell seems to be attractive; self-pollination also occurs.

SAMBU'CUS

215. *Sambucus E'bulus.*   **Danewort, Dwarf Elder.**

Coarse, perennial herb, 2–3 ft., locally found in shady waste places through most of Britain; I. Flowers white, tinged purple, late summer. Rhizome woody, branching, and throwing up stout, herbaceous, grooved shoots. Leaves opposite, pinnately compound. Leaflets long, lance-shaped, toothed; stipules leafy; glabrous. Flowers small, in close, nearly flat, false corymbs, with purplish stamens. Fruit black. S. NI'GRA, the *Elder*, is a small tree with flat corymbs of cream-coloured, fragrant flowers, ovate leaflets, and black fruits. S. RACEMO'SA, the *Red-berried Elder*, is frequently naturalized in thickets.

VIBU'RNUM

216. *Viburnum O'pulus.*   **Guelder-rose.**

Shrub, 6–10 ft., common in hedges in England, rare in Scotland; I. Flowers white, summer. Leaves broad, 3-lobed, the lobes notched, dark green, glabrous; stipules very narrow. Flowers in a close corymb, the central flowers of which are small and the sterile marginal flowers have large, flat, showy corollas. Fruit a rounded, translucent, red drupe. Flowers pollinated by short-tongued beetles and flies, the nectar being easily reached in the shallow corolla.

214.
Moschatel

216. Guelder-rose

213. Dwarf Cornel

15. Danewort

217. Wayfaring-tree

220. Wild Madder

219. Honeysuckle

218. Linnaea

217. *Viburnum Lanta'na.* Wayfaring-tree.

Shrub, 6–12 ft., common in hedges and copses on calcareous soils in southern England. Flowers cream, early summer. Leaves oval or ovate, with heart-shaped base, finely toothed, whitish with down below; stipules absent. Flowers in rounded corymbs; corolla shortly funnel-shaped. Fruit a flattened drupe, red when unripe and turning black.

LINNAE'A

218. *Linnaea borea'lis.* Linnaea.

A creeping shrub with flowering shoots about 4 in., rare, but locally abundant in pine woods in mid- and northern Scotland. Flowers pink, late summer. Stem slender, creeping, branching, and rooting. Leaves opposite, shortly stalked, round or ovate, with few teeth, glabrous, evergreen. Flower-stalks erect with 2 small bracts and 2 apical, drooping, bell-shaped flowers. The flowers have a faint scent and produce nectar, but are very little visited and fruit is very rare.

LONI'CERA

219. *Lonicera Pericly'menum.* Honeysuckle, Woodbine.

Woody twiner, common in hedges and thickets throughout Britain; I. Flowers cream, tinged yellow and red, summer. Leaves opposite, shortly stalked or sessile, oval or ovate, entire, slightly hairy. Flowers sessile, in terminal clusters of about 12. Corolla tube about 1 in., splitting into 2 spreading, unequal lips. Berries crimson. L. CAPRIFO'LIUM, the *Garden Honeysuckle*, sometimes found as an escape, has bluish-green leaves, more or less united round the stem, and scarlet berries. The flowers are visited for the nectar at the base of the corolla tube by long-tongued moths at night, when they are most fragrant; on the evening the flower first opens, the stamens stand straight out and are brushed by the moth, the style is bent down; on the second evening the stamens wither away and the style now stands out and is touched, so that cross-pollination is effected.

RUBIACEAE. BEDSTRAW FAMILY
RU'BIA

220. *Rubia peregri'na.* Wild Madder.

Perennial, 1–2 ft., not uncommon in rough places, especially near the sea, in south-western England; I. Flowers yellowish, summer. Rhizome and base of stem woody; stem branched, 4-angled. Leaves in whorls of 4–6, elliptical, with bristly margins, evergreen. Flowers in small, loose, leafy panicles. Fruit a small, black berry, rounded with 1 seed, or lobed with 2.

GA'LIUM

221. *Galium borea'le*. Northern Bedstraw.

Perennial, 9–12 in., not uncommon on river shingles and moist stony uplands, in northern England and Scotland. Flowers white, summer. Stems erect, branched. Leaves in whorls of 4, lance-shaped, slightly hairy. Flowers small, in a rather close terminal panicle.

222. *Galium Crucia'ta*. Crosswort.

Perennial, 1–1½ ft., common in shady places from mid-Scotland southwards; I. Flowers yellow, early summer. Stem branched at the base, weak, more or less erect above. Leaves in whorls of 4, oval, softly hairy. Flowers in small clusters in the leaf axils.

223. *Galium ve'rum*. Lady's Bedstraw.

Perennial, 1–1½ ft., common on dry banks, pastures, and links on light soils, throughout Britain; I. Flowers yellow, summer. Rhizome woody, giving rise to many erect stems. Leaves about 8 in a whorl, very narrow, finely pointed, the margins rolled back, finely hairy. Flowers in a showy, terminal panicle. Nectar is fully exposed on a ring round the base of the style; flowers visited by many small insects; self-pollination may also occur by movements of the stamens towards the stigma.

224. *Galium Mollu'go*. Hedge Bedstraw.

Perennial, 2–4 ft., common in hedgerows and thickets in southern Scotland and England; I. Flowers white, summer. Stems much branched, spreading and rambling, square. Leaves 6–8 in a whorl, reverse lance-shaped, pointed, rough. Flowers in loose panicles with spreading branches. Fruit small, black, smooth. G. ERE'CTUM is a very similar plant of more upright habit with erect flowering branches, less coarse in habit.

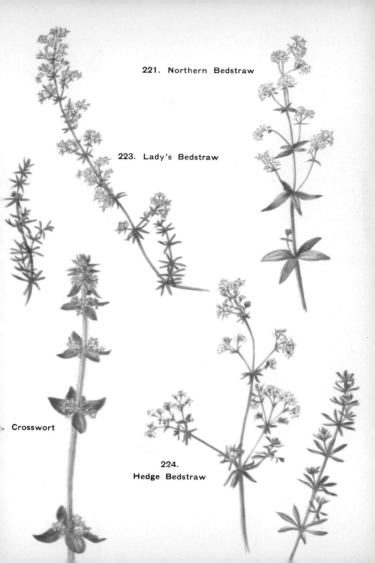

221. Northern Bedstraw

223. Lady's Bedstraw

Crosswort

224.
Hedge Bedstraw

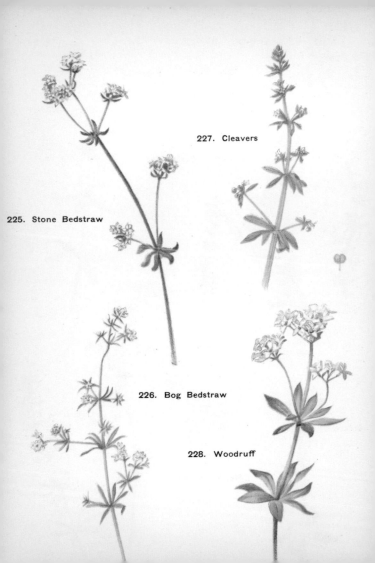

225. Stone Bedstraw

227. Cleavers

226. Bog Bedstraw

228. Woodruff

225. *Galium saxa'tile*.   **Stone Bedstraw, Heath Bedstraw.**

Perennial, ½–1 ft., common on heaths and upland pastures throughout Britain; I. Flowers white, summer. Stem prostrate, with many spreading branches. Leaves about 6 in a whorl, reverse-ovate, with fine points. Flowers in small cymes in the leaf axils. Fruit rough with bristles.

226. *Galium uligino'sum*.   **Bog Bedstraw.**

Perennial, 1–2 ft., in ditches and wet places throughout Britain; I. Flowers white, late summer. Stems branched, weak and straggling, rough with small prickles. Leaves 6–8 in a whorl, narrowly lance-shaped or elliptical, with fine points. Flowers in small groups. G. PALU'STRE, the *Marsh Bedstraw*, is a similar common plant with larger leaves, 4–5 in a whorl, which go black on drying.

227. *Galium Apari'ne*.   **Cleavers, Goosegrass.**

Annual, 2–4 ft., common in thickets and waste places throughout Britain; I. Flowers white, summer. Stem branched, weak, straggling, with 4 prominent ridges. Leaves 6–8 in a whorl, narrowly reverse lance-shaped, like the stem very rough with bristles. Flowers in small inconspicuous groups. Fruit covered with hooks which aid in dispersal. G. TRICO'RNE is a similar plant found as a field weed in England, smaller, and without hooks on the fruits.

ASPE'RULA

228. *Asperula odora'ta*.   **Woodruff.**

Perennial, 6–9 in., not uncommon in shady places throughout Britain; I. Flowers white, early summer. Rhizome branched and spreading, stems erect, little branched. Leaves about 8 in a whorl, reverse lance-shaped or elliptical, glabrous, rather rough. Flowers in terminal corymbs. Fruits with hooks. Plant fragrant when dry.

229. *Asperula cyna'nchica*.   **Squinancywort.**

Perennial, 6–8 in., local on calcareous pastures, especially in southern England; I. Rhizome woody, branched. Stems erect, in tufts. Leaves 4 in a whorl, 2 large and 2 small, narrow. Flowers in loose panicles.

SHERA'RDIA

230. *Sherardia arve'nsis*.   **Field Madder.**

Annual, about 6 in., common as a weed of cultivated ground throughout Britain; I. Flowers lilac, spring to autumn. Stem branching from the base, branches spreading on the ground. Leaves 4–6 in a whorl, reverse-ovate or elliptical. Flowers in small terminal heads.

VALERIANACEAE.   VALERIAN FAMILY
VALERIA'NA

231. *Valeriana officina'lis*.   **Valerian.**

Perennial, 2–3 ft., common in damp meadows and shady places throughout Britain; I. Flowers pink, summer. Stems erect. Leaves pinnately compound. Leaflets lance-shaped, with large teeth, nearly glabrous. Flowers in terminal corymbs. Fruits with feathery pappus. The plant spreads by runners and suckers. The flowers are visited by bees, butterflies, and other insects for nectar in the pouch of the corolla; as the stamens project before the stigmas and shed their pollen, cross-pollination is usual. V. DIOI'CA, the *Marsh Valerian*, is a smaller plant of marshes in southern Scotland and England; flowers pink, early summer; lower leaves entire, ovate, upper deeply lobed with a large terminal lobe.

VALERIANE'LLA

232. *Valerianella olito'ria*.   **Lamb's-lettuce, Corn Salad.**

Annual, 6–12 in., not uncommon in fields and waste places throughout Britain; I. Flowers pale blue or lilac, early summer. Stem soft and juicy, forking repeatedly. Leaves oblong or lance-shaped, blunt, glabrous. Flowers very small, in close terminal heads. Of several other species V. DENTATA is the commonest; leaves narrow, upper toothed; fruit crowned by the small spoon-shaped calyx tube. The flowers are visited by small flies, beetles, and other insects, but self-pollination also occurs.

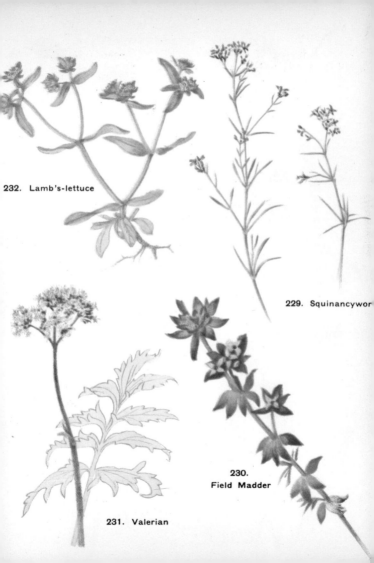

232. Lamb's-lettuce

229. Squinancywor

230.
Field Madder

231. Valerian

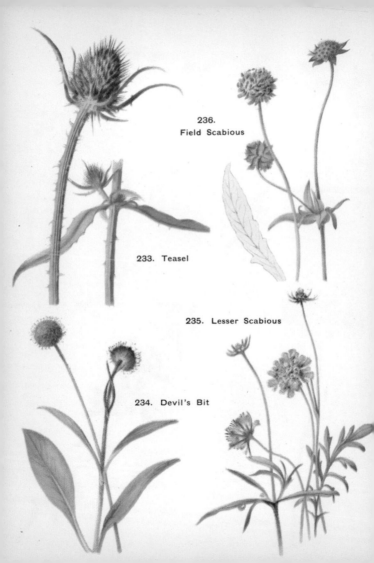

236.
Field Scabious

233. Teasel

235. Lesser Scabious

234. Devil's Bit

DIPSACEAE. TEASEL FAMILY
DI'PSACUS

233. *Dipsacus sylve'stris*.   **Teasel.**

Perennial, 3–5 ft., not uncommon in waste places in southern Scotland and England; I. Flowers pale purple, autumn. Stem erect, branched above, stout, ribbed. Radical leaves in a rosette withering after the 1st year; stem leaves opposite, long, lance-shaped and, like the stem, prickly. Flowers in dense ovoid heads; individual bracts projecting beyond the flowers and hardening into straight spines in the fruiting head. D. FULLO'NUM, the *Fuller's Teasel*, found as an escape, has hooked spines; the heads are used in dressing woollens. D. PILOSUS, the *Small Teasel*, a slender, less common plant, has whitish flowers, divided leaves, and rounded heads.

SCABIO'SA

234. *Scabiosa succi'sa*.   **Devil's Bit.**

Perennial, 1–2 ft., common in pastures, heaths, and open woods throughout Britain; I. Flowers bright blue-purple, summer. Stock short, stem erect, branched above. Radical leaves oval-oblong, narrowing to a stalk, entire, hairy; upper leaves elliptical, often toothed. Flowers in small, dense, hemispherical heads; petals 4.

235. *Scabiosa Columba'ria*.   **Lesser Scabious.**

Perennial, 1–1½ ft., common on calcareous pastures especially in southern England. Flowers lilac, late summer. Stem slender, erect, branched above. Radical leaves elliptical, oval, or oblong, the first formed bluntly toothed, the later pinnately lobed, with broad, toothed lobes; upper leaves cut into very narrow segments; slightly hairy. Flowers in heads which owe their elegance to the very much enlarged, outer petals of the outer flowers; petals 5. Bracts narrow and green.

236. *Scabiosa arve'nsis*.   **Field Scabious.**

Perennial, 2–3 ft., a handsome wayside plant, common except in northern Scotland; I. Flowers pinkish-lilac, summer. Stem erect and branched, from a stout rhizome. Leaves elliptical or oblong, the lowest bluntly toothed, the upper cut into oblong, widely spaced segments; hairy. Flowers in terminal heads, 1½ in. Petals usually 4, the outer ones of the outer flowers enlarged. Outer bracts ovate; individual bracts replaced by tufts of hairs. All the stamens of a head mature and shed their pollen before the styles project. Many insects visit the flowers for pollen and for the nectar in the corolla tube, but pollination is usually effected by a small bee which is always associated with this plant.

COMPOSITAE. DAISY FAMILY

EUPATO'RIUM

237. Eupatorium cannabi'num.   **Hemp Agrimony.**

Perennial, 2–3 ft., in damp grassy places throughout Britain, not common in Scotland; I. Flowers pale purple, summer. Stems coarse, erect, in clumps from a woody stock. Leaves shortly stalked, divided into 3–5 leaflets or lobes; leaflets lance-shaped, notched or toothed, hairy. Flowers in small heads, massed in a large terminal corymb. Fruit ribbed.

SOLIDA'GO

238. Solidago Virgau'rea.   **Golden Rod.**

Perennial, 1–2 ft., common in thickets and stream banks throughout Britain; I. Flowers yellow, summer. Rhizome woody, stems erect, little branched, round. Leaves elliptical, narrowing to a stalk, entire or toothed, slightly hairy. Flower-heads small, massed in a terminal panicle.

BE'LLIS

239. Bellis pere'nnis.   **Daisy.**

Perennial, 2–6 in., common in lawns and pastures throughout Britain; I. Flowers white and pink, spring to autumn. Stock branching, and giving rise to rosettes of leaves. Leaves spoon-shaped, narrowing to a stalk, toothed, hairy. Flower-heads solitary on naked stalks. Ray flowers white, female, disk flowers yellow, hermaphrodite. The daisy owes its predominance on neglected lawns to the branching stock which spreads it, and to the way the leaves are close pressed to the ground, thus escaping the mower and suppressing grassblades.

A'STER

240. Aster Tripo'lium.   **Sea Aster.**

Perennial, 1–2 ft., common in salt marshes throughout Britain; I. Flowers blue-purple, summer. Stem branched, erect. Lower leaves elliptical, narrowing to a stalk, upper strap-shaped, sometimes toothed. The whole plant glabrous and fleshy. Flowers in rather small heads with a purple ray, which is sometimes missing, and yellow disk. Pappus of abundant fine hairs. A. LINOSY'RIS, *Goldilocks*, is a very rare plant of cliffs in south-west England with yellow flower-heads without rays.

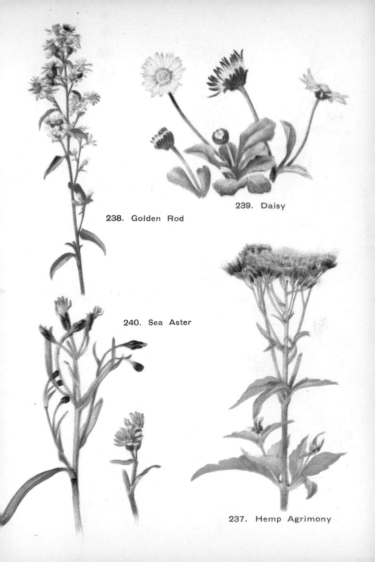

238. Golden Rod

239. Daisy

240. Sea Aster

237. Hemp Agrimony

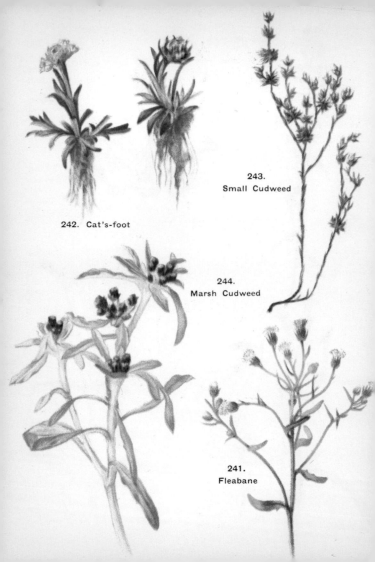

242. Cat's-foot

243.
Small Cudweed

244.
Marsh Cudweed

241.
Fleabane

ERI'GERON

241. Erigeron a'cre.   **Fleabane.**

Biennial, about 1 ft., not uncommon in dry places in England, rare in Scotland; I. Flowers purplish, late summer. Stem erect, little branched, reddish. Leaves elliptical, narrowing to a stalk, the upper narrow, entire, hairy. Flower-heads small, numerous, with yellow disk and inconspicuous, narrow, purplish ray flowers. Pappus of abundant long hairs. E. ALPI'NUM, the *Alpine Fleabane*, is a very rare Scottish alpine with few rather large heads, having a conspicuous ray of narrow, purple flowers.

ANTENNA'RIA

242. Antennaria dioi'ca.   **Cat's-foot, Mountain Everlasting.**

Perennial, 4–5 in., common on upland heaths, especially in northern England and Scotland; I. Flowers pink or white, summer. Leafy shoots prostrate and flowering stems upright. Leaves spoon-shaped, those on the flowering stems very narrow, entire, white and silky beneath. Flower-heads few, crowded at the tip of the stem and showy because of the expanded tips of the bracts.

FILA'GO

243. Filago mi'nima.   **Small Cudweed.**

Annual, 3–5 in., a rather uncommon plant of dry places through most of Britain; I. Flowers greyish-yellow, late summer. Stem branched from the base, branches slender, upright, or prostrate. Leaves small, narrow, pressed to the stem; whole plant white and woolly. Flower-heads in numerous small clusters about the tips of the branches, ovoid and greyish, opening out and becoming brownish in fruit. Of several other species, F. GERMANICA, rather common in dry places in England, has broader leaves and clusters of about 20 flower-heads which are tipped with brown or yellow.

GNAPHA'LIUM

244. Gnaphalium uligino'sum.   **Marsh Cudweed.**

Annual, common in damp fields throughout Britain; I. Flowers pale brown, autumn. Stem much branched and spreading at the base. Leaves strap-shaped, or spoon-shaped, finely pointed; whole plant downy. Flower-heads in small clusters at the branch tips; bracts pale brown or yellow. G. SYLVA'TICUM, the *Wood Cudweed*, a common plant of heaths and pastures, has erect unbranched stems about 8 in., long, narrow leaves, flower-heads in a long, terminal spike, bracts ruddy brown. G. SUPI'NUM, *Dwarf Cudweed*, is a dwarf, tufted, alpine found on mountains in Scotland.

I'NULA

245. Inula Cony'za.   **Ploughman's Spikenard.**

Biennial, $1\frac{1}{2}$–3 ft., not uncommon in copses and dry places, especially on calcareous soils in England. Flower-heads yellow, tinged purple, late summer. Stems stout, erect, branched above, purple. Leaves broadly lance-shaped or elliptical, shortly stalked, finely hairy. Flower-heads small, numerous in a terminal corymb. The inner bracts are tinged with purple and the ray flowers are small and inconspicuous. INULA HELE'NIUM, the *Elecampane*, occasionally found naturalized, has stout stems, 3–5 ft., and yellow flower-heads 3 in. across. I. CRITHMOI'DES, the *Golden Samphire*, a plant of the south and west coasts, has fleshy leaves and bright yellow flower-heads.

246. Inula Pulica'ria.   **Lesser Fleabane.**

Annual, $\frac{1}{2}$–1 ft., uncommon in damp sandy places and roadsides in southern England. Flowers yellow, autumn. Stem branched. Leaves wavy, oblong, slightly toothed, hairy. Flower-heads numerous, small, ray flowers small. Pappus hairs surrounded by minute scales. I. DYSENTE'RICA, the *Greater Fleabane*, is a commoner plant, 1–2 ft., leaves woolly beneath, clasping the stem; flower-heads nearly 1 in., with conspicuous ray flowers.

BI'DENS

247. Bidens triparti'ta.   **Bur-marigold.**

Annual, 1–2 ft., common in ditches and marshy places in England, rarer in southern Scotland; I. Flowers dull yellow, autumn. Stems erect, simple or branched. Leaves lance-shaped, coarsely and sharply toothed, notched or 3-lobed. Outer bracts large and leafy. Fruit with 2 barbed bristles. B. CE'RNUA is a similar plant with undivided, toothed leaves, drooping heads and fruits with 3–4 bristles.

245. Ploughman's
Spikenard

246. Lesser Fleabane

247. Bur-marigold

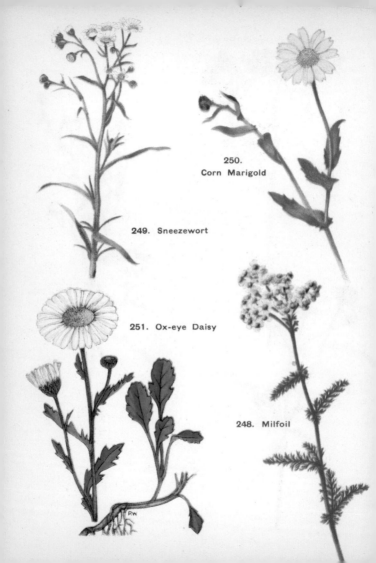

250.
Corn Marigold

249. Sneezewort

251. Ox-eye Daisy

248. Milfoil

ACHILLE'A

248. *Achillea Millefo'lium*. **Milfoil, Yarrow.**

Perennial, $\frac{1}{2}$–$1\frac{1}{2}$ ft., common on roadsides and pastures throughout Britain; I. Flowers white, summer. Rhizome woody; spreads by suckers; stem stiff, erect, little branched. Radical leaves long-stalked, stem leaves sessile, oblong, pinnately compound, the many leaflets twice deeply divided into fine segments; softly hairy. Flower-heads small, with 4–6 ray flowers, massed in a showy corymb.

249. *Achillea Pta'rmica*. **Sneezewort.**

Perennial, $\frac{1}{2}$–$1\frac{1}{2}$ ft., common in pastures and waste places throughout Britain; I. Flowers white or pink, late summer. Rhizome long, branched; stem stiff, erect. Leaves sessile, strap-shaped, finely toothed, finely hairy. Flower-heads with about 12 ray flowers, in a loose terminal corymb.

CHRYSA'NTHEMUM

250. *Chrysanthemum se'getum*. **Corn Marigold.**

Annual, 1–$1\frac{1}{2}$ ft., common as a cornfield weed throughout Britain; I. Flowers yellow, summer. Stem erect, with spreading branches. Leaves notched or pinnately cut, toothed, glabrous, bluish-green, rather fleshy, aromatic. Flower-heads large, solitary, both ray and disk rich yellow.

251. *Chrysanthemum Leuca'nthemum*. **Ox-eye Daisy.**

Perennial, 1–2 ft., common in meadows throughout Britain; I. Flowers white, summer. Stem erect, slightly branched, furrowed. Lower leaves spoon-shaped, notched or pinnately lobed, the terminal lobe largest, narrowed to a stalk, glabrous, dark green; the upper narrow and toothed, sessile. Flower-heads large, solitary, ray white, disk yellow. Pollen is shed into the tube formed by the anthers and is pushed out of this by the style as it lengthens with the 2 stigmas closed together. Insects, visiting young heads for the nectar formed in the corolla tube, become covered with pollen. Later the style pushes right out of the anther tube and the 2 stigmas separate and are exposed; if cross-pollination fails they bend back and touch the pollen lying about the mouth of the corolla; the ray flowers are female, those of the disk hermaphrodite. This is the standard type of pollination in the family. C. PARTHE'NIUM, the *Feverfew*, has a branched stem, deeply lobed and notched leaves, and a corymb of many, rather small, white heads.

A'NTHEMIS

252. Anthemis arve'nsis.   **Corn Camomile.**

Annual, ½–1½ ft., not uncommon as a field weed in England and southern
Scotland; I. Flowers white, summer. Stem much branched from, and
prostrate at the base. Leaves twice deeply and pinnately cut into fine segments, whitish with hairs. Flower-heads terminal, on long stalks; disk
conical. The scales of the receptacle have long points and are about as long
as the disk flowers. A. NO'BILIS, the *Camomile*, is an uncommon plant of
pastures in southern England, very aromatic; leaf segments very narrow;
scales of receptacle blunt. A. CO'TULA, the *Stinking Mayweed*, a rather
common weed in England, has an unpleasant scent, very narrow pointed
scales, and a granular fruit.

MATRICA'RIA

253. Matricaria inodo'ra.   **Scentless Mayweed.**

Annual, ½–1½ ft., common as a field weed throughout Britain; I. Flowers
white, summer. Stem branched, erect, or spreading. Leaves twice or thrice
cut deeply and pinnately into very fine segments, glabrous. Flower-heads
rather large, disk rounded, yellow. Bracts with a brown membranous
margin. Somewhat aromatic. A fleshy, perennial variety is found on sea
cliffs. M. CHAMOMI'LLA, the *False Camomile*, has a conical disk, bracts without the brown border, and a strong scent. M. DISCOI'DEA, the *Rayless
Mayweed*, is a North American species without ray flowers which has spread
greatly in waste places, especially near the coast, in recent years.

TANACE'TUM

254. Tanacetum vulga're.   **Tansy.**

Perennial, 2–3 ft., common in waste places as an outcast from gardens
throughout Britain; I. Flowers yellow, autumn. Rhizome woody; spreads
by suckers. Stems tough, erect, ridged. Leaves pinnately compound;
leaflets lance-shaped, deeply cut into toothed segments, glabrous, dark green,
aromatic. Flower-heads button-like, massed in broad terminal corymbs.

ARTEMI'SIA

255. Artemisia vulga'ris.   **Mugwort.**

Perennial, 2–3 ft., common in waste places throughout Britain; I. Flowers
dull yellow and grey, autumn. Stems stiff, and erect from a woody stock,
reddish. Leaves pinnately cut into notched, lance-shaped segments, glabrous
above and woolly white below. Flower-heads small, ovoid, in long, narrow,
terminal panicles. Aromatic. A. ABSI'NTHIUM, the *Wormwood*, is an uncommon plant of waste places with drooping, rounded, yellow flower-heads.
A. MARI'TIMA, the *Sea Southernwood*, is a hoary plant of salt marshes with
ovoid, brownish, drooping heads.

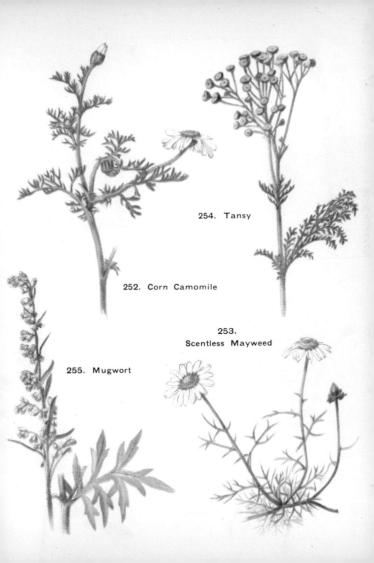

254. Tansy

252. Corn Camomile

253.
Scentless Mayweed

255. Mugwort

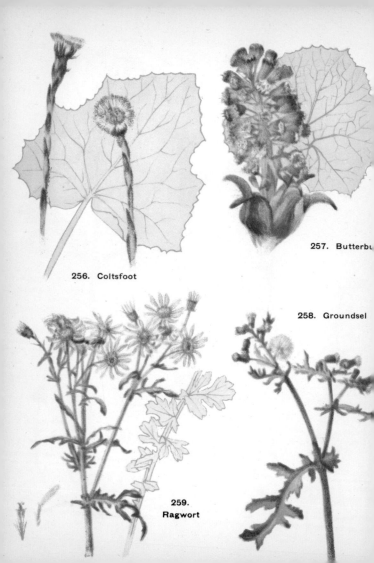

256. Coltsfoot

257. Butterbu

258. Groundsel

259.
Ragwort

TUSSILA'GO

256. Tussilago Fa'rfara. Coltsfoot.

Perennial, ½–1 ft., a common weed throughout Britain; I. Flowers yellow, spring. The plant has a deep, extensively branching rhizome, which makes it difficult to eradicate. Leaves all radical, stalked, broadly heart-shaped with scalloped and toothed margins, covered below with cobwebby hairs. The flowering stalks, which come up in tufts before the leaves, bear only small scales and a single terminal flower-head. The head droops in the bud and again after flowering, but becomes erect when the fruits are ripe, by which time the stalk has doubled its length. The disk flowers have only stamens, those of the ray only carpels, the stigmas of which are receptive before the pollen is shed. The early flowers are visited by many insects. The heads open by day and close at night or in cold weather; the closing movement may bring the stigmas into contact with pollen and effect self-pollination.

PETASI'TES

257. Petasites vulga'ris. Butterbur.

Perennial, ½–1 ft., locally common in damp places in England and southern Scotland; I. Flowers pale purple, spring. Rhizome branched and fleshy. Leaves very broadly heart- or kidney-shaped, with scalloped and sharply toothed margins and cobwebby hairs; when fully grown nearly a yard across. Flowering stems appear before the leaves, with massive, pyramidal panicles of small flower-heads. P. A'LBUS is an introduced species with creamy flowers; P. FRA'GRANS, the *Winter Heliotrope*, is another introduced species, extensively naturalized, with fragrant mauve flowers in winter.

SENE'CIO

258. Senecio vulga'ris. Groundsel.

Annual, 6–8 in., a common weed throughout Britain; I. Flowers yellow, spring to autumn. Stem rather succulent, branched, erect or spreading, ribbed, often tinged red. Leaves sessile, clasping, pinnately cut, with notched segments, glabrous. Flower-heads small, ovoid in loose terminal clusters; ray flowers usually absent. S. SYLVA'TICUS, the *Heath Groundsel*, a similar plant common in sandy places, has small ray flowers, an erect stem, and hairy fruits. S. VISCO'SUS, the *Stinking Groundsel*, has very sticky hairs and glabrous fruits.

259. Senecio Jacobae'a. Ragwort.

Perennial, 2–3 ft., common in pastures and waste places throughout Britain; I. Flowers yellow, summer. Stem tough, erect, branched above. Radical leaves ovate, coarsely toothed, with a few small lobes at the base; stem leaves sessile, clasping, pinnately lobed and toothed; glabrous. Flower-heads massed in showy terminal corymbs. S. AQUA'TICUS, the *Marsh Ragwort*, is a common plant of wet places with less cut stem-leaves, the terminal lobe of which is always the largest. There are several other uncommon species.

CARLI'NA

260. *Carlina vulga'ris*.   **Carline Thistle.**

Biennial, $\frac{1}{2}$–$1\frac{1}{2}$ ft., in pastures in England and southern Scotland, common
in the south; I. Flower-heads yellowish-purple, summer and autumn. A tap-
root and leaf-rosette is formed in the first year and the stout, erect, flowering
stem in the second. Leaves oblong, sessile, clasping, pinnately cut into spiny
teeth. Flower-heads few, about 1 in., in a terminal cluster. Outer bracts
green and spiny, inner brownish-purple, with spreading yellowish tips;
flowers pale purple.

A'RCTIUM

261. *Arctium mi'nus*.   **Lesser Burdock.**

Biennial, 2–3 ft., common in shady waste places throughout Britain; I.
Flowers dingy purple, late summer. Stem stout, with many spreading
branches. Leaves stalked, broadly ovate or heart-shaped, margin wavy,
sometimes toothed, glabrous or downy; lower leaves very large. Heads nearly
1 in., solitary or in groups towards the branch tips, closely surrounded by
the bracts. The fruiting heads, with their hooked spines, stick to passing
animals and are so dispersed.

CA'RDUUS

262. *Carduus lanceola'tus*.   **Spear Thistle.**

Biennial, 2–5 ft., common in waste places and pastures throughout Britain; I.
Flowers purple, late summer. Stem stout, erect, with spiny wings. Leaves
lance-shaped, waved, cut into lobes which are usually forked and terminate
in stout spines. Heads large, urn-shaped, with spiny bracts. CARDUUS
NU'TANS, the *Musk Thistle*, is a smaller plant of somewhat similar appearance
of southern England, distinguished by the drooping heads with spreading
bracts, and the simple pappus hairs.

263. *Carduus hetero'phyllus*.   **Melancholy Thistle.**

Perennial, 2–3 ft., not uncommon in upland pastures in northern England
and southern Scotland. Flowers purple, late summer. Stems erect, furrowed,
little branched. Spreads by suckers. Stem leaves sessile, lance-shaped, with
fine marginal spines, but not prickly, lower sides and stem white with hairs.
Heads with green bracts from which the deep purple flowers spread out.
C. PRATE'NSIS, a plant of moist pastures and marshes in southern England,
is distinguished by its wavy, more or less notched, somewhat prickly leaves.

260.
Carline Thistle

261. Lesser Burdock

262.
Spear Thistle

263. Melancholy Thistle

265. Field Thistle

267. Knapweed

264.
Ground Thistle

266.
Sawwort

264. *Carduus acau'lis*. Ground Thistle.

Perennial, 3–6 in., common on calcareous pastures in southern England. Flowers purple, late summer. The woody stock gives rise to a rosette of leaves in the centre of which are 1 or few, almost sessile, heads. Leaves cut into broad lobes which are toothed and spiny, glabrous. Bracts with very short spiny points.

265. *Carduus arve'nsis*. Field Thistle.

Perennial, 2–4 ft., common in fields, pastures, and waste places throughout Britain; I. Flowers pale purple, late summer. The plant spreads by an extensive branching rhizome and is difficult to eradicate. Stems erect, little branched, angled. Leaves sessile, oblong, waved and lobed, with spiny margins, glabrous or woolly beneath. Heads rather small, numerous, in loose corymbs; bracts pointed. Some plants bear only male and others female and hermaphrodite flowers. The flowers, as with other thistles, are visited by many insects, especially by bees able to reach the nectar in the rather long corolla tubes. C. PALU'STRIS, the *Marsh Thistle*, is another common thistle with numerous small heads found in damp meadows and marshes, distinguished by its winged, spiny stems, and hairy leaves.

SERRA'TULA

266. *Serratula tincto'ria*. Sawwort.

Perennial, 1–2 ft., not uncommon in open woods and thickets in England. Flowers purple, late summer. Stem erect, slender, branched above. Leaves stalked, the lower deeply pinnately lobed; lobes elliptical toothed; upper leaves notched, sessile. Flower-heads in a loose corymb; bracts fringed with hairs, purple-brown.

CENTAURE'A

267. *Centaurea ni'gra*. Knapweed, Hardheads.

Perennial, 1–3 ft., common in pastures throughout Britain; I. Flowers red-purple, summer. Stem upright, tough, little branched. Leaves lance-shaped, entire or slightly lobed, hairy, dark green, the upper sessile. Heads about 1 in., at the tips of the branches; the flowers may be all the same and rather small, or the outer row may be much larger, making the head more showy. of short bristles or o. A very variable plant in the appearance of both leaves and flower-heads.

268. *Centaurea Scabio'sa*.   **Great Knapweed.**

Perennial, 1–3 ft., common in pastures in England, less so in southern
Scotland; I. Flowers purple, late summer. Stock woody, stem erect,
branched. Leaves pinnately cut with oval, toothed or notched segments
which stand out with wide spaces between; hairy. Heads 1½ in., on the
branch tips. Marginal flowers very large and showy, sterile. Bracts green,
with a dark brown, toothed margin and tip. Pappus of stiff bristles.

269. *Centaurea Cy'anus*.   **Cornflower, Bluebottle.**

Annual, 1–2 ft., an occasional cornfield weed throughout Britain; I. Flowers
blue, summer. Stem slender, erect, with ascending branches. Leaves sessile,
narrow and pointed, lower with a few teeth or notches; with sparing woolly
hair. Heads on the branch tips; bracts with a membranous fringe; outer
flowers much larger than central and brighter blue. Pappus of short bristles.
As in other species the filaments of the stamens are sensitive and, when
rubbed by an insect, contract suddenly, pulling the anther tube down over
the style and so ejecting the pollen. Nectar collects in the wider, upper part
of the corolla tube and is reached by bees and other insects; the large sterile
flowers greatly increase the conspicuousness of the head.

270. *Centaurea Calci'trapa*.   **Star-thistle.**

Biennial, ½–1½ ft., a rare plant of waste places in southern England. Flower-
heads rose and yellow, late summer. Stem stiff, with spreading branches.
Leaves pinnately cut into narrow toothed segments. Bracts terminating in
prominent yellow spines 1 in. long, and radiating in every direction. Flowers
rosy purple.

CICHO'RIUM

271. *Cichorium I'ntybus*.   **Chicory, Succory.**

Perennial, 1–3 ft., not uncommon in dry places in England, doubtfully native
in the north and in Scotland; I. Flowers blue, summer and autumn. Stem
erect and branched, from a fleshy tap-root. Lower leaves large, elliptical, with
deep, backward-pointing, toothed lobes, upper leaves notched or toothed,
clasping the stem; hairy. Heads 1½ in., withering after 1 day.

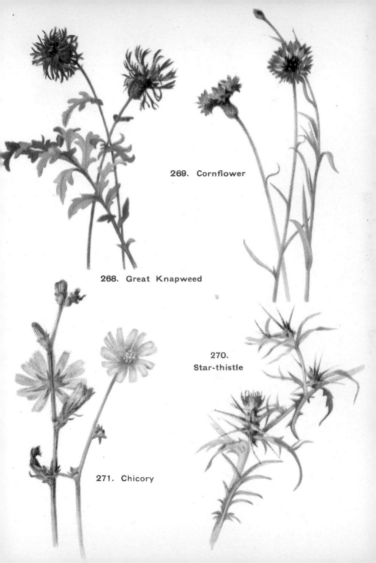

269. Cornflower

268. Great Knapweed

270.
Star-thistle

271. Chicory

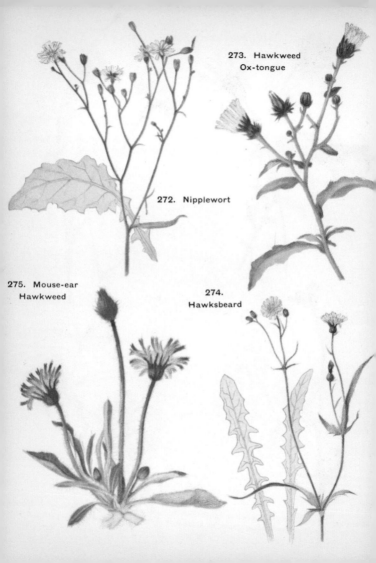

273. Hawkweed Ox-tongue

272. Nipplewort

275. Mouse-ear Hawkweed

274. Hawksbeard

LA'PSANA

272. *Lapsana commu'nis*.   Nipplewort.

Annual, 1–3 ft., common in waste places throughout Britain; I. Flowers yellow, late summer and autumn. Lower leaves stalked, with a large ovate or heart-shaped terminal segment and 1–2 pairs of smaller segments; upper leaves elliptical, toothed or entire; hairy. Flower-heads ¼ in., in a very loose, terminal corymb.

PI'CRIS

273. *Picris hieracioi'des*.   Hawkweed Ox-tongue.

Biennial, 1–3 ft., not uncommon in dry waste places in England and southern Scotland. Stem stout, branched. Leaves strap- or lance-shaped, the lower tapering to a stalk, the upper wavy, coarsely toothed; roughly hairy. Flower-heads ¾ in., in a loose terminal corymb; outer bracts spreading. Fruit not beaked. P. ECHIOI'DES, the *Ox-tongue*, is a coarse plant of shady waste places; leaves broadly lance-shaped, with bristly margins, the upper clasping; outer bracts broad, leafy; fruit with a beak crowned by the pappus.

CRE'PIS

274. *Crepis capilla'ris*.   Hawksbeard.

Annual, 1–2 ft., common in fields and waste places throughout Britain; I. Flowers yellow, late summer and autumn. Stem usually much branched. Leaves mostly radical, elliptical, with numerous short lobes, the upper leaves clasping with narrow lobes or only toothed; nearly glabrous. Flower-heads numerous, rather small, in an open corymb. Outer bracts small, awl-shaped. Fruit not beaked. Pappus white. There are several other species. C. PALU-DO'SA, the *Marsh Hawksbeard*, is not uncommon in moist upland meadows in northern England and Scotland; leaves broadly lance-shaped, with coarse, backward-pointing teeth; pappus dirty white; fruit strongly ribbed. C. TARAXACIFOLIA, the *Beaked Hawksbeard*, a not uncommon plant of southern England, has hairy leaves, cut like those of a dandelion; fruit with a long beak crowned by the pappus.

HIERA'CIUM

275. *Hieracium Pilose'lla*.   Mouse-ear Hawkweed.

Perennial, about 6 in., common in pastures and heaths throughout Britain; I. Flowers yellow, summer. Rhizome, woody, giving off runners, by which the plant spreads, tufts of leaves and flowering stems. Leaves spoon-shaped, elliptical or lance-shaped, narrowed to a stalk, softly hairy. Heads solitary on slender, leafless stalks.

276. *Hieracium muro'rum.* Wall Hawkweed.

Perennial, 1–2 ft., common in upland shady and stony places throughout Britain; I. Flowers yellow, summer. Radical leaves in a rosette, ovate, pointed, toothed, softly hairy. Flowering stems with a few small leaves or none. Flowering heads rather large, in a small terminal corymb. H. AURA'N-TIACUM, the *Cockscomb*, sometimes found as an escape, is a plant of similar habit with orange flowers.

HYPOCHOE'RIS

277. *Hypochoeris radica'ta.* Cat's-ear.

Perennial, $\frac{1}{2}$–1 ft., common on pastures and heaths throughout Britain; I. Flowers yellow, summer. Tap-root thick and woody. Leaves in a rosette, oblong, with small lobes often pointing back, hairy. Heads few, on an erect, forked stem bearing a few small scales. Pappus on a beak. H. GLA'BRA is an uncommon plant of dry places, smaller, glabrous, and an annual. The rare H. MACULA'TA has slightly toothed, spotted leaves.

LEO'NTODON

278. *Leontodon autumna'lis.* Hawkbit.

Perennial, $\frac{1}{2}$–1$\frac{1}{2}$ ft., common in pastures and waste places throughout Britain; I. Flowers yellow, late summer and autumn. Leaves in a rosette, long, strap-shaped, with small, spreading lobes or coarse teeth, glabrous. Flowering stems erect, branched, bearing a few small scales; below each head the stem is swollen and hollow. Pappus not on a beak. L. HI'SPIDUS, the *Rough Hawkbit*, a common pasture plant in England and southern Scotland, has coarsely toothed, hairy leaves and unbranched flowering stems, bearing large solitary heads.

TARA'XACUM

279. *Taraxacum officina'le.* Dandelion.

Perennial, $\frac{1}{2}$–1 ft., a very common weed throughout Britain; I. Flowers yellow, spring to autumn. Tap-root long and fleshy; if damaged it sends up fresh shoots, increasing the plant and making it difficult to eradicate. Leaves in a rosette, more or less deeply cut into sharp, backward-pointing lobes, glabrous. Heads large, solitary, on hollow, naked stalks which elongate after flowering. There are several varieties; that figured is VAR. ERYTHRO-SPE'RMUM, common on sand dunes, with deeply cut leaves and red-brown fruits.

278. Hawkbit

277. Cat's-ear

276. Wall Hawkweed

279. Dandelion

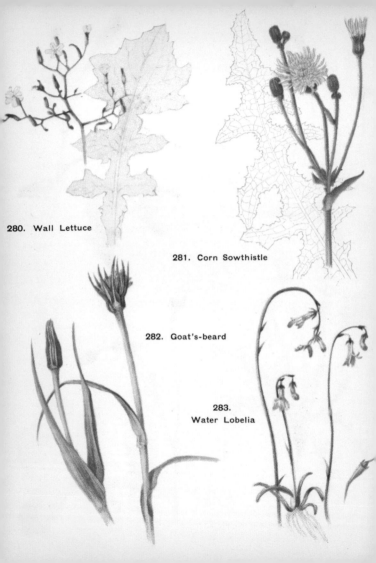

280. Wall Lettuce

281. Corn Sowthistle

282. Goat's-beard

283.
Water Lobelia

LACTU'CA

280. Lactuca mura'lis. **Wall Lettuce.**

Annual, 1–2 ft., rather uncommon on old, shady walls from mid-Scotland southwards; I. Flowers yellow, summer. Stems slender, branched. Leaves pinnately lobed, the apical lobe ivy-shaped and largest, toothed, glabrous, and bluish-green below. Heads very small and numerous, in a large, loose panicle. Beak shorter than fruit. L. VIRO′SA, the *Wild Lettuce*, an uncommon plant of waste places in England has oblong, undivided, sharply toothed, and clasping leaves; beak as long as the fruit.

SO'NCHUS

281. Sonchus arve'nsis. **Corn Sowthistle.**

Perennial, 2–3 ft., common in arable land throughout Britain; I. Flowers yellow, late summer and autumn. Spreads by slender suckers. Stem erect, little branched, hollow, succulent. Leaves lance-shaped with sharply toothed, backward-pointing lobes, clasping the stem with rounded ears; uppermost leaves toothed only; glabrous. Heads rather large, in terminal panicles; flower-stalks with sticky hairs. S. OLERA′CEUS, the *Common Sowthistle*, is a common annual weed with notched or cut leaves, the terminal lobe often almost triangular, sharply toothed, and clasping the stem with long, pointed ears.

TRAGOPO'GON

282. Tragopogon prate'nsis. **Goat's-beard, Jack-go-to-Bed-at-Noon.**

Biennial, 1–2 ft., common in grassy places in England, less so in Scotland; I. Flowers yellow, summer. Stems erect, little branched, from a fleshy tap-root. Leaves clasping the stem, lower long and narrow, upper lance-shaped, narrowing into a long point; glabrous. Flower-heads large, solitary, the bracts usually longer than the flowers. The head is open in the early morning and closes before midday. T. PORRIFO′LIUS, the *Salsify*, occasionally found as an escape, has purple flowers.

CAMPANULACEAE. BELLFLOWER FAMILY

LOBE'LIA

283. Lobelia Dortma'nna. **Water Lobelia.**

Aquatic perennial, 1–1½ ft., not uncommon near the margins of mountain lakes in northern England, Wales, and Scotland; I. Flowers lilac, late summer. Stock short; spreading by suckers. Leaves submerged, tufted, cylindrical, fleshy, each with 2 hollow tubes. The simple flowering stem bears a few scales and brings the raceme of flowers above water.

JASI'ONE

284. Jasione monta'na.   **Sheep's-bit.**

Annual, $\frac{1}{2}$–1 ft., not uncommon in heaths and pastures on sandy soils in
southern England, less common in the north and in southern Scotland; I.
Flowers light blue, summer. Stem erect, slender, branched from the base.
Rosette leaves stalked, elliptical or spoon-shaped; stem leaves sessile, narrow,
oblong, small; hairy. Flower-heads small, solitary, on long stalks.

PHYTEU'MA

285. Phyteuma orbicula're.   **Round-headed Rampion.**

Perennial, $\frac{1}{2}$–1 ft., a rare plant of the chalk downs of southern England.
Flowers deep blue, late summer. A fleshy tuber gives rise to several erect
flowering stems and tufts of leaves. Radical leaves ovate or lance-shaped,
stalked, toothed; stem leaves shortly stalked or sessile, narrowly lance-shaped.
Heads solitary, dense, rounded.

WAHLENBE'RGIA

286. Wahlenbergia hedera'cea.   **Ivy-leaved Bellflower.**

Small creeping perennial, not uncommon in shady, marshy places in south-
western England, rarer in the north and in southern Scotland; I. Flowers
pale blue or lilac, late summer. Stem very slender, branched. Leaves long-
stalked, thin, kidney-shaped, with about 5 shallow, angular lobes. Flowers
solitary, drooping, on thread-like stalks; corolla $\frac{1}{3}$ in., bell-shaped.

CAMPA'NULA

287. Campanula glomera'ta.   **Clustered Bellflower.**

Biennial, $\frac{1}{2}$–1$\frac{1}{2}$ ft., not uncommon in pastures and thickets from mid-Scotland southwards. Flowers bright purple-blue, summer. Stem erect, un-
branched. Radical leaves long-stalked, narrowly heart-shaped or broadly
lance-shaped, bluntly toothed; stem leaves sessile, lance-shaped; hairy.
Flowers large, erect, sessile in a terminal cluster with a few lower on the
stem. Capsules erect, with pores at the top of the capsule just below the
sepals; the seeds cannot fall but must be jerked out by wind or passing
animals and so are scattered.

284. Sheep's-bit

286. Ivy-leaved Bellflower

285. Round-headed Rampion

287. Clustered Bellflower

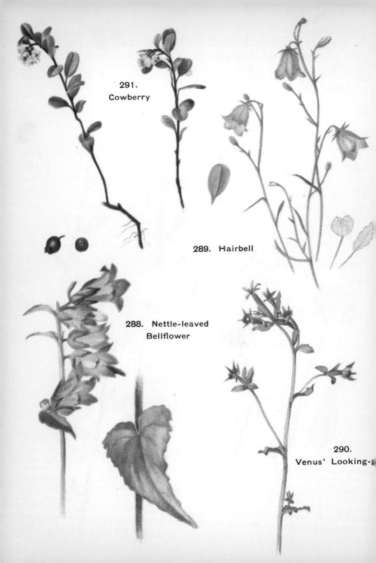

291.
Cowberry

289. Hairbell

288. Nettle-leaved
Bellflower

290.
Venus' Looking-g

288. *Campanula Trache'lium.* **Nettle-leaved Bellflower.**

Biennial, 1–3 ft., not uncommon in thickets in southern England, rarer in the north and in Scotland; I. Flowers purplish-blue, late summer. Stem erect, unbranched. Leaves heart-shaped, ovate or lance-shaped, lower stalked, upper sessile, coarsely toothed, hairy. Flowers large, inclined, in a leafy terminal panicle; calyx hairy. The capsule is drooping, the pores are at its base, and the seeds cannot fall out. C. LATIFO'LIA, the *Giant Bellflower* or *Throatwort*, is common in thickets of northern England and southern Scotland; leaves ovate-lance-shaped toothed; flowers solitary, in the axils of the upper leaves; calyx glabrous. C. PA'TULA is a rare annual of southern England, distinguished by its leafless panicle of widely open, purple flowers.

289. *Campanula rotundifo'lia.* **Hairbell, Harebell.**

Perennial, ½–1½ ft., common on pastures, heaths, and links throughout Britain; I. Flowers blue or white, late summer. Rhizome slender, giving off suckers. Flowering stems wiry, erect. The lowest leaves are long-stalked, heart-shaped, finely toothed; they are followed by ovate, lance-shaped, and, finally, linear leaves which often alone persist when the plant is flowering. Flowers drooping, in loose panicles. In shady places prostrate, non-flowering plants are often found. In this, as in other species, the stamens in the young flower are closely pressed to the style and shed their pollen on it in a mass; as it lengthens they wither away and visiting insects, chiefly bees, receive pollen. Later the stigmas open out and are receptive; if not pollinated they curl back and touch the pollen on the style. The nectary is on the top of the ovary, protected by the broad bases of the stamens and the nectar can be reached only by the fine, long tongue of an insect passing between these.

SPECULA'RIA

290. *Specularia hy'brida.* **Venus's Looking-glass.**

Annual, ½–1 ft., a not uncommon weed of arable land on light soil in southern England, rare farther north. Flowers blue-purple, late summer. Stem branched from the base; branches spreading or erect. Leaves small, oblong with wavy margins, hairy. Flowers in small clusters at the branch tips; sepals longer than the petals. Capsule as long as 1 in., narrow, angled, and crowned by the pointed sepals.

ERICACEAE. HEATH FAMILY

VACCI'NIUM

291. *Vaccinium Vi'tis-idae'a.* **Cowberry, Red Whortleberry.**

Shrub, ½–1½ ft., common on upland heaths in northern England and Scotland; I. Flowers pink, summer. Much branched, more or less prostrate. Leaves shortly stalked, oval, oblong or reverse-ovate, notched at the tip, margins rolled back, evergreen, glossy, dark green above, pale and dotted below. Flowers in small terminal racemes; corolla bell-shaped. Berries deep red; this is the *Cranberry* of Scotland.

292. *Vaccinium Myrti'llus.*   Bilberry, Blaeberry, Whortleberry.
Shrub, up to 2 ft., common in heaths and open woods throughout Britain; I.
Flowers rose, tinged green, early summer. A creeping, woody rhizome gives
rise to erect, much-branched stems; young shoots green and ridged.
Leaves shortly stalked, ovate, finely toothed, deciduous, glabrous. Flowers solitary;
corolla urn-shaped. Berry black with a bluish bloom. Nectar is produced
by a disk surrounding the base of the style; owing to the narrow mouth of
the corolla only long-tongued bees can reach it. On visiting the pendulous
flower the insect touches the pin-head stigma which stands at the mouth
of the corolla; its proboscis then jars the long tails which project from the
back of the stamens and the powdery pollen falls on the insect's head; it
may also fall on the stigma and self the flower if cross-pollination fails.
V. ULIGINO'SUM, the *Bog Whortleberry*, is a local mountain plant, distinguished by its entire leaves and the young shoots, which are not ridged.

293. *Vaccinium Oxyco'ccus.*   Cranberry.
Creeping shrub of peat bogs, commonest in the north but nowhere abundant; I. Flowers rose, late summer. The creeping rhizome gives off slender,
prostrate stems. Leaves ovate, shining, green above, whitish below, evergreen. Flowers solitary, on erect stalks, drooping. The 4 narrow petals are
reflexed, and the yellow or purple stamens project from them. Berries red.

ARCTOSTA'PHYLOS

294. *Arctostaphylos U'va-u'rsi.*   Bearberry.
Trailing shrub, locally common on mountain heaths in northern England and
Scotland; I. The much-branched, woody stem forms trailing mats. Leaves
shortly stalked, reverse-ovate or oval, entire, fringed with fine hairs, leathery,
evergreen; veins forming a prominent network. Flowers in small apical
racemes; corolla urn-shaped. Berries bright red. A. ALPI'NA, the *Black
Bearberry*, is a rare plant of Scottish mountains with spoon-shaped, serrate
leaves and black berries.

ANDRO'MEDA

295. *Andromeda polifo'lia.*   Andromeda.
Shrub, ½–1 ft., of peat moors from mid-Scotland southwards, commoner
in the south; I. Flowers pink, summer. Stem woody, prostrate, and rooting
below, with erect branches. Leaves narrowly elliptical, pointed, margins
rolled back, leathery, bluish below, evergreen. Flowers in short, terminal
racemes, drooping, with urn-shaped corolla. Capsule erect.

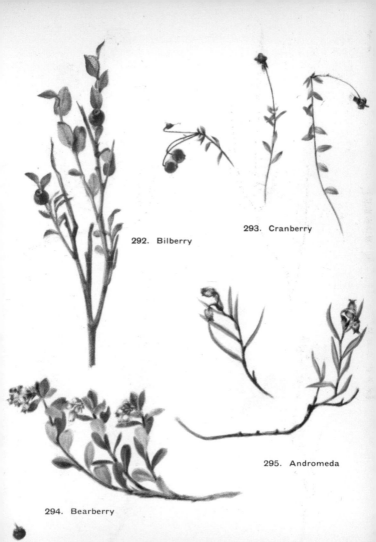

292. Bilberry

293. Cranberry

294. Bearberry

295. Andromeda

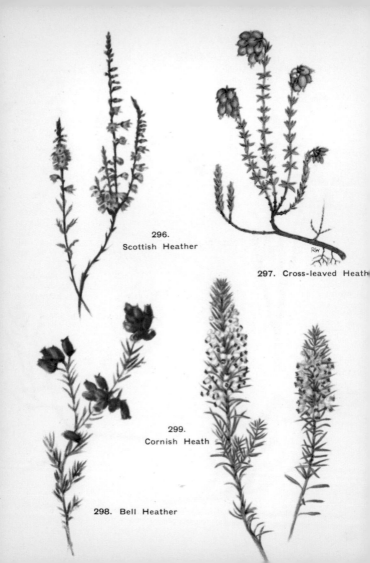

296.
Scottish Heather

297. Cross-leaved Heath

299.
Cornish Heath

298. Bell Heather

CALLU'NA

296. *Calluna vulga'ris.*   **Scottish Heather, Ling.**

Shrub, ½–3 ft., common on heaths and moors throughout Britain; I. Flowers rosy purple, sometimes white, late summer. An underground, woody rhizome branches profusely and throws up much-branched, erect stems. Leaves very small and numerous, in 4 rows, 3-cornered, with a basal prolongation, glabrous or finely hairy. Flowers in dense spikes near the branch tips, inclined, bell-shaped; both sepals and petals coloured. The plant occurs in extensive masses; heather moors used for grouse shooting are burnt over in sections about every 3 years so that the plants do not reach the tall, straggly, mature form. The flowers are much visited by bees and yield a characteristic brown honey; the pollen is shaken out by the insect striking the anther spurs; it has been stated that wind-pollination also occurs, the pollen being very powdery.

E'RICA

297. *Erica Te'tralix.*   **Cross-leaved Heath.**

Shrub, ½–1½ ft., common on moist heaths throughout Britain; I. Flowers pink, rarely white, late summer. Stems erect, branched, slender. Leaves in whorls of 4, narrow, blunt, with margins rolled back, often greyish with fine hairs especially on young shoots. Flowers in terminal, drooping clusters. Corolla urn-shaped, anthers hidden, spurred.

298. *Erica cine'rea.*   **Bell Heather.**

Shrub, ½–1½ ft., common on dry heaths throughout Britain; I. Flowers crimson, summer, making a brilliant, though more restricted, display before the ling, especially on places which have been burnt over. Stem much branched, prostrate or straggling, the branches erect. Leaves about 3 in a whorl, with short, leafy shoots in the axils, so that they appear tufted, narrow, pointed, the margins folded completely back. Flowers in dense terminal clusters; corolla, urn-shaped; anthers hidden, spurred. E. CILIA'RIS, a rare plant of south-western England, has spikes of bright crimson, rather large flowers; mouth of corolla squint; anthers hidden, without spurs.

299. *Erica va'gans.*   **Cornish Heath.**

Shrub, 1–3 ft., locally abundant on heaths in the west of Cornwall. Flowers pink, late summer. Stem stout, with many stiff, erect branches. Leaves rather long, narrow, pointed, glabrous, margins folded right back. Flowers in dense, leafy spikes. Corolla bell-shaped; anthers protruding, not spurred, brown.

PY'ROLA

300. *Pyrola mi'nor.*   **Wintergreen.**

Perennial, ½–1 ft., locally common in open woods in Scotland and northern
England, rare in the south; I. Flowers white, tinged rose, summer. Rhizome
slender, branching. Leaves radical, stalked, broadly oval or round, rather
leathery, glabrous. Flowering stem erect, with a terminal raceme of drooping
flowers. Stamens as long as the style. P. ME′DIA is a similar plant with
a straight style longer than the stamens. P. ROTUNDIFOL′IA is a rarer plant,
distinguished by its large, pure white, bell-shaped flowers and long, curved
style. P. SECU′NDA, locally common on heaths in Scotland, has ovate, pointed,
toothed leaves and greenish white flowers on one side of the stem. P.
UNIFLO′RA has a solitary flower, terminal on a stem 2–3 in. high.

MONO'TROPA

301. *Monotropa Hypopithys.*   **Bird's-nest.**

Perennial, ½–1 ft., occasionally found in beech and pine woods in England
and southern Scotland; I. Stem rather fleshy, swollen at the base, cream-
coloured and clad with brownish scales, terminating in a raceme of bell-
shaped flowers which droops when young and becomes erect in the fruit.
The plant is a saprophyte devoid of the green pigment chlorophyll, drawing
nourishment from decaying matter in the soil.

PLUMBAGINACEAE.   THRIFT FAMILY

STA'TICE

302. *Statice Limo'nium.*   **Sea-lavender.**

Perennial, ½–1 ft., common on muddy shores of England and southern
Scotland; I. Flowers bluish-purple, late summer. Rhizome thick and
woody. Leaves radical, large, elliptical or oval, with a prominent mid-rib,
narrowed to a stalk, glabrous. Flowering stem leafless, branched above into
the corymb. There are several less common species with small leaves,
about 1 in. long; S. BINERVO′SA, with spoon-shaped leaves, is found locally
on rocky shores in England.

ARME'RIA

303. *Armeria mari'tima.*   **Thrift, Sea-daisy.**

Perennial, 3–9 in., common on rocky coasts throughout Britain and also
occurring as an alpine; I. Flowers bright pink, summer. Stock stout and
woody, with several apices which bear tufts of long, very narrow leaves.
Flowering stems slender, grooved, terminating in a rounded head. The
plant found on some Scottish mountains has rather broader leaves.

300.
Wintergreen

302. Sea-lavender

303. Thrift

301. Bird's-nest

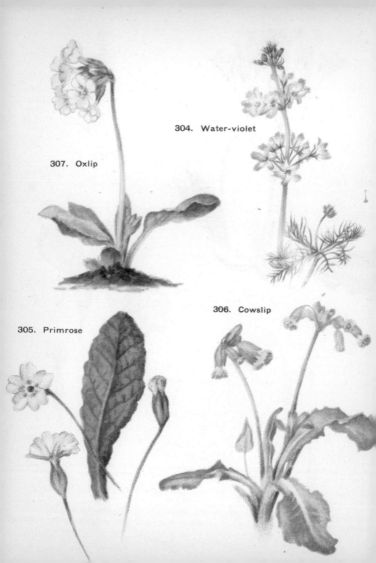

307. Oxlip

304. Water-violet

305. Primrose

306. Cowslip

PRIMULACEAE. PRIMROSE FAMILY

HOTTO'NIA

304. *Hottonia palu'stris*. **Water-violet.**

Aquatic perennial, 1–2 ft., a rather uncommon plant of ponds and ditches in most of England; I. Flowers lilac with yellow eye, summer. The flowering stem rises above the surface and from its base leafy branches spread out under water. Leaves in irregular whorls, deeply pinnately cut into linear, pointed segments. Flowers in whorls in a terminal raceme; corolla ¾ in., salver-shaped.

PRI'MULA

305. *Primula vulga'ris*. **Primrose.**

Perennial, about 6 in., common in woods, hedgerows, and banks throughout Britain; I. Flowers yellow, spring. Stem a stout, subterranean stock, rough with the bases of old leaves. Leaves in a rosette, oval, narrowing to the stalk, with a toothed, scalloped edge, wrinkled; under surface softly hairy. Corolla salver-shaped, with thickenings at the throat. The flowers are of two sorts on separate plants: (a) *pin-eyed*, with long styles and stamens set half-way down the tube of the corolla, and (b) *thrum-eyed*, with short styles and stamens in the mouth of the tube. Pollen is transferred from the stamens of the one sort to the stigma of the other, so that cross-pollination takes place. The chief visitors are bees and hoverflies.

306. *Primula ve'ris*. **Cowslip, Paigle.**

Perennial, 4–9 in., common in meadows in England, rare in Scotland; I. Flowers deep yellow with orange spots, early summer. Stem a stout stock. Leaves with a winged stalk, ovate, toothed, wrinkled. Flower-stalks stout, terminating in an umbel of drooping flowers; corolla small, bell-shaped, with thickenings at the throat.

307. *Primula ela'tior*. **Oxlip.**

Perennial, 6–12 in., common in woods on calcareous soil on the borders of Suffolk, Essex, Cambridge, and Herts. Flowers yellow, spring. Stem a stout stock. Leaves with a winged stalk, ovate, toothed, and wrinkled. Flower-stalk tall, terminating in an umbel of inclined flowers; corolla widely bell-shaped, without thickenings at the throat. The False Oxlip is a hybrid between the Primrose and the Cowslip, found where these two occur together and may be distinguished from the true Oxlip by the presence of thickenings at the mouth of the corolla tube.

308. *Primula farino'sa*.　　　　　　　　**Bird's-eye Primrose.**

Perennial, about 6 in., locally common in wet pastures in northern England.
Flowers lilac purple with yellow eye, summer. Leaves small, in a rosette,
spoon-shaped, finely toothed towards the tip, mealy below. Flower stalk
terminating in a crowded umbel of small flowers; corolla salver-shaped, petals
standing apart. P. SCO'TICA is a similar plant, 2–3 in., with broader leaves
and overlapping petals, of pastures in Orkney and the extreme north of
Scotland.

LYSIMA'CHIA

309. *Lysimachia vulga'ris*.　　　　　　　　**Yellow Loosestrife.**

Perennial, 2–3 ft., marshes and stream sides in England, rare in Scotland; I.
Flowers yellow, summer. The rhizome gives off suckers and stiff, erect,
flowering stems. Leaves in pairs or whorls of 3–4, sessile, ovate-lance-
shaped, finely hairy below. Flowers in showy terminal panicles. Corolla
bell-shaped, with orange spots. L. THYRSIFLO'RA, the *Tufted Loosestrife*, is
a rare plant of similar habit and situation with paired, lance-shaped leaves
and small flowers in stalked clusters in the leaf axils. Flowers visited by
bees for pollen.

310. *Lysimachia ne'morum*.　　　　　　　　**Yellow Pimpernel.**

Perennial, 6–12 in., common in shady places throughout Britain; I. Flowers
yellow, summer. Stem slender, creeping, rooting below and rising at the tip.
Leaves opposite, shortly stalked, ovate, pointed, glabrous. Flowers solitary,
on thread-like stalks; sepals narrow, pointed; corolla almost flat, $\frac{1}{2}$ in.
L. NUMMULA'RIA, *Moneywort*, a similar plant of moist, shady places, has
more rounded leaves, ovate sepals, and a larger flower; corolla $\frac{3}{4}$ in.

TRIENTA'LIS

311. *Trientalis europae'a*.　　　　　　　　**Chickweed Wintergreen.**

Perennial, about 6 in., a common and characteristic plant of conifer woods
in mid- and northern Scotland, rare in northern England. Flowers white,
summer. Spreads by suckers; stem erect, slender, bearing 1 whorl of 5–6
oval or reverse-ovate, pointed, glabrous leaves. From this spring 1–4
delicate flower-stalks, each with a single flower. Corolla $\frac{3}{4}$ in., almost flat.

308. Bird's-eye
Primrose

309.
Yellow Loosestrife

Yellow Pimpernel

311. Chickweed Wintergre

313. Scarlet Pimpernel

312. Sea-milkwort

315. Brookweed

314. Bog Pimpernel

GLAUX

312. *Glaux mari'tima*.   **Sea-milkwort, Black Saltwort.**

Perennial, 3–9 in., common on sandy and muddy shores throughout Britain and also in the salt districts of the midlands; I. Flowers pink, summer. Spreading vigorously by suckers; stems prostrate. Leaves small, opposite, sessile, oval, fleshy, and glabrous. Flowers small, sessile in the leaf axils, with a bell-shaped, pink calyx.

ANAGA'LLIS

313. *Anagallis arve'nsis*.   **Scarlet Pimpernel, Poor-Man's-Weather-glass.**

Annual, ½–1 ft., common as a weed of arable land in England, less common in eastern Scotland; I. Flowers scarlet, summer and autumn. Stem branched at the base; branches square, prostrate, and spreading. Leaves opposite, sessile, ovate, glabrous. Flowers on slender stalks in the leaf axils. The fruiting stalks curl, with the globular capsules, under the leaves. The style is so placed between the stamens that it must be touched first by visiting insects, but the flower has no nectar and is rarely visited; the red colour, to which many insects are colour-blind, may partly account for the scarcity of visits. The flower closes in the evening and does not open in cool weather, and, when the corolla closes, the stamens are brought in contact with the stigma. A blue-flowered variety is also found.

314. *Anagallis tene'lla*.   **Bog Pimpernel.**

Perennial, 3–4 in., a not uncommon plant of bogs in England and western Scotland; I. Flowers pink, late summer. Stem slender, branched, prostrate. Leaves more or less opposite, shortly stalked, rounded, ovate, glabrous. Flowers erect, on thread-like stalks in the leaf axils; corolla bell-shaped. CENTU'NCULUS MI'NIMUS, the *Bastard Pimpernel* or *Chaffweed*, is a small annual, 1–2 in., rare in moist, sandy places in England, with alternate leaves and very small, sessile, pink or white flowers; parts of the flower in fours.

SA'MOLUS

315. *Samolus Valera'ndi*.   **Brookweed.**

Perennial ½–1½ ft., not uncommon in wet places, especially near the west coast from mid-Scotland southwards; I. Flowers white, summer and autumn. Stem erect, with spreading branches at the base. Leaves reverse-ovate, rounded, glabrous. Flowers small, in racemes terminal and in the leaf axils.

OLEACEAE. ASH FAMILY
FRA'XINUS

316. Fraxinus exce'lsior.   **Ash.**

Tree, up to 80 ft., forming open woods on calcareous soils in the midlands
and south-west of England; I. Common along roads where it has been
planted for the use of wheelwrights. Flowers green, tinged crimson, spring.
Bark smooth, grey. Branches erect; branchlets stout, sweeping. Buds
opposite, small, pointed, black. Leaves pinnately compound; leaflets elliptical, toothed, glabrous. Flowers in dense panicles, before the leaves,
pollinated by wind. Fruit a green, winged key 1–2 in. long, oblong.

LIGU'STRUM

317. Ligustrum vulga're.   **Privet.**

Shrub, 7–8 ft., common in hedgerows and thickets on calcareous soil in
mid- and southern England, planted in hedges throughout Britain; I.
Flowers white, summer. Much branched. Leaves opposite, stalked, elliptical
or lance-shaped, entire, glabrous, evergreen except in hard winters. Flowers
small, in showy terminal panicles. Fruit a small, black berry.

APOCYNACEAE. PERIWINKLE FAMILY
VI'NCA

318. Vinca mi'nor.   **Periwinkle.**

Perennial, 1–2 ft., common in woods and hedgerows throughout Britain,
but usually an escape; I. Flowers blue, spring and summer. Stem trailing,
branching and rooting. Leaves opposite, shortly stalked, elliptical or lance-
shaped, evergreen, glabrous and shining. Flowering stems short, erect;
flowers solitary, on short stalks in the leaf axils. Corolla salver-shaped.
V. MA'JOR, a larger plant, with erect or arching stems and ovate leaves, is
always planted or an escape. The stamens shed their sticky pollen on the
top of the stigma but it cannot reach the receptive surface underneath the
edge except through the agency of bees seeking nectar secreted by 2 yellow
nectaries at the bottom of the long corolla tube.

GENTIANACEAE. GENTIAN FAMILY
BLACKSTO'NIA

319. Blackstonia perfolia'ta.   **Yellow Centaury, Yellowwort.**

Annual, ½–1 ft., not uncommon in pastures and banks on calcareous soils,
especially in the south; I. Flowers yellow, summer. Stem erect, tough,
branched from the base or simple. Radical leaves in a rosette; stem leaves
ovate, pointed, joined round the stem by their broad bases, pale bluish-green.
Flowers in terminal false corymbs; corolla funnel-shaped.

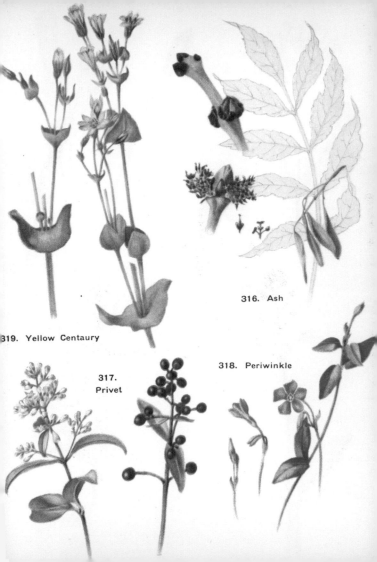

316. Ash

319. Yellow Centaury

318. Periwinkle

317.
Privet

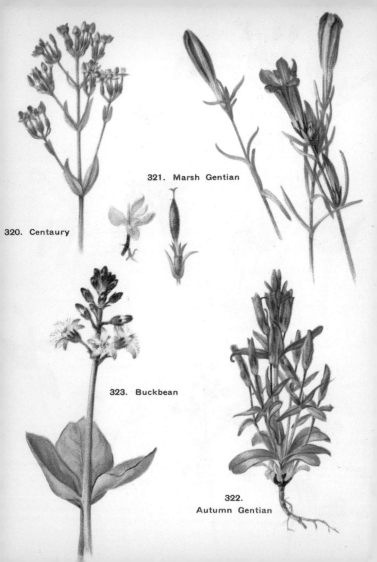

320. Centaury

321. Marsh Gentian

323. Buckbean

322.
Autumn Gentian

ERYTHRAE'A

320. Erythraea Centau'rium. Centaury.

Annual, 2–18 in., locally common in pastures and sandy places throughout Britain, especially in the south; I. Stem simple or branched, erect. Radical leaves oval; stem leaves elliptical, oblong, glabrous. Flowers in a terminal corymb or small head. This plant is very variable and a number of closely similar species differing in size, inflorescence, and details of floral structure are recognized by specialists.

GENTIA'NA

321. Gentiana Pneumona'nthe. Marsh Gentian.

Perennial, $\frac{1}{2}$–$1\frac{1}{2}$ ft., a rare plant of moist heaths in England, commonest in the north. Flowers deep blue, late summer. Stems slender, erect from near the base, simple. Leaves linear, blunt, glabrous. Flowers solitary or few, terminal. Corolla, 1–$1\frac{1}{2}$ in. long, narrowly bell-shaped, striped with green outside. G. NIVALIS is a rare Scottish alpine with small, bright blue flowers. G. VE'RNA is a rare dwarf alpine of northern England and Ireland.

322. Gentiana Amare'lla. Autumn Gentian, Felwort.

Annual, 3–9 in., rather common in upland pasture and roadsides throughout Britain; I. Flowers pale purple, autumn. Stem erect, branched. Radical leaves spoon-shaped; stem leaves sessile, lance-shaped. Sepals 5, equal. Corolla bell-shaped, the throat fringed with hairs. G. CAMPE'STRIS, the *Field Gentian*, is a very similar species with 4 sepals and petals, 2 of the sepals being much larger than the others. Nectar is formed by nectaries at the base of the long corolla tube and can be reached only by the long-tongued bees which pollinate the flowers; small insects are prevented from entering by the hairs in the throat.

MENYA'NTHES

323. Menyanthes trifolia'ta. Buckbean, Bogbean.

Perennial, $\frac{1}{2}$–1 ft., common in marshes throughout Britain; I. Flowers white, tinged pink, early summer. Rhizome stout and branching in the mud. Leaves alternate, stalked, 3-foliate; leaflets oval, entire, glabrous. Flowers in showy terminal racemes on naked stems; corolla funnel-shaped, fringed with conspicuous white hairs. Fruit a capsule, opening by 2 valves; seeds orange. The flowers are of 2 sorts on separate plants: (*a*) with long styles and short stamens, and (*b*) with short styles and long stamens, so that cross-pollination is favoured by the transference of pollen to the stigma at the corresponding level; bees, flies, and small beetles visit the flowers for nectar.

BORAGINACEAE. FORGET-ME-NOT FAMILY
CYNOGLO'SSUM

324. Cynoglossum officina'le.   **Hound's-tongue.**

Biennial, 1–2 ft., an uncommon plant of waste places and sandhills from mid-Scotland southwards; I. Flowers dull purple, summer. Tap root fleshy, black, with a tuft of oval leaves the first year and a stout, erect, flowering stem the second. Stem leaves sessile, oblong, elliptical, with rather soft, adpressed hairs, greyish. Flowers in numerous racemes curled in when young. Fruit dispersed by its hooks catching in animals. C. MONTA'NUM is a rare plant of southern England with greener leaves.

SY'MPHYTUM

325. Symphytum officina'le.   **Comfrey.**

Perennial, 1½–3 ft., common in moist meadows and shady places from mid-Scotland southwards; I. Flowers dirty white or dull purple, summer. Rhizome stout. Stems stout, erect, branched. Leaves large, lance-shaped, the lower broad and stalked, the upper sessile and running down the stem as wings. Flowers in numerous, forked, 1-sided, few-flowered, curved and drooping racemes. Nectar is secreted by a disk at the base of the ovary and can be reached only by long-tongued bees, the scales preventing small insects from creeping in. S. TUBERO'SUM is a smaller species common in shady places in Scotland, rare in England; rhizome tuberous, stem scarcely winged, leaves ovate, flowers cream.

ANCHU'SA

326. Anchusa sempervi'rens.   **Evergreen Alkanet.**

Perennial, 1–2 ft., occasionally abundant on banks and waste places throughout Britain, usually introduced; I. Flowers bright blue, with a white eye, summer. Stem, stout, erect simple. Leaves ovate, pointed, the lower long-stalked, the upper short-stalked or sessile; roughly hairy. Flowers in small paired cymes, at the end of long stalks in the axils of the upper leaves.

LYCO'PSIS

327. Lycopsis arve'nsis.   **Bugloss.**

Annual, 1–1½ ft., common as a field weed throughout Britain; I. Flowers blue, with white eye, summer. Stem erect, branched. Leaves strap-shaped, the upper sessile, margins waved or toothed; the whole plant very roughly hairy. Flowers small, in forked cymes curled in when young and straightening out later. The sepals enlarge greatly in the fruit.

Hound's-tongue

327. Bugloss

325. Comfrey

326.
Evergreen Alkanet

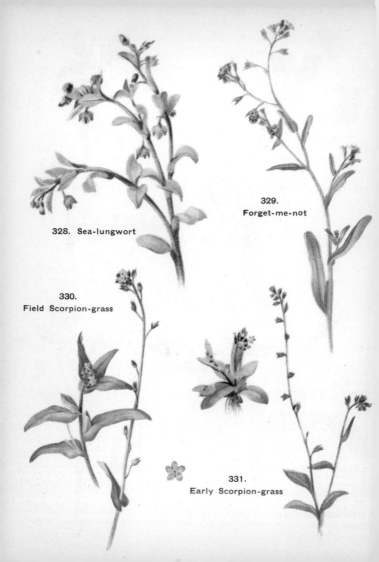

328. Sea-lungwort

329.
Forget-me-not

330.
Field Scorpion-grass

331.
Early Scorpion-grass

MERTE'NSIA

328. *Mertensia mari'tima*.   **Sea-lungwort, Oyster Plant.**

Perennial, 1–2 ft., not uncommon on shingle shores in northern Scotland, rare elsewhere; I. Stock fleshy, spreading by suckers. Stems branched, prostrate at the base and spreading. Lower leaves stalked, upper sessile, oval, ovate or reverse-ovate, very blue and almost glabrous, fleshy. Flowers in long, forked cymes, pink changing to purple-blue.

MYOSO'TIS

329. *Myosotis scorpioi'des*.   **Forget-me-not.**

Perennial, 1–2 ft., common in ditches and damp places throughout Britain; I. Flowers blue, with yellow eye, summer. Rhizome long, spreading by runners or suckers. Stem prostrate and rooting at base, then erect. Leaves narrowly oblong or spoon-shaped, finely hairy with spreading hairs, shining green. Spikes forked, terminal, curled in when young, then straightening. Calyx divided less than half its length, with adpressed hairs. Corolla large, ⅓ in. across. M. CAESPITO'SA is a common plant of damp situations distinguished by its smaller flowers, ⅛ in. across, and the adpressed hairs of the stem. Flowers visited by flies and small bees which can reach the nectar at the bottom of the short tube; self-pollination also takes place by pollen falling on the stigmas.

330. *Myosotis arve'nsis*.   **Field Scorpion-grass.**

Annual, ½–1½ ft., common in fields and waste places throughout Britain; I. Flowers blue, with yellow eye, summer. Stem branched from the base, erect, with spreading hairs. Leaves oblong, pointed, upper sessile, lower narrowing to stalks. Flowers small in forked spikes, on stalks a little longer than the calyx, which is divided to half its length, is covered with spreading, hooked hairs, and is closed in the fruit. M. SYLVA'TICA, the *Wood Scorpion-grass*, is a similar, less common plant of shady places with large, bright blue flowers and the calyx deeply cleft.

331. *Myosotis colli'na*.   **Early Scorpion-grass.**

Annual, 2–6 in., common on dry banks and sand-dunes, except in north western Scotland; I. Flowers bright blue, spring. Stems simple or much branched. Leaves elliptical or oblong, sessile, hairy. Flowers in terminal spikes on stalks about the length of the calyx, which is covered with spreading hairs and is open in the fruit. Corolla small, funnel-shaped. An ephemeral which flowers early and passes the dry season as seed. M. VERSI'COLOR, the *Variegated Scorpion-grass*, is a common plant of waste ground, about 1 ft., with small flowers which change from yellow when young to blue when fully opened; summer.

LITHOSPE'RMUM

332. *Lithospermum arve'nse*.   **Corn Gromwell.**

Annual, 1–1½ ft., a not uncommon weed of cultivated ground through most of Britain; I. Flowers white, summer. Stem erect, branched, with short bristles. Leaves sessile, narrowly elliptical or oblong. Corolla just longer than the narrow sepals which lengthen in the fruit. Nutlets grey, wrinkled, and hard. L. OFFICINA'LE, the *Gromwell*, is a rather uncommon plant of thickets and roadsides, with yellowish flowers and white, smooth nutlets, only 1 or 2 of which ripen. L. PURPU'REO-CAERU'LEUM is a very rare plant of south-western England with purple-blue flowers.

E'CHIUM

333. *Echium vulga're*.   **Viper's Bugloss.**

Biennial, 1–3 ft., in dry places throughout Britain, rare in the north; I. Flowers blue, summer. Stem stout, erect, from a thick tap-root, leafy. Leaves sessile, oblong lance-shaped, pointed; the whole plant rough with stiff hairs. Corolla large, with an open mouth, pink when young and turning bright blue. E. PLANTAGI'NEUM, found in Jersey, has heart-shaped upper leaves and large, violet-blue flowers. The flowers of both are visited by many insects, bees, hoverflies, and butterflies. The stamens ripen first and later the style elongates and the forked stigmas diverge and become receptive.

CONVOLVULACEAE. BINDWEED FAMILY

CONVOL'VULUS

334. *Convolvulus se'pium*.   **Greater Bindweed.**

Perennial climber, 2–5 ft., common in hedges and as a garden weed throughout Britain; I. Flowers white, summer. Stem weak, twining round more or less upright supports. Leaves stalked, heart-shaped or arrow-shaped, with pointed corners, glabrous. Flowers solitary in the leaf axils, each with 2 large heart-shaped bracteoles immediately below the calyx; corolla 2 in.

335. *Convolvulus Soldane'lla*.   **Sea Bindweed.**

Perennial ½–1 ft., local on sandy and shingle shores, from mid-Scotland southwards; I. Flowers pink, summer. Spreads by an extensive, branching rhizome. Leaves stalked, kidney-shaped, with a few shallow lobes, glabrous, fleshy. Flowers solitary in the leaf axils, with 2 blunt, oval bracteoles immediately below the calyx; corolla 2 in.

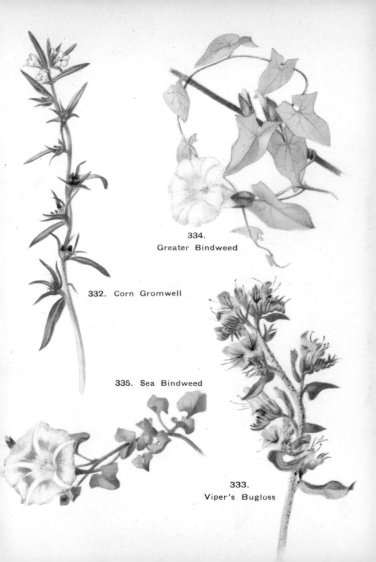

334.
Greater Bindweed

332. Corn Gromwell

335. Sea Bindweed

333.
Viper's Bugloss

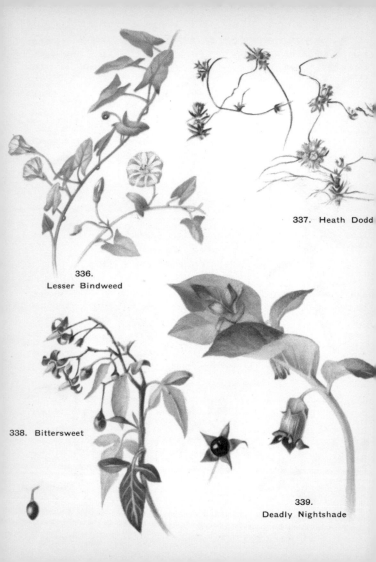

337. Heath Dodd

336.
Lesser Bindweed

338. Bittersweet

339.
Deadly Nightshade

336. *Convolvulus arve'nsis*. **Lesser Bindweed.**

Perennial, 1–3 ft., common on banks and in cornfields in England, less common in Scotland; I. Flowers pink, summer. Stem weak, trailing or twining. Leaves stalked, broadly arrow- or halbert-shaped, blunt, glabrous. Flowers solitary or paired, in the leaf axils, with 2 small bracteoles about ½ in. below the calyx. Nectar is produced at the base of the ovary and, though the corolla tube is wide, it cannot be reached by small insects, as it is covered by the broad bases of the stamens; between these bees, butterflies, and other insects must insert their tongues; the stigma is touched before the stamens. The flower lasts only a day and then droops; in this position pollen may fall on the stigma.

CU'SCUTA

337. *Cuscuta Epithy'mum*. **Heath Dodder.**

Parasitic annual, ½–1½ ft., locally abundant on furze, thyme, and ling on heaths in England and southern Scotland; I. Flowers pink, late summer. Stem reddish, thread-like, much branched and often forming dense mats over the host plants into which it sends suckers. Corolla with 4–5 spreading teeth. A variety is sometimes a pest on clover. C. EUROPAE'A, the *Great Dodder*, with coarse, yellow stems and small, forked corolla scales, is a rare parasite on nettles and other plants.

SOLANACEAE. NIGHTSHADE FAMILY
SOLA'NUM

338. *Solanum Dulcama'ra*. **Bittersweet.**

Perennial, 2–6 ft., common in hedges and thickets throughout England, less common in southern Scotland; I. Flowers purple and yellow, summer. Stem shrubby below, much branched, weak and rambling. Leaves stalked, ovate, heart- or halbert-shaped, or with 3 deep lobes, entire, hairy. Corolla bright purple; stamens yellow. Berries ovoid, scarlet. S. NI'GRUM, the *Black Nightshade*, is a common weed in southern England, less common in the north; much branched, 1–1½ ft., leaves rhomboidal, coarsely toothed, flowers small, dirty white, berries globular, black.

ATROPA

339. *Atropa Bellado'nna*. **Deadly Nightshade, Dwale.**

Perennial, 2–3 ft., a rare plant of waste places on calcareous soils in England and southern Scotland; I. Usually an escape. Flowers dingy purple, summer. Rhizome stout, spreading by suckers; stems erect, forking. Leaves shortly stalked, broadly ovate, pointed, finely hairy, often occuring in pairs of which one is smaller. Flowers solitary, drooping; corolla rather large, bell-shaped. Berry round, purple-black. Very poisonous; source of the alkaloid *atropine*. Pollinated by humble-bees.

HYOSCY'AMUS

340. Hyoscyamus ni'ger.   **Henbane.**

Biennial, 1–2 ft., occasionally found in waste places near old buildings from mid-Scotland southwards; I. Flowers dirty yellow and purple, summer. Stem branched. Radical leaves stalked, ovate; stem leaves sessile, oblong-ovate, notched; soft with sticky hairs. Flowers in a double row on one side of the stem, the apex of this spike curled in when young. The globular, lower part of the calyx tightly encloses the capsule, the lid of which breaks off at the level of the expanded, upper part of the calyx. Very poisonous; source of the alkaloid *hyoscyamine*. Pollinated by humble-bees.

SCROPHULARIACEAE.   FOXGLOVE FAMILY

VERBA'SCUM

341. Verbascum Tha'psus.   **Great Mullein, Aaron's Rod.**

Biennial, 3–4 ft., not uncommon in waste places and roadsides in England and southern Scotland; I. Flowers yellow, summer. Stem stout, erect, un-branched. Radical leaves in a rosette, stem leaves running down the stem forming wings, large, oval, with very slight indentations and very woolly. Flowers in long terminal spikes; corolla ¾ in.; stalks of 3 stamens with white hairs. The flowers are pollinated by bees and hover-flies which are said to eat the staminal hairs, as nectar is scanty, and collect pollen; the stigma is touched before the stamens. There are several other species, of which V. NI'GRUM, the *Black Mullein*, is native in southern England and occurs as an escape elsewhere; 2–3 ft., with ovate or heart-shaped, stalked leaves, almost glabrous above; flowers yellow with purple staminal hairs.

LINA'RIA

342. Linaria Cymbala'ria.   **Ivy-leaved Toadflax.**

Trailing perennial, ½–2 ft., not a native, but naturalized on old walls and common throughout England and southern Scotland; I. Flowers lilac, summer. Stems slender, much branched, creeping and trailing. Leaves long-stalked, ivy-shaped, glabrous, rather fleshy. Flowers solitary, on long stalks in the leaf axils; corolla with a short, blunt spur. After flowering the stalks bend away from the light and bring the fruit into crevices of the wall.

343. Linaria vulga'ris.   **Yellow Toadflax.**

Perennial, 1–2 ft., common along waysides from mid-Scotland southwards; I. Flowers bright yellow, late summer. Spreads by suckers; stem stiff, erect. Leaves numerous, linear, glabrous. Flowers in a close, terminal raceme; corolla with a long spur, yellow with orange mouth. Only long-tongued bees are able to force open the mouth of the corolla and reach the nectar at the bottom of the long spur, pollinating the flowers; in southern Europe certain moths are able to insert their tongues between the closed lips, reach the nectar, and transfer pollen on their tongues. L. PURPU'REA, the *Purple Toadflax*, with slender spikes of small, bright purple flowers, is sometimes found as an escape.

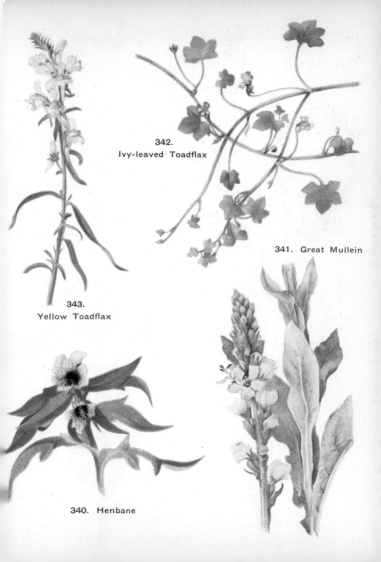

342.
Ivy-leaved Toadflax

341. Great Mullein

343.
Yellow Toadflax

340. Henbane

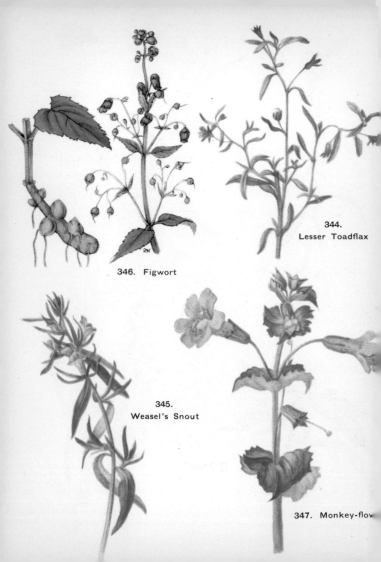

344.
Lesser Toadflax

346. Figwort

345.
Weasel's Snout

347. Monkey-flo

344. *Linaria mi'nor.*   **Lesser Toadflax.**

Annual, ½–1 ft., not uncommon as a weed of fields and gardens in most of England, rare farther north; I. Flowers pale purple and yellow, summer and autumn. Stem branched, branches spreading and then erect. Leaves narrow, lance-shaped or linear, hairy. Flowers small, solitary in the leaf axils; corolla with a short blunt spur, pale purple with a yellow mouth. L. SPU'RIA, the *Male Fluellen*, a cornfield weed of southern England, is prostrate; leaves ovate with sticky hairs; corolla yellow, with purple tip and a pointed spur at right-angles to the tube. L. ELATI'NE, the *Sharp-leaved Fluellen*, is a similar weed of cornfields, with halbert-shaped leaves. There are three other rare species.

ANTIRRHI'NUM

345. *Antirrhinum Oro'ntium.*   **Weasel's Snout.**

Annual, ½–1½ ft., not uncommon as a field and garden weed in England, especially in the south; I. Flowers rose-purple, late summer and autumn. Stem erect, branched. Leaves shortly stalked, narrowly lance-shaped, slightly hairy. Flowers in the axils of the upper leaves; sepals very long and narrow. Only bees are able to force open the flower, reach the nectar at the base of the ovary, and carry out pollination. A. MA'JUS, the *Snapdragon*, is often found naturalized on old walls.

SCROPHULA'RIA

346. *Scrophularia nodo'sa.*   **Figwort.**

Perennial, 2–3 ft., common in damp, shady places throughout Britain; I. Flowers brown, late summer. The branched, erect, 4-angled stem rises from a stout, knotty rhizome. Leaves stalked, opposite, heart-shaped, coming to a point, toothed, hairless. Flowers in a loose terminal panicle. S. AQUA'TICA, the *Water-betony*, is a similar plant, common in wet places in England, with narrower, bluntly toothed leaves and a winged stem. S. SCORODO'NIA is a rare plant of Cornwall and Devon with downy leaves.

MI'MULUS

347. *Mimulus gutta'tus.*   **Monkey-flower.**

Perennial, 1–2 ft., a native of N. America, frequently naturalized in ditches, especially in Scotland; I. Flowers bright yellow, late summer. The short rhizome gives rise to prostrate barren stems and erect, flowering stems. Leaves opposite, upper sessile, ovate, pointed, coarsely toothed, glabrous. Flowers long-stalked, large, in the axils of the upper leaves, forming a showy raceme. Pollinated by bees; the stigmas are sensitive and close together after they have been rubbed by an insect.

DIGITA'LIS

348. *Digitalis purpu'rea*.   **Foxglove.**

Biennial, 2–5 ft., common in pastures, heaths, and open woods, especially on light soils in upland districts, throughout Britain; I. Flowers purple with white spots, summer. In the first year a rosette of leaves is formed, and, in the second a tall, stout, flowering stem. Leaves with winged stalks, the upper sessile, long, ovate, coarsely toothed, softly hairy. Flowers large, drooping, in a long, handsome raceme. Poisonous; the source of the glucoside *digitalin*. Pollinated by humble-bees; the pollen is shed before the stigmas are receptive.

VERO'NICA

349. *Veronica hederaefo'lia*.   **Ivy-leaved Speedwell.**

Annual, ½–1 ft., a common weed of cultivated ground throughout Britain; I. Flowers lilac, spring to autumn. Stems much branched from the base, prostrate. Leaves alternate, stalked, very broadly ovate, with 3–5 shallow lobes, hairy. Flowers solitary in the leaf axils. Capsule swollen, rounded.

350. *Veronica pe'rsica*.   **Greater Field Speedwell.**

Annual, ½–1 ft., a common weed of cultivated ground throughout Britain; I. Flowers bright blue, spring to autumn. Stem much branched from the base, prostrate. Leaves alternate, shortly stalked, ovate or heart-shaped, toothed, sparsely hairy. Corolla nearly ½ in. Capsule twice as broad as long, with lobes pointing outwards. V. AGRE'STIS, the *Lesser Field Speedwell*, is a similar but smaller common weed; flowers about ¼ in., capsule not twice as broad as long, with erect lobes.

351. *Veronica serpyllifo'lia*.   **Thyme-leaved Speedwell.**

Perennial, 3–9 in., common in open woods, pastures, and road-sides throughout Britain; I. Flowers pale lilac with darker stripes, late summer. Stem branched, rooting at the base, prostrate, with erect tips. Leaves opposite, shortly stalked or sessile, ovate or oval, blunt, almost glabrous. Flowers in slender, terminal racemes; corolla ¼ in. Capsule heart-shaped. V. ALPI'NA, the *Alpine Speedwell*, is a rare Scottish alpine with erect stems and short racemes of blue flowers.

349.
Ivy-leaved Speedwell

348. Foxglove

350. Greater
Field Speedwell

351.
Thyme-leaved Speedwell

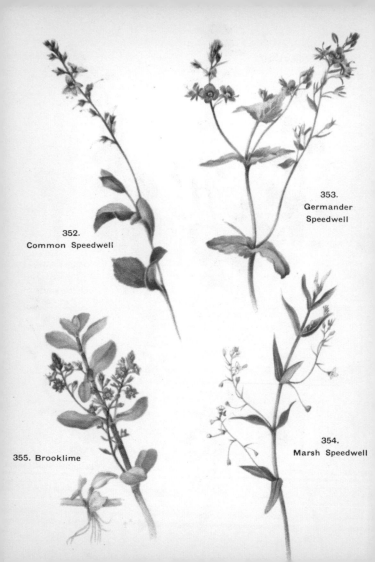

352.
Common Speedwell

353.
Germander Speedwell

355. Brooklime

354.
Marsh Speedwell

352. *Veronica officina'lis.* Common Speedwell.

Perennial, 3–9 in., common in pastures and open woods throughout Britain; I. Flowers lilac-purple, summer. Stems branched, prostrate, rooting below, hairy all round. Leaves opposite, oval, narrowing to short stalks, sharply toothed, hairy. Flowers in erect spikes in the leaf axils. Capsule heart-shaped. V. ARVE'NSIS, the *Wall Speedwell*, is a common annual of dry places, with stem branched below, branches more or less erect, terminating in spikes of small, pale blue flowers; leaves opposite, sessile, ovate or heart-shaped, coarsely toothed.

353. *Veronica Chamae'drys.* Germander Speedwell.

Perennial, ½–1½ ft., common in pastures and open woods throughout Britain; I. Flowers bright blue, early summer. Stem prostrate, branching and rooting below; branches erect, with 2 lines of hairs. Leaves opposite, sessile, ovate or heart-shaped, deeply toothed, hairy. Flowers large, in racemes in the leaf axils; corolla ½ in. Nectar is secreted at the base of the ovary and is protected by hairs in the throat of the corolla. The stigma points down and the stamens to the side. The flowers are pollinated by hover-flies which brush the stigma and, settling on the flower, pull the stamens, brushing pollen from them. The flower remains closed in cold weather and may be self-pollinated. V. MONTA'NA, the *Mountain Speedwell*, a plant of similar habit, is not uncommon in moist woods from mid-Scotland southwards. Flowers smaller and paler, leaves stalked, stem hairy all round.

354. *Veronica scutella'ta.* Marsh Speedwell.

Perennial, ½–1 ft., rather uncommon in wet and boggy places throughout Britain; I. Flowers pale lilac or pink. Stem brittle, rooting and giving off runners at the base; branches erect. Leaves opposite, sessile, narrowly lance-shaped, glabrous. Flowers small, in loose alternate racemes in the leaf axils; flower-stalks much longer than the bracts. V. ANAGA'LLIS, the *Water Speedwell*, a rather commoner plant of wet places, is coarser; leaves opposite, lance-shaped, toothed; flowers small, lilac in opposite racemes in the leaf axils; flower-stalks about as long as the bracts.

355. *Veronica Beccabu'nga.* Brooklime.

Perennial, 1–2 ft., common in ditches throughout Britain; I. Flowers bright blue, late summer. Stem prostrate and rooting below; branches erect. Leaves opposite, shortly stalked, oval, with shallow teeth, glabrous. Flowers in racemes in the leaf axils.

EUPHRA'SIA

356. Euphrasia officina'lis.   **Eyebright.**

Annual, 2–9 in., common on heaths and pastures throughout Britain; I.
Flowers of varied shades of lilac, often striped, with a yellow spot, summer.
Stem stiff, simple or branched, erect. Leaves opposite, sessile, ovate or
lance-shaped, toothed or notched. Flowers in terminal and lateral, leafy
spikes. The eyebright is a partial parasite drawing water and salts from the
roots of grasses and other plants with which it makes connexion through its
roots. It is a very variable plant and many species and varieties are recognized.

BA'RTSIA

357. Bartsia Odonti'tes.   **Red Eyebright, Red Bartsia.**

Annual, ½–1 ft., not uncommon along waysides throughout Britain; I.
Flowers dull red, late summer. Stem tough, 4-angled, branched, erect.
Leaves opposite, sessile, lance-shaped, coarsely toothed. Flowers in 1-sided
spikes. B. ALPI'NA, a rare alpine of northern England and Scotland, has
hairy, ovate or heart-shaped leaves, and reddish flowers. B. VISCO'SA, a plant,
locally abundant in damp pastures in southern England, has yellow flowers.
All are semi-parasites.

PEDICULA'RIS

358. Pedicularis palu'stris.   **Marsh Lousewort, Red Rattle.**

Annual, ½–1½ ft., common in marshes and wet fields throughout Britain; I.
Flowers purple-pink, summer. Stem erect, branched. Leaves mostly
alternate, deeply pinnately cut into toothed segments. Flowers in leafy
spikes; calyx with 2 cut lobes; corolla with a long, bent tube, upper lip with
2 small teeth. Pollinated by humble-bees which touch the protruding stigma
first. P. SYLVA'TICA, the *Heath Lousewort*, a common plant of damp, open
woods and heaths, has spreading, half-prostrate branches; calyx with 5
irregular, notched teeth; corolla rose, without teeth. Both species are partial
root parasites.

RHINA'NTHUS

359. Rhinanthus Cri'sta-ga'lli.   **Yellow Rattle.**

Annual, ½–1½ ft., common in fields and roadsides throughout Britain; I.
Flowers yellow with a purple spot, summer and autumn. Stem erect, stiff,
4-angled, simple or branched. Leaves opposite, sessile, narrowly lance-
shaped, toothed. Spikes 1-sided. A partial root-parasite.

358.
Marsh Lousewort

357. Red Eyebright

359.
Yellow Rattle

356. Eyebright

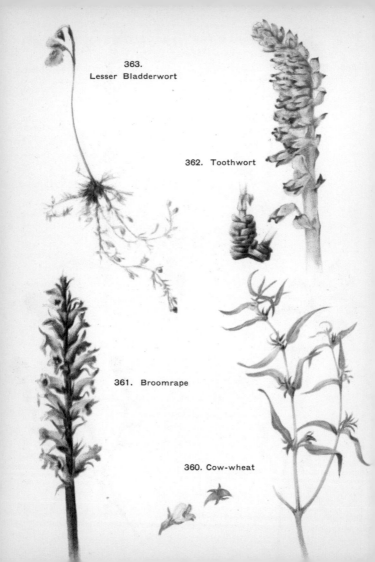

363.
Lesser Bladderwort

362. Toothwort

361. Broomrape

360. Cow-wheat

MELAMPY'RUM

360. *Melampyrum sylva'ticum*. **Cow-wheat.**

Annual, ½–1 ft., rather uncommon in upland woods of northern England and Scotland; I. Flowers yellow, late summer. Stem stiff, erect, with spreading branches. Leaves opposite, shortly stalked, narrowly lance-shaped. Flowers solitary, in the leaf axils, pointing to one side of the stem; corolla twice as long as the calyx. The seeds are distributed by ants. M. PRATE'NSE, the *Common Cow-wheat*, a not uncommon plant of open woods and pastures, has flowers in leafy spikes, with toothed bracts and a corolla 4 times as long as the calyx. M. CRISTA'TUM and M. ARVE'NSE are rare weeds of south-eastern England with inflorescences striking from their purple bracts. Partial root-parasites.

OROBANCHACEAE. BROOMRAPE FAMILY.

OROBA'NCHE

361. *Orobanche He'derae*. **Broomrape.**

Parasitic perennial, ½–1½ ft., not uncommon on ivy in south-western England; I. Flowers pale purplish-brown, late summer. The stems have only a few small scale leaves and terminate in long spikes of flowers in the axils of brownish bracts. Other species grow on thyme, bedstraw, broom, and furze.

LATHRAE'A

362. *Lathraea squama'ria*. **Toothwort.**

Perennial, ½–1 ft., occasionally found under hazel, ash, and other trees, on the roots of which it is parasitic, from mid-Scotland southwards; I. Flowers pale lilac, spring and early summer. The branching rhizome is thickly beset with fleshy, hollow scales. Stems fleshy, whitish. Flowers inclined to one side.

LENTIBULARIACEAE. BUTTERWORT FAMILY

UTRICULA'RIA

363. *Utricularia mi'nor*. **Lesser Bladderwort.**

Aquatic perennial, 3–6 in., not uncommon in moorland pools throughout Britain; I. Flowers yellow, summer. The plant consists of a submerged mass of branching stems and leaves which are very finely divided; they bear many minute bladders, about $\frac{1}{12}$ in., into which small water-animals are sucked by a peculiar mechanism and digested; the plant is insectivorous. Flowers on slender stems, projecting 3–4 in. above water; seldom seen in the north; spur very short and blunt. U. VULGA'RIS, the *Greater Bladderwort*, is a commoner and coarser plant of ditches and pools; bladders $\frac{1}{8}$ in. long; flowers large, bright yellow. There are several other rare species.

PINGUI'CULA

364. Pinguicula vulga'ris.   **Butterwort.**

Perennial, 3–6 in., frequent in bogs and wet, sandy places throughout
Britain; I. Flowers bright violet, early summer. Leaves in a rosette,
sessile, oval blunt, fleshy, edges inturned, covered with sticky glands.
Flowers solitary, on slender, leafless stalks; corolla ½ in. with spreading
petals. The plant is insectivorous and insects are caught and digested by
the sticky secretion of the leaf glands. P. GRANDIFLO'RA, the *Irish Butterwort*,
found only in Ireland, has flowers 1 in. with overlapping petals. P. LUSI-
TA'NICA, the *Western Butterwort*, found in Ireland, south-western England,
and western Scotland, has a pale lilac corolla with 5, almost equal lobes.
P. ALPI'NA, the *Alpine Butterwort*, a rare Scottish alpine, has yellowish white
flowers.

VERBENACEAE. VERVAIN FAMILY

VERBE'NA

365. Verbena officina'lis.   **Vervain.**

Perennial, 1–2 ft., occasionally found in dry waste places, especially in
southern England; I. Flowers pale lilac-blue, late summer. Stem erect,
from a woody rhizome, with stiff branches. Leaves opposite, stalked or
sessile, oval, notched or pinnately cut into toothed segments, hairy. Flowers
in slender spikes. Not scented.

LABIATAE. MINT FAMILY

ME'NTHA

366. Mentha aqua'tica.   **Water Mint.**

Perennial, 2–3 ft., common in ditches and wet places throughout Britain; I.
Flowers pale purple, summer and autumn. Spreads vigorously by suckers;
stem erect, branched above. Leaves shortly stalked, ovate, toothed, hairy.
Flowers in rounded, lateral and terminal heads. M. LONGIFO'LIA, the *Horse
Mint*, sometimes found in damp places, has sessile, narrowly ovate, toothed
leaves, greyish with hairs below, and flowers in slender spikes. There are
several other similar species; all hybridize with each other and with the
following species, so that many intermediate types occur.

367. Mentha arve'nsis.   **Corn Mint.**

Perennial, ½–1½ ft., in arable fields throughout Britain; I. Flowers pale
purple, autumn. Spreads by suckers; stem much branched, branches spreading or erect. Leaves shortly stalked, oval, ovate or rounded, toothed, hairy.
Flowers in dense whorls in the leaf axils; calyx teeth short, triangular.

364. Butterwort

366. Water Mint

365. Vervein

367. Corn Mint

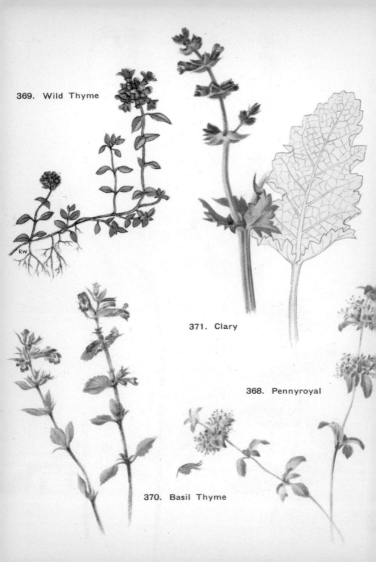

369. Wild Thyme

371. Clary

368. Pennyroyal

370. Basil Thyme

368. *Mentha Pule'gium*.   **Pennyroyal.**

Perennial, ½–1 ft., rather uncommon on damp heaths and pastures, throughout England and southern Scotland; I. Flowers lilac, autumn. Stem weak, prostrate, branched. Leaves very shortly stalked, small, oval, scarcely toothed, hairy. Flowers in dense whorls; calyx 2-lipped, with a hairy throat.

THY'MUS

369. *Thymus Serpy'llum*.   **Wild Thyme.**

Small shrub, 3–9 in., common in pastures, heaths, and rocky places throughout Britain; I. Flowers purple, summer. Stems branching out from a woody stock, prostrate, forming mats. Leaves small, shortly stalked, ovate or oval, slightly hairy, leathery, evergreen. Flower-whorls in small, terminal clusters. Aromatic. T. OVA'TUS, a less common, upland, plant has more erect shoots, ovate leaves and flower-whorls in a spike terminating in a head. Pollinated by bees, flies, and butterflies; stamens and stigmas stand far apart. ORI'GANUM VULGA'RE, the *Marjoram*, is a common plant of dry banks from mid-Scotland southward. Stem 1–2 ft., branched; leaves ovate, softly hairy, aromatic; flowers small, pale purple, in conspicuous corymbs, summer.

CALAMI'NTHA

370. *Calamintha A'cinos*.   **Basil Thyme.**

Annual or biennial, 3–9 in., rather uncommon on dry banks and fields, from mid-Scotland southwards; I. Flowers bright blue-purple, summer. Stems slender, branching from the base, spreading. Leaves stalked, ovate or oval, slightly toothed, slightly hairy. Flower whorls in the leaf axils; calyx inflated at the base and contracted below the teeth. C. VULGA'RE, the *Wild Basil*, a common plant of banks and bushy places from mid-Scotland southwards, has erect stems and softly hairy, ovate leaves; flowers red-purple, in crowded whorls in the leaf axils and at the tip of the stem. C. OFFICINA'LIS, the *Calamint*, is not uncommon in thickets in England; stem 2 ft., erect, with straggling branches; whorls of pale purple flowers in leafy spikes.

SA'LVIA

371. *Salvia Verbena'ca*.   **Clary, Wild Sage.**

Perennial, 1–2 ft., common in dry places in England, rare in eastern Scotland. Flowers blue-purple, summer. Stem erect, from a woody stock. Lower leaves stalked, oblong or heart-shaped, with shallow lobes and rounded teeth, wrinkled, slightly hairy; upper leaves sessile, toothed. Flower-whorls in the axils of small, broadly ovate, pointed bracts, in slender spikes. Pollinated by bees; the insect pushes against the lower half of the anther and brings the upper half down on its back, thus becoming dusted with pollen. The flowers sometimes remain closed and are self-pollinated. S. PRATE'NSIS, the *Meadow Sage*, a rare plant of southern England has large blue flowers, 1 in. long.

NE′PETA

372. Nepeta hedera′cea.   **Ground-ivy.**

Perennial, ½–1½ ft., common in shady places throughout Britain; I. Flowers bright purple-blue, spring and early summer. Stem branched, creeping, rooting at the nodes and so spreading and forming new plants. Leaves stalked, broadly heart-shaped or kidney-shaped, with very large, blunt teeth; slightly hairy. Flowering stems more or less erect, with whorls of about 6 flowers in the leaf axils. N. CATA′RIA, the *Cat-mint*, is an uncommon plant of waste places with erect, branching stems and terminal spikes of pale purplish-white flowers. Pollinated by bees which receive pollen in young flowers and brush it on the stigmas of older flowers.

SCUTELLA′RIA

373. Scutellaria galericula′ta.   **Skull-cap.**

Perennial, ½–2 ft., of ditches and the sides of streams and lakes, common in England, less so in Scotland; I. Flowers purple-blue, late summer. Rhizome branching, stems erect, branched. Leaves shortly stalked, broadly lance-shaped, with heart-shaped base and rounded teeth. Flowers in the axils of the upper leaves, all the pairs pointing towards the same side of the stem. S. MI′NOR, the *Lesser Skull-cap*, is a plant of swamps, commonest in the west, with pink flowers; about 6 in.

PRUNE′LLA

374. Prunella vulga′ris.   **Self-heal.**

Perennial, ½–1 ft., common in grassy places throughout Britain; I. Flowers blue-purple, summer and autumn. Stem branched from the base, branches rooting and spreading. Leaves stalked, ovate, irregularly toothed, hairy. Flowers in dense, terminal, cylindrical spikes; bracts very broad, sharply pointed, edged with purple; calyx purple.

STA′CHYS

375. Stachys officina′lis.   **Wood Betony.**

Perennial, ½–2 ft., common in thickets and pastures in England and southern Scotland; I. Flowers red-purple, summer. Stem stiff, erect, un-branched, hairy. Leaves stalked, oblong heart-shaped, the upper narrow with large blunt teeth. Lower flower-whorls in the axils of small leaves, upper in a head with small bracts.

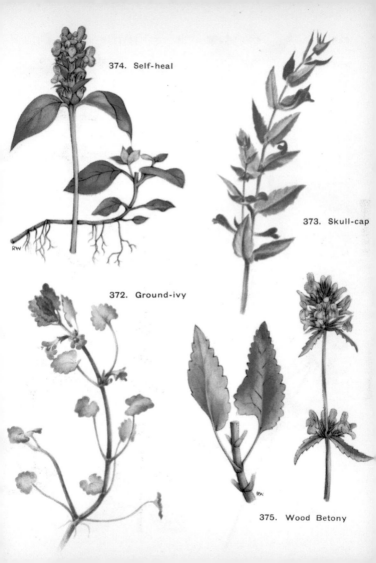

374. Self-heal

373. Skull-cap

372. Ground-ivy

375. Wood Betony

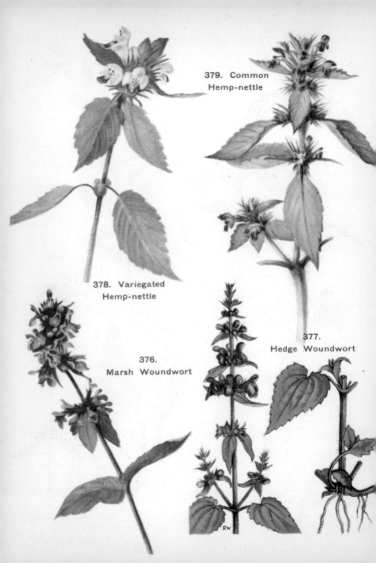

379. Common
Hemp-nettle

378. Variegated
Hemp-nettle

376.
Marsh Woundwort

377.
Hedge Woundwort

376. *Stachys palu'stris.*   Marsh Woundwort.

Perennial, 1–3 ft., common in damp fields throughout Britain; I. Flowers purple, late summer. Spreads extensively by suckers; stems erect, stout, hollow, simple or branched. Leaves shortly stalked or sessile, long, lance-shaped, toothed, hairy. Flowers few in a whorl, in a long, leafy spike.

377. *Stachys sylva'tica.*   Hedge Woundwort.

Perennial, 2–3 ft., common in shady places throughout Britain; I. Flowers reddish purple with white spots, late summer. Spreads by suckers; stems erect, unbranched, stout, hollow, hairy. Leaves stalked, heart-shaped, coming to a point, sharply toothed, hairy. Flowers few in a whorl in the axils of lance-shaped, entire bracts, in a long slender spike. Whole plant with an unpleasant smell. Visited by bees, which transfer the pollen from younger to the stigmas of older flowers. S. ARVE′NSIS, the *Field Woundwort*, common in fields in England, has branching, spreading stems, ovate leaves, flower-whorls in short leafy spikes; corolla pale purple, just longer than the calyx.

GALEO'PSIS

378. *Galeopsis specio'sa.*   Variegated Hemp-nettle.

Annual, 1–2 ft., a weed of fields with root-crops on light soils, especially in the north; I. Flowers bright yellow and purple, autumn. Stem stout, with spreading branches. Leaves stalked, ovate or broadly lance-shaped, toothed, hairy. Flower-whorls in the axils of the leaves near the tips; corolla 1½ in. long, handsome. The very long corolla tube can be probed only by very long-tongued bees and moths. G. DU′BIA, the *Downy Hemp-nettle*, a rare weed of north England, has softly hairy leaves and pale yellow flowers.

379. *Galeopsis Te'trahit.*   Common Hemp-nettle.

Annual, 1–2 ft., common as a weed of arable land throughout Britain; I. Flowers pale purple, autumn. Stem stout, erect, with spreading branches. Leaves stalked, ovate or broadly lance-shaped, toothed, hairy. Corolla less than 1 in. long, pale purple or whitish. G. LA′DANUM, the *Red Hemp-nettle*, is a field weed commonest in southern England, about 1 ft., with lance-shaped leaves and flowers mostly in terminal heads.

LA'MIUM

380. Lamium amplexicau'le. Henbit Dead-nettle.

Annual, ½–1 ft., a not uncommon weed of cultivated ground throughout
Britain; I. Flowers red-purple, summer and autumn. Stems branching
from the base, spreading and then erect. Lower leaves stalked, upper sessile,
round with rounded, toothed, lobes; meeting round the stem; almost
glabrous. Flower-whorls in the axils of the upper leaves; corolla tube thrice
as long as the calyx; calyx teeth meeting over the nutlets.

381. Lamium purpu'reum. Red Dead-nettle.

Annual, ½–1½ ft., a very common garden and field weed throughout Britain; I.
Flowers red-purple, almost throughout the year. Stems branching from the
base, weak and straggling. Leaves stalked, ovate or heart-shaped, blunt, with
rounded teeth, slightly hairy. Flowers in small whorls in the axils of the
crowded upper leaves; calyx teeth spreading in the fruit; corolla tube not
twice as long as the calyx.

382. Lamium a'lbum. White Dead-nettle.

Perennial, 1–2 ft., common along roadsides and in waste places throughout
Britain; I. Flowers white, summer. Spreads by suckers and generally grows
in dense clumps; stem rooting at the base and then erect, unbranched.
Leaves stalked, ovate or heart-shaped, coming to a point, with large teeth;
hairy. Flower-whorls in the axils of the upper leaves; corolla large, with
much-arched upper lip. Only long-tongued humble-bees can probe the long
tube; small insects are excluded from the nectar by a ring of hair in the
tube. L. MACULA'TUM, *Spotted Dead-nettle*, is a somewhat smaller plant,
occasionally found as an escape from cottage gardens; flowers red-purple;
leaves often with white markings.

383. Lamium Galeo'bdolon. Yellow Archangel.

Perennial, 1–2 ft., not uncommon in thickets and hedgerows on various
soils, especially in southern England; I. Flowers yellow, orange spotted,
summer. The stock gives rise to prostrate barren shoots and erect, unbranched, flowering stems; spreads by suckers. Leaves stalked, ovate,
pointed, coarsely toothed, hairy. Flower-whorls in the axils of the upper
leaves; corolla large, upper lip much arched.

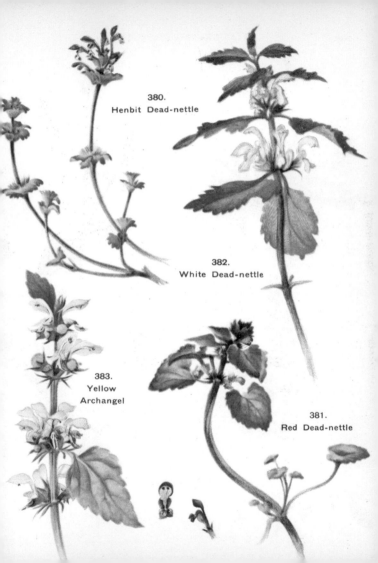

380.
Henbit Dead-nettle

382.
White Dead-nettle

383.
Yellow
Archangel

381.
Red Dead-nettle

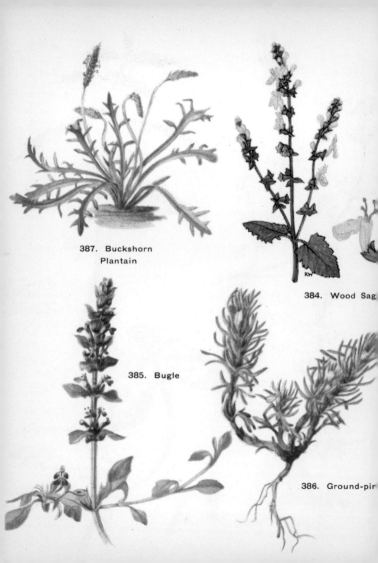

387. Buckshorn
Plantain

384. Wood Sage

385. Bugle

386. Ground-pir

TEU'CRIUM

384. *Teucrium Scorodo'nia*.   **Wood Sage.**

Perennial, $\frac{1}{2}$–$1\frac{1}{2}$ ft., common in dry woods and heaths throughout Britain; I. Flowers cream, with purple stamens, late summer. The rhizome gives rise to suckers and the erect, branching stem. Leaves shortly stalked, oblong heart-shaped, bluntly toothed, wrinkled, hairy. Flowers solitary in the axils of small, opposite, ovate bracts in slender racemes; all the flowers pointing to one side. In young flowers the stamens stick straight out and are touched by visiting bees; in older flowers the stamens bend back and the stigmas take their place; as the older flowers are at the bottom of the raceme, and the bee works regularly upwards, cross-pollination takes place. T. Sco'RDIUM, the *Water Germander*, is a very rare plant of wet meadows in eastern England; leaves sessile, oblong; flowers pale purple.

A'JUGA

385. *Ajuga re'ptans*.   **Bugle.**

Perennial, $\frac{1}{2}$–1 ft., common in shady places and pastures throughout Britain; I. Flowers bright purple-blue, summer. The rhizome gives off long, prostrate runners and erect flowering stems; the runners root at the tip and form new plants the following year. Lower leaves stalked, upper sessile; oval, blunt, slightly toothed, nearly glabrous. Flower-whorls in the axils of the upper leaves, forming a loose spike.

386. *Ajuga Chamae'pitys*.   **Ground-pine.**

Annual, 3–6 in., locally abundant in fields in south-eastern England on calcareous soils. Flowers yellow, summer. Stem branching from the base, branches spreading, then erect. Leaves crowded, divided into 3 linear segments, hairy. Flowers solitary, in the axils of the upper leaves. Aromatic.

PLANTAGINACEAE. PLANTAIN FAMILY

PLANTA'GO

387. *Plantago Corono'pus*.   **Buckshorn Plantain.**

Annual or biennial, 2–6 in., common in dry places, especially near the sea, throughout Britain; I. Flowers greenish, summer. The short stock runs down into a long tap-root. Leaves in a rosette, long and narrow, pinnately divided into narrow, notched segments, hairy. Flowers in a close, cylindrical spike on a leafless hairy stem. Bracts longer than the calyx. P. MARI'TIMA, the *Sea Plantain*, is a common plant of moist places near the sea with linear, entire, rather fleshy leaves.

388. *Plantago lanceola'ta.*   Ribwort Plantain.

Perennial, ½–1½ ft., common in grassy places throughout Britain; I. Flower-heads dark brown–black, summer. Stock woody, often forked. Leaves in tufts, long lance-shaped, narrowing to a stalk, about 5-ribbed, slightly hairy. Flower-heads usually cylindrical on long, ribbed stalks. In dry bare places the leaves are short and form a flat rosette and the flower-heads are small and ovoid. Pollinated, as are the other species, by wind; in young flowers the slender, hairy styles may be seen protruding from the closed corolla; later these wither, the corolla opens and the 4 stamens, on their long stalks, hang out and liberate their dusty pollen; both stigmas and stamens are fully exposed, and the latter are easily shaken by the wind.

389. *Plantago ma'jor.*   Great Plantain, Waybread.

Perennial, ½–1 ft., common in waste and grassy places throughout Britain; I. Flower-heads brownish-green, summer and autumn. Leaves in a rosette from a short stock, stalked, ovate or oval, irregularly toothed, nearly hairless. Flowers in a long, slender spike; stalks of stamens short, whitish, anthers purple. The plantain is a troublesome weed on lawns as the flat rosettes prevent the growth of grass and themselves escape the mower. P. ME'DIA, the *Hoary Plantain*, is a similar species, common in grassy places on calcareous soils, especially in England; leaves almost sessile, ovate, downy; flowers in dense spikes of a silvery lilac; stalks of stamens purple, anthers yellow.

LITORE'LLA

390. *Litorella uniflo'ra.*   Shoreweed.

Perennial, 2–3 in., not uncommon in shallow water along the margins of lakes throughout Britain; I. Flowers greenish-brown, summer. The stock gives rise to tufts of leaves and to slender runners, which root at intervals and produce new plants. Leaves sheathing, long, linear, hollow, glabrous. Male flowers solitary, at the tips of long stalks; stamens with stalks ¾ in. long; female flowers concealed among the leaf bases. The plants flower only when the water dries up, and are wind pollinated.

ILLECEBRACEAE. KNAWEL FAMILY

SCLERA'NTHUS

391. *Scleranthus a'nnuus.*   Knawel.

Annual, 2–6 in., common in fields and waste places throughout Britain; I. Flowers greenish, summer. Stem branched from the base, branches spreading, prostrate or rising at the tips. Leaves opposite, sessile and united round the stem, awl-shaped, pointed. Flowers numerous, sepals pointed. S. PEREN-NIS is a very similar rare perennial of southern England. The inconspicuous flowers are seldom visited by insects and are usually self-pollinated.

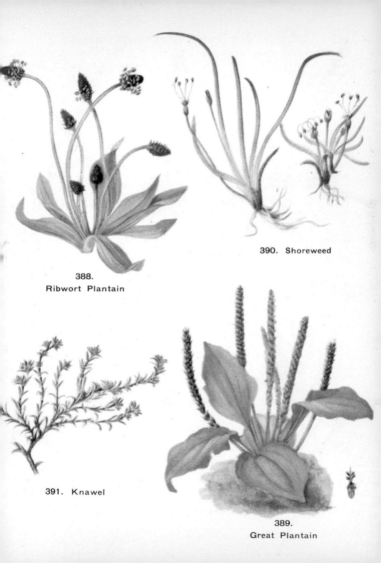

388.
Ribwort Plantain

390. Shoreweed

391. Knawel

389.
Great Plantain

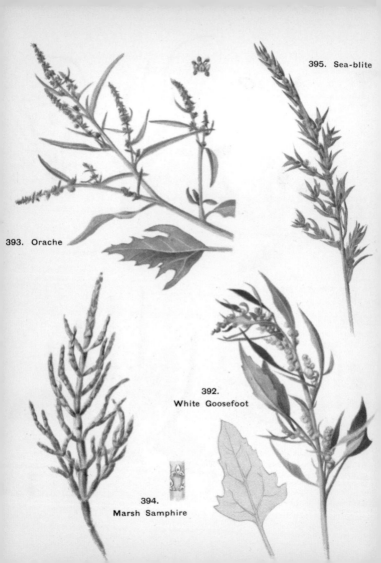

395. Sea-blite

393. Orache

392.
White Goosefoot

394.
Marsh Samphire

CHENOPODIACEAE. GOOSEFOOT FAMILY
CHENOPO'DIUM

392. *Chenopodium a'lbum*.   White Goosefoot, Fat Hen.

Annual, 1–2 ft., common as a weed of gardens and root crops, also on rubbish heaps, throughout Britain; I. Flowers green, autumn. Stem erect, branched, ribbed. Leaves stalked, rhomboidal or ovate, irregularly toothed, the upper lance-shaped, mealy below (sometimes quite green). Flowers in small clusters, in axillary and terminal spikes. Probably pollinated by small crawling insects. C. VULVA'RIA, the *Stinking Goosefoot*, occasionally found in waste places, has spreading branches, rhomboidal, mealy, entire leaves and an unpleasant smell. C. POLYSPE'RMUM is a similar plant with green leaves. C. RU'BRUM, the *Red Goosefoot*, is a variable plant of waste places, upright; leaves rhomboidal, coarsely notched, not mealy; stem and fruits often tinged red. C. BO'NUS-HENRI'CUS, *Good King Harry*, formerly grown as a vegetable and often found naturalized near villages, is perennial, with a stout tap-root and large triangular, soft, dark green leaves.

A'TRIPLEX

393. *Atriplex pa'tula*.   Orache.

Annual, 1–3 ft., common in waste places throughout Britain; I. Flowers reddish green, summer. Stem much branched, sometimes spreading on the ground. Leaves stalked; the lower rhomboidal or halbert-shaped; upper lance-shaped; more or less mealy. Flower clusters grouped in terminal leafy panicles; male and female flowers mixed together; fruiting bracts usually toothed and warty. This plant is very variable and has been divided by specialists into several species of which A. BABINGTONII with prostrate stems is common on sand and shingle beaches. A. PORTULACOI'DES, the *Sea Purslane*, not uncommon on seaside marshes and cliffs, is a shrubby, silvery grey plant, with entire elliptical leaves.

SALICO'RNIA

394. *Salicornia herba'cea*.   Marsh Samphire, Glasswort.

Annual, 3 in. to 1½ ft., locally abundant in salt marshes throughout Britain; I. Flowers green, autumn. Stem erect, much branched with opposite branches; these are cylindrical, jointed, succulent. A colonizer of the bare mud on the outer fringe of salt marshes the plant can withstand immersion by every tide. It is very variable and has been divided into several separate species. S. PERE'NNIS, a perennial, shrubby species found only in England, is rare.

SUAE'DA

395. *Suaeda mari'tima*.   Sea-blite.

Annual, ½–1½ ft., common in salt marshes throughout Britain; I. Flowers greenish, autumn. Stem tough, much branched, erect, spreading or prostrate. Leaves linear, fleshy, rounded below, flat above. Flowers small, solitary or in small groups in the axils of the upper leaves. S. FRUTICOSA is a rare shrubby species.

SA'LSOLA

396. Salsola Ka'li.   Saltwort.

Annual, $\frac{1}{2}$–$1\frac{1}{2}$ ft., common on sandy shores throughout Britain; I. Flowers greenish or pinkish, late summer. Stem branched, spreading or prostrate. Leaves linear or awl-shaped, ending in a prickle, fleshy, with hairy margins. Flower in the axil of a leaf, with a leafy bract on each side. Sepals with membranous wings in the fruit.

POLYGONACEAE. DOCK FAMILY

POLY'GONUM

397. Polygonum Convo'lvulus.   Black Bindweed.

Annual, 1–3 ft., common as a weed of arable land throughout Britain; I. Flowers pinkish-green, autumn. Stem branched, straggling or twining round thin supports. Leaves stalked, heart- or arrow-shaped, pointed, glabrous. Flowers in spikes, in the leaf axils. Nutlets black, 3-angled, enclosed by the enlarged sepals, of which the 3 outer sometimes develop narrow wings on the back. Flowers, as are those of the two following species, seldom visited by insects and usually self-pollinated.

398. Polygonum avicula're.   Knotgrass.

Annual, $\frac{1}{2}$–3 ft., common as a garden and field weed throughout Britain; I. Flowers pink, summer. Stems much branched, prostrate. Leaves almost sessile, elliptical or lance-shaped. Flowers in small clusters in the leaf axils all over the plant.

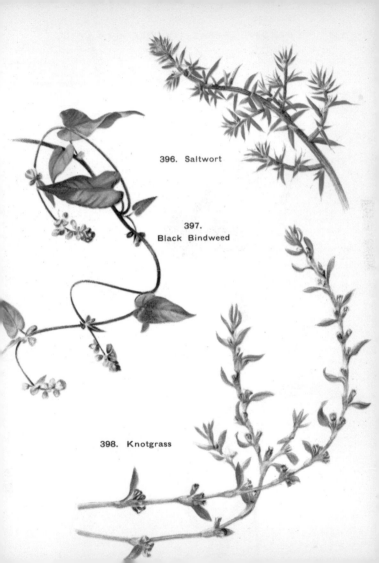

396. Saltwort

397.
Black Bindweed

398. Knotgrass

399. Water-pepp

402. Bistort

401. Amphib
Persicary

400.
Spotted Persicary

399. *Polygonum Hydropi'per.*   Water-pepper.

Annual, 1–2 ft., common in wet places in England and southern Scotland, rare in the north; I. Flowers pinkish-green, late summer. Stems much branched, branches spreading, prostrate at the base. Leaves shortly stalked, lance-shaped, wavy. Flowers in very loose, slender, half-drooping spikes. The leaves have a peppery taste.

400. *Polygonum Persica'ria.*   Spotted Persicary.

Annual, 1–2 ft., common as a garden and field weed throughout Britain; I. Flowers pink, sometimes white or greenish, late summer. Stem branched, branches spreading, prostrate at the base, nodes swollen. Leaves sessile or shortly stalked, lance-shaped, glabrous or slightly hairy, often with a dark brown blotch; stipules fringed. Flowers in terminal and lateral spikes. The flowers are pollinated by flies and small bees seeking nectar produced in a small nectary at the base of each stamen; when young the stamens stand out, away from the stigma, but in older flowers they bend in and self-pollination may take place. P. LAPATHIFO'LIUM, the *Pale Persicary*, is a common plant of wet places and damp fields distinguished by the pale green, unspotted leaves, the absence of a fringe on the stipules and the greenish, creamy flowers.

401. *Polygonum amphi'bium.*   Amphibious Persicary.

Perennial, 2–3 ft., common in ponds and wet places throughout Britain; I. Flowers pink, late summer. On damp ground the branched stem is prostrate at the base and the shortly stalked leaves are lance-shaped and finely hairy. In water the stems are thick and limp; leaves long stalked, floating, oblong with heart-shaped base, glabrous, waxy and unwettable. The two forms are very distinct, yet may be assumed by different branches of the same plant. Flowers in dense terminal spikes.

402. *Polygonum Bisto'rta.*   Bistort, Snakeweed.

Perennial, 1–2 ft., not uncommon in damp meadows and shady places, especially in southern Scotland and northern England; I. Flowers pink, summer. Rhizome branched and twisted. Radical leaves with a long, winged stalk, bluntly heart-shaped; stem leaves nearly sessile, ovate; glabrous. Flowers in a short, dense, terminal spike. Nectar is formed by a small nectary at the base of each stamen and the flowers are visited and pollinated by a variety of flies and bees; stamens ripe some time before the stigmas.

403. *Polygonum vivi'parum*.   **Alpine Persicary.**

Perennial, 4–9 in., not uncommon in damp upland pastures in northern England and Scotland; I. Flowers pink, summer. Rhizome woody, stem slender, erect. Radical leaves, stalked, narrowly lance-shaped; stem leaves almost sessile, linear, with slightly rolled margins; glabrous. Flowers in a slender, terminal spike. The flowers, although visited by insects, seldom set fruits and the lower are usually replaced by small bulbils which propagate the plant.

OXY'RIA

404. *Oxyria di'gyna*.   **Mountain Sorrel.**

Perennial, ½–1 ft., not uncommon along streams and wet rocks in the mountains of northern England, Wales, and Scotland; I. Stems and leaves in tufts, from a woody stock. Leaves long, stalked, kidney-shaped, glabrous, somewhat fleshy. Flowers in a terminal panicle. Fruit flattened, round, with a fringed wing.

RU'MEX

405. *Rumex obtu'sifo'lius*.   **Broad-leaved Dock.**

Perennial, 2–3 ft., common in waste places throughout Britain; I. Flowers green, tinged red, summer and autumn. Stem stout, erect, furrowed. Leaves stalked, large, oblong-ovate or heart-shaped, upper leaves smaller and lance-shaped. Flowers in small whorls in large terminal panicles. In the fruit the inner sepals are enlarged, toothed at the base and 1 or more has a rounded tubercle on the back. There are several other large species of dock and many hybrids. R. CRI'SPUS, the *Curled Dock*, another common species, has narrower leaves, with very wavy margins; fruiting sepals entire. R. PU'LCHER, the *Fiddle Dock*, a plant of southern England, has the leaves narrowed near the base so as to have the shape of the body of a violin. R. SANGUI'NEUS, the *Bloody Dock*, has lance-shaped leaves with red veins. R. HYDROLA'PATHUM, the *Water Dock*, is a very large plant of ditch-sides in England with oblong leaves; sepals entire, all tubercled. R. MARITIMUS, the *Golden Dock*, an uncommon plant of marshes near the sea in England, has crowded clusters of brownish flowers.

406. *Rumex Aceto'sa*.   **Sorrel.**

Perennial, 1–2 ft., common in fields and roadsides throughout Britain; I. Flowers crimson and green, summer. Stem erect, from a stout rhizome. Leaves arrow-shaped, succulent, the lower stalked, the upper sessile and clasping. Flowers in terminal panicles, male and female on separate plants.

403.
Alpine Persicary

406. Sorrel

405.
Broad-leaved
Dock

404.
Mountain Sorrel

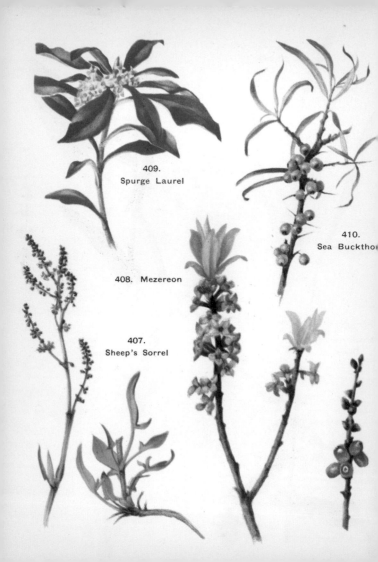

409.
Spurge Laurel

410.
Sea Buckthor

408. Mezereon

407.
Sheep's Sorrel

407. *Rumex Acetose'lla*.   Sheep's Sorrel.

Perennial, ½–1½ ft., common in fields, pastures, and waste places, especially
on light soils, throughout Britain; I. Flowers crimson and green, summer.
Spreads by slender, much branched underground shoots; a troublesome
weed. Stems erect unbranched. Leaves stalked, halbert-shaped. Male and
female flowers on separate plants. As in all other species of Rumex pollination is by wind.

THYMELEACEAE. SPURGE LAUREL FAMILY
DA'PHNE

408. *Daphne Meze'reum*.   Mezereon.

Shrub, 2–3 ft., a rare shrub of woods and copses, native only in southern
England. Flowers pink, spring. Stem much branched. Leaves deciduous,
spoon-shaped, pointed, glabrous. Flowers in small clusters towards the tips
of the stems, appearing before the leaves. Fruit an ovoid, scarlet berry;
poisonous. Pollinated by bees and butterflies seeking nectar at the base of
the tube.

409. *Daphne Lau'reola*.   Spurge Laurel.

Shrub, 2–3 ft., occasionally found in woods and copses on heavy soils in
England. Flowers greenish-yellow, spring. Stem little branched. Leaves
elliptical or reverse lance-shaped, leathery, evergreen. Flowers in small
clusters in the upper leaf axils. Fruit an ovoid, black berry, poisonous.

ELAEAGNACEAE. SEA BUCKTHORN FAMILY
HI'PPOPHAE

410. *Hippophae Rhamnoi'des*.   Sea Buckthorn.

Shrub, 1–12 ft., abundant in some places on the east coast of England,
occasionally planted elsewhere. Flowers greenish-white, summer. Much
branched, spreading vigorously by suckers; many twigs end in spines.
Leaves alternate, very shortly stalked, narrowly lance- or strap-shaped,
silvery below with scales. Fruit globular, fleshy, orange.

SANTALACEAE. SANDALWOOD FAMILY
THE'SIUM

411. *Thesium humifu'sum*.　　　　　　　**Bastard Toadflax.**
Perennial, $\frac{1}{2}$–1 ft., uncommon in pastures on calcareous soil in southern England. Flowers greenish white, summer. Stems slender, very numerous, bushy and straggling from a woody rhizome. Leaves alternate, small, linear, yellowish-green. Flowers inconspicuous, in loose terminal racemes. The plant is a partial parasite on grass roots.

EUPHORBIACEAE. SPURGE FAMILY
EUPHO'RBIA

412. *Euphorbia Heliosco'pia*.　　　　　　　**Sun Spurge.**
Annual, $\frac{1}{2}$–1$\frac{1}{2}$ ft., common as a weed of fields and gardens throughout Britain; I. Flowers yellow-green, summer. Stem stiff, erect, usually unbranched. Leaves alternate, shortly stalked, reverse ovate, finely toothed, glabrous. Inflorescences in a 5-rayed umbel; nectaries oval; leafy bracts ovate, yellowish. Fruit smooth. In this, as in other species, the nectar is completely exposed and is sought for by flies, which carry out cross-pollination, as the female flowers are mature before the male. The seed has a fleshy outgrowth sought for by ants which aid in dispersal. E. PLATYPHY'LLOS is a rare weed of southern England distinguished by warty fruits.

413. *Euphorbia amygdaloi'des*.　　　　　　　**Wood Spurge.**
Perennial, 1–2 ft., common in woods and hedges in mid- and southern England; I. Flowers yellowish-green, spring. Rhizome woody, stem stout, erect, unbranched, leafy the first year. Leaves alternate, reverse lance-shaped, narrowing to a stalk, entire, slightly hairy. Inflorescences in a panicle; nectaries crescent-shaped; leafy bracts opposite, semi-circular, yellow.

414. *Euphorbia Pe'plus*.　　　　　　　**Petty Spurge.**
Annual, $\frac{1}{2}$–1 ft., common as a garden and field weed throughout Britain; I. Flowers green, late summer. Stem erect, branched. Leaves alternate, shortly stalked, oval or ovate, entire, glabrous. Inflorescences in a 3-rayed umbel; nectaries crescent-shaped, with pointed horns; leafy bracts ovate, green. Capsules with a narrow, double wing down the edges. E. EXI'GUA, the *Dwarf Spurge*, a not uncommon weed in England and southern Scotland, is distinguished by its lance-shaped leaves and bracts, and the absence of the wings on the capsule. There are several other species, some very rare. E. PARA'LIAS, the *Sea Spurge*, and E. PORTLA'NDICA, the *Portland Spurge*, are bushy plants of sandy coasts in the south and west; in the former the leaves are oval, thick, and leathery, in the latter reverse-ovate, pointed, and bluish-green.

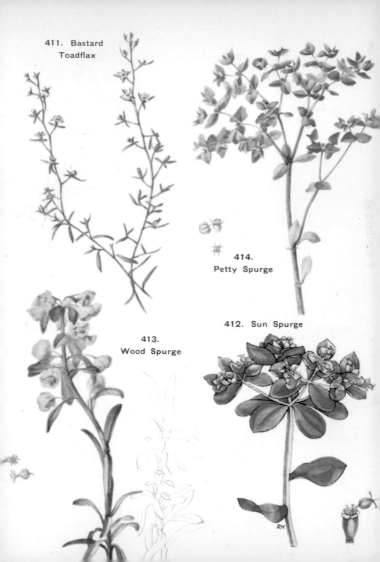

411. Bastard
Toadflax

414.
Petty Spurge

413.
Wood Spurge

412. Sun Spurge

417. Wych Elm

415. Box

416.
Dog's Mercury

418.
Stinging Nettle

BU'XUS

415. Buxus sempervi'rens.   **Box.**

Shrub, 6–12 ft., native in some localities on chalk hills in southern England.
Flowers greenish, early summer. Much branched. Leaves opposite, oval or
oblong, blunt or with a notched tip, shining, leathery, evergreen. Fruit a
leathery capsule with a crest formed by the 3 hardened styles.

MERCURIA'LIS

416. Mercurialis pere'nnis.   **Dog's Mercury.**

Perennial, ½–1½ ft., common in woods and shady banks throughout Britain; I.
Female flowers green, male yellowish, spring. Spreads vigorously by suckers
and generally grows in masses. Stem erect, unbranched. Leaves opposite,
stalked, ovate or oval, toothed, hairy. Male flowers numerous, in long-
stalked spikes in the leaf axils, conspicuous from the yellow stamens; female
flowers few, in short spikes, green and inconspicuous. Pollinated by wind.
M. A'NNUA, the *Annual Mercury*, is a common weed in southern England;
stem branched; leaves ovate, glabrous; male and female flowers sometimes
on the same plant.

ULMACEAE. ELM FAMILY
U'LMUS

417. Ulmus gla'bra.   **Wych Elm.**

Tree, 60–120 ft., common in woods and along roads and fields, native in
northern England and Scotland; I. Flowers crimson, early spring. A large
tree with spreading branches, fine twigs, and furrowed bark. Leaves very
shortly stalked, oval oblong, with a tapered point, doubly toothed, roughly
hairy, unequal at the base. Flowers in roundish clusters near the tips of the
twigs, before the leaves. Fruit round, with the seed in the centre of the wing.
U. CAMPE'STRIS, the *Common Elm*, abundant along fields in southern England,
has smaller, blunter leaves, fruit less round, with the seed (which is infertile)
near the top; it throws up abundant suckers from the roots, often at a con-
siderable distance from the trunk. Several other closely similar species of
restricted distribution are distinguished.

URTICACEAE. NETTLE FAMILY
URTI'CA

418. Urtica dioi'ca.   **Stinging Nettle.**

Perennial, 2–4 ft., common in waste places throughout Britain; I. Flowers
green, summer. Rhizome branching and spreading vigorously. Stem erect,
little branched, square. Leaves opposite, stalked, ovate or lance-shaped,
with a heart-shaped base, deeply and sharply toothed, coming to a point,
covered with stinging hairs. Male and female flowers on separate plants, in
loose panicles, longer than the leaf-stalks. The hairs are hollow with brittle
tips which break off and penetrate the skin, injecting an irritating fluid.
Pollinated by wind; the stamens are bent in the bud and, when the flower
opens, spring out and scatter their pollen. U. U'RENS, the *Small Nettle*, is

a less common annual weed with dense panicles shorter than the leaf stalks. U. PILULI'FERA, the *Roman Nettle*, a rare species introduced in eastern England, has the female flowers in globular heads.

PARIETA'RIA

419. *Parietaria officina'lis*.   **Pellitory-of-the-wall.**

Perennial, $1-1\frac{1}{2}$ ft., not uncommon on old walls in England and southern Scotland; I. Flowers reddish green, summer. Stems spreading out from the wall in clumps, reddish. Leaves alternate, without stipules, stalked, oval or elliptical, softly hairy. Small clusters of male, female, and hermaphrodite flowers in the leaf axils. The stamens are bent in under the tips of the sepals; a slight shock liberates them and they spring out violently scattering their pollen, which is caught and dispersed in air currents.

MYRICACEAE. BOG-MYRTLE FAMILY

MYRI'CA

420. *Myrica Ga'le*.   **Bog Myrtle, Sweet Gale.**

Shrub, 2–3 ft., of moist, peaty moors throughout Britain, but commonest in the north; I. Flowers brownish-green, spring, before the leaves. Spreads vigorously by branching, underground, woody shoots which throw up shrubby clumps. Leaves alternate, stalked, reverse lance-shaped, toothed at the tip, glabrous, pale below. The roots bear small forked nodules in which live bacteria which fix nitrogen and so aid in the nutrition of the plant on barren moors. Pollination by wind; male and female catkins generally on separate plants.

BETULACEAE. BIRCH FAMILY

BE'TULA

421. *Betula a'lba*.   **Birch.**

Tree, reaching 40–50 ft., common in oak scrub and open pine woods and heaths throughout Britain; I. Bark silvery. Young twigs with granular glands. Leaves on slender stalks, ovate or rhomboidal, sharply toothed. Fruit a small, winged nut, dispersed by wind. B. PUBE'SCENS, a closely similar tree, has more rounded, ovate leaves and softly hairy young twigs. B. NA'NA, the *Dwarf Birch*, is an alpine shrub of northern England and Scotland with shortly stalked, almost round leaves.

A'LNUS

422. *Alnus glutino'sa*.   **Alder.**

Tree, reaching 50 ft., common along streams and in marshy woods throughout Britain; I. Flowers in spring before the leaves. Much branched, often from the base. Leaves stalked, almost round, with broadly wedge-shaped base and very shallow lobes, toothed, glabrous, dark, glossy green. Female catkin ripens to a woody cone; seeds winged. Roots form nodules often as large as a cricket ball with bacteria which fix nitrogen.

421. Birch

422. Alder

420.
Bog Myrtle

419.
Pellitory-of-the-Wall

424. Hazel

423. Hornbeam

425. Oak

CARPI'NUS

423. Carpinus Be'tulus.   **Hornbeam.**

Tree, reaching 60 ft., native and forming woods in south-eastern England,
occasionally planted elsewhere; often pollarded. Trunk often flattened and
twisted; bark smooth, dull grey. Leaves stalked, oblong oval or ovate, doubly
toothed, pointed, glabrous; stipules long, falling early. Male catkins brownish, conspicuous; female catkins forming inconspicuous tufts at the tips of
the shoots, lengthening as they mature into long leafy clusters; fruit a small
nut with a 3-lobed green wing, 1 in. or more long.

CO'RYLUS

424. Corylus Avella'na.   **Hazel.**

Large shrub, occasionally a small tree, common in hedges and thickets
throughout Britain; I. Catkins expanding before the leaves, early spring.
Leaves large, reverse ovate or round, with an unequal heart-shaped base,
shortly pointed, coarsely double-toothed. Male catkins yellow, conspicuous,
shedding very abundant, dusty pollen. Female catkins differing from the
leaf buds only in their slightly larger size and in the tuft of crimson stigmas
projecting from the tip. Nuts in clusters, each enclosed by a leafy husk.
'Cobs', with broad nuts, and 'filberts', with narrow nuts, are cultivated
varieties.

FAGACEAE. BEECH FAMILY

QUE'RCUS

425. Quercus Ro'bur.   **Oak.**

Tree, 60–80 ft., common and native from mid-Scotland southwards; I.
Catkins expand with the young leaves in early summer. Grown in the open
the oak has a short, rugged bole and spreading branches; in woods it is
usually coppiced, that is, cut down at intervals of about 12 years, new shoots
coming up from the stools. Leaves stalked, reverse ovate-oblong, with
many, rounded lobes, glabrous. The fruit is the acorn, a nut set in a cup
of fused bracts. 2 species are now recognized: Q. SESSILIFLO'RA, the *Durmast
Oak*, which grows on light soils, with the groups of acorns nearly sessile,
leaf stalks rather long, the base of the blade tapering into the stalk; Q. PEDUN-
CULA'TA, the *Common Oak*, which grows on heavy, clay soils, with the groups
of acorns stalked, leaf stalks short, the base of the blade forming small,
rounded ears. Q. I'LEX, the *Holm Oak*, with evergreen, entire leaves, is
widely grown as an ornamental tree.

FA'GUS

426. Fagus sylva'tica.   **Beech.**

Tree up to 100 ft., forming native woods on calcareous soils in southern England and extensively planted elsewhere; I. Catkins with the leaves in early summer. Trunk tall, with smooth, grey bark; twigs slender, sweeping upwards. Leaves stalked, ovate, almost entire or with shallow, blunt teeth, fringed with fine hairs, glossy, green. Nuts 3-angled, brown, in a spiny, woody, brown, 4-valved cupule.

SALICACEAE. WILLOW FAMILY

SA'LIX

427. Salix tria'ndra.   **Almond-leaved Willow.**

Large shrub or tree, up to 30 ft., common along rivers from mid-Scotland southwards and planted in willow beds; I. Catkins in early summer, with the young leaves. Leaves shortly stalked, up to 4 in., oblong lance-shaped or elliptical, pointed, finely toothed, glossy above, paler below; stipules large, rounded, falling early. Catkins on short, leafy stalks, long and rather loose; male flowers with 3 stamens. S. PENTA'NDRA, the *Bay-leaved Willow*, has broader, shining leaves; buds and young leaves rather sticky, scented; male flowers with about 5 stamens.

428. Salix a'lba.   **White Willow.**

Tree, up to 60 ft., of wet places throughout Britain, often planted; I. Catkins with the leaves in spring. Leaves stalked, narrowly elliptical, tapering above and below, pointed, very finely toothed, white with silky hairs below; stipules small, falling early. Catkins on short leafy stalks, slender and loose; male flowers with 2 stamens. The *Cricket Bat* or *Blue Willow* is a variety of this species in which the old leaves are bluish below. S. FRA'GILIS, the *Crack Willow* or *Withy*, is distinguished by its broader, less silky leaves, large stipules, and the ease with which the twigs can be broken off.

426. Beech

427. Almond-leaved
Willow

428.
White Willow

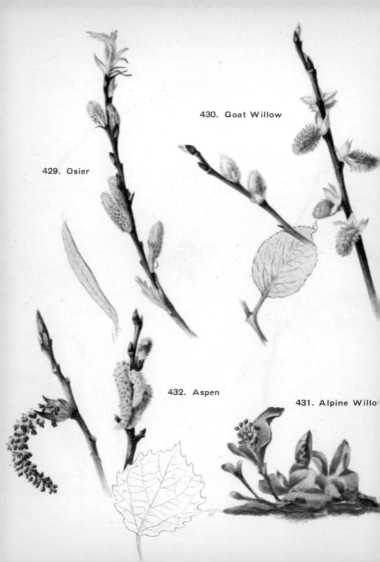

429. Osier

430. Goat Willow

431. Alpine Willow

432. Aspen

429. *Salix vimina'lis.* Osier.

Large shrub or tree up to 30 ft., common in wet places, except in northern Scotland, and planted in willow beds; I. Catkins before the leaves, spring. Young shoots form the long, straight rods used in basket-making. Leaves stalked, up to 10 in., narrowly oblong, tapering above and below, margin entire, rather wavy, white and silky below; stipules narrow, pointed, falling early. Catkins almost sessile, short, dense, the male bright yellow; stamens 2.

430. *Salix Ca'prea.* Goat Willow, Sallow.

Small bushy tree, common in thickets and hedgerows throughout Britain; I. Catkins before the leaves, spring. Leaves stalked, oval, ovate, or reverse ovate, somewhat wrinkled above, downy beneath, margins almost entire. Catkins sessile; the young, downy catkin is the 'pussy willow' or 'palm' of country children. Male catkin bright yellow and conspicuous. The flowers, like those of other willows, are insect pollinated and are much visited by early bees and other insects for their abundant nectar. The seeds are minute, hairy, and scattered by wind; they are remarkably short-lived, remaining viable for a week only after being shed.

431. *Salix herba'cea.* Alpine Willow.

Dwarf shrub, common at high altitudes in Wales, northern England, and Scotland; I. Catkins after the leaves, summer. The stem creeps and branches in the surface soil and sends up numerous short twigs with a few leaves. Leaves almost round, finely toothed, surface netted and shining. Catkins few, on short stalks, at the tips of the shoots. S. RE'PENS, a shrub with creeping stems and erect shoots, $\frac{1}{2}$–$1\frac{1}{2}$ ft., is common on heaths throughout Britain.

PO'PULUS

432. *Populus tre'mula.* Aspen.

Tree, up to 70 ft., of open woods and heaths throughout Britain, often planted; I. Leaves broadly ovate, heart-shaped, or almost round in outline, pointed, coarsely toothed, on long stalks, the flattening of which is responsible for the trembling of the leaf. Buds not sticky. Catkins before the leaves in April. Pollinated by wind. P. A'LBA, the *White Poplar* or *Abele*, a tree up to 80 ft., of open woods, has very broadly ovate leaves with a lobed or wavy margin, white with cottony hairs below, buds not sticky. P. NI'GRA, the *Black Poplar*, with rhomboidal, glabrous, toothed leaves and sticky, fragrant buds, is often planted, as is its variety, the *Lombardy Poplar*; several North American species are also planted and are remarkable for their rapid growth.

EMPETRACEAE. CROWBERRY FAMILY
EMPE'TRUM

433. *Empetrum ni'grum.* **Crowberry.**

Creeping, dwarf shrub of upland heaths and turfy places near the sea, commonest in northern England and Scotland; I. Flowers pink, early summer. Much branched, prostrate, forming mats. Leaves crowded, ¼ in. linear, with the margins folded back and meeting in a line down the centre of the lower surface, leathery, evergreen. Flowers inconspicuous, in small clusters in the leaf axils. Berries deep purple-black, sweet.

CERATOPHYLLACEAE. HORNWORT FAMILY
CERATOPHY'LLUM

434. *Ceratophyllum deme'rsum.* **Hornwort.**

Perennial, submerged aquatic, rather uncommon in ponds and ditches from mid-Scotland southwards, commonest in the south; I. Flowers inconspicuous, green, formed only in shallow water, summer. Stems ½–3 ft., branched. Leaves in whorls of about 8, forked 2–3 times, segments narrow, spreading; at the tips of the shoots the leaves are packed closely into a thick tassel. The pollen is transported by water currents.

MONOCOTYLEDONS
HYDROCHARIDACEAE. FROGBIT FAMILY
ELO'DEA

435. *Elodea canade'nsis.* **Water-thyme.**

A submerged aquatic, native in North America, introduced in 1836 and now found abundantly in ditches and slow streams throughout Britain; I. Flowers small, purplish, late summer. Stem slender, much branched, rooting in the mud and forming dense masses. Leaves sessile, opposite below, in whorls of 3 above, oval-oblong, pointed, up to ½ in. The female flowers reach the surface of the water on the long calyx tube; the male flowers (which have been found in this country only near Edinburgh) are detached and float to the surface, where they burst open, scattering their pollen, which floats to the stigmas.

HYDRO'CHARIS

436. *Hydrocharis Mo'rsus-ra'nae.* **Frogbit.**

Perennial, of ponds and ditches in England, commonest in the south; I. Flowers white, late summer. Leaves in a rosette, stalked, floating, kidney-shaped. Flowers raised above the surface, nearly 1 in. across. Nectar is produced at the base of the petals and the flowers are pollinated by honey-bees. In autumn small, ovoid, green buds are liberated and sink into the mud; in spring these float to the surface and start new rosettes; long runners are formed by the original rosettes and spread and multiply the plant rapidly.

433. Crowberry

434. Hornwort

435. Water-thyme

436. Frogbit

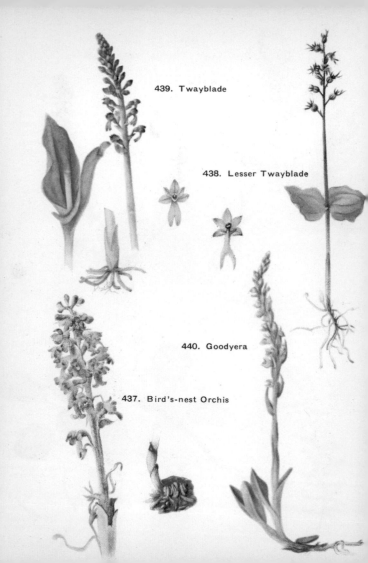

439. Twayblade

438. Lesser Twayblade

440. Goodyera

437. Bird's-nest Orchis

ORCHIDACEAE. ORCHIS FAMILY.

NEO'TTIA

437. *Neottia Ni'dus-a'vis*.   **Bird's-nest Orchis.**
Perennial, 1–1½ ft., occasionally found in woods from mid-Scotland southwards; I. Flowers brown, summer. The flowering stem, bearing brownish
scale-leaves, rises from the branched, matted rhizome which gives the plant
its name; there are no true roots and the plant absorbs organic food from
the leaf mould through the rhizome; this is always infected with a fungus,
probably concerned with the plant's nutrition. CORALLORHI'ZA TRI'FIDA,
the *Coralroot*, another saprophyte, is a smaller plant of yellowish colour,
rare in sandy woods of eastern Scotland.

LI'STERA

438. *Listera corda'ta*.   **Lesser Twayblade.**
Perennial, 4–8 in., of upland moors and woods throughout Britain, commoner in the north; I. Flowers brownish-green, late summer. Stem slender,
angled. Leaves sessile, ovate or heart-shaped, glabrous. Lip deeply forked,
with 2 side lobes near the base.

439. *Listera ova'ta*.   **Twayblade.**
Perennial, 1–2 ft., not uncommon in meadows and the margins of woods
throughout Britain; I. Flowers green, summer. Stem erect, round. Leaves
sessile, large, broadly oval, glabrous. Lip long and conspicuous, deeply
forked, without side lobes. Nectar is formed in a groove of the lip and is
sucked by small flies, which remove the pollen masses and transport them
to the stigma of another flower.

GOODYE'RA

440. *Goodyera re'pens*.   **Goodyera.**
Perennial, ½–1 ft., not uncommon in conifer woods in north-eastern Scotland.
Flowers white, tinged green, summer. Rhizome branching in the surface
mould, flowering stem erect, with leaves near the base. Leaves oval or ovate,
tapering to a stalk, finely hairy below. Bracts green, flowers twisted to one
side of the stem. SPIRA'NTHES SPIRA'LIS, *Lady's Tresses*, a rather rare plant
of pastures, commonest in southern England, is of similar appearance, but
has a twisted spike and tuberous roots.

EPIPA'CTIS

441. *Epipactis palu'stris.*   **Marsh Helleborine.**

Perennial, 1–1½ ft., uncommon in marshes and wet meadows in southern Scotland and England; I. Flowers greenish-white, tinged rose, summer. Leaves lance-shaped, clasping the stem and tapering to a point. Racemes loose, bracts leafy, shorter than the flowers; lip toothed. E. LATIFO'LIA, an uncommon woodland plant, has broader leaves and bracts longer than the flowers.

O'RCHIS

442. *Orchis ustula'ta.*   **Dwarf Orchis, Burnt Orchis.**

Perennial, about 3–9 in., found locally on calcareous pastures in England, especially in the south. Flowers dark purple, early summer. Root tubers ovoid. Leaves lance-shaped. Flowers small, in a dense spike; sepals hooded, dark purple; lip white, spotted with purple, spur half the length of the ovary.

443. *Orchis Mo'rio.*   **Green-winged Orchis.**

Perennial, 4–12 in., common in meadows and pastures in England, especially in the south; I. Flowers purple, early summer. Root tubers globular. Leaves strap-shaped. Spikes loose; bracts purple; sepals hooded, purple, with green veins; lip broad, 3-lobed; spur pointing upwards, nearly as long as the ovary.

444. *Orchis ma'scula.*   **Early Purple Orchis.**

Perennial, ½–1½ ft., not uncommon in open woods and pastures throughout Britain; I. Flowers red-purple, early summer. Leaves strap-shaped, blunt, often spotted. Spike loose, many-flowered; bracts purplish, 1-veined, as long as the ovary; side sepals, spreading; lip broad, notched; spur rather longer than the ovary. O. PYRAMIDA'LIS, found in calcareous pastures in England, has a close spike of rose-coloured flowers; lip with 3 broad lobes; spur longer than the ovary.

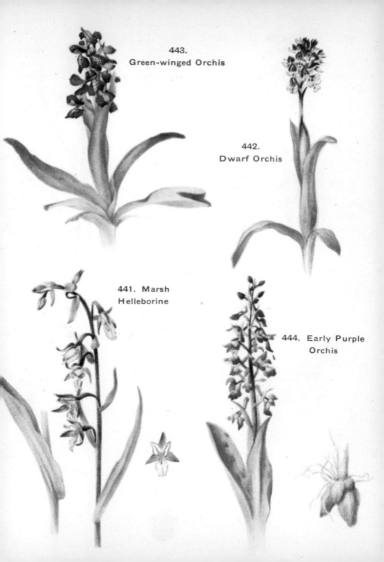

443.
Green-winged Orchis

442.
Dwarf Orchis

441. Marsh
Helleborine

444. Early Purple
Orchis

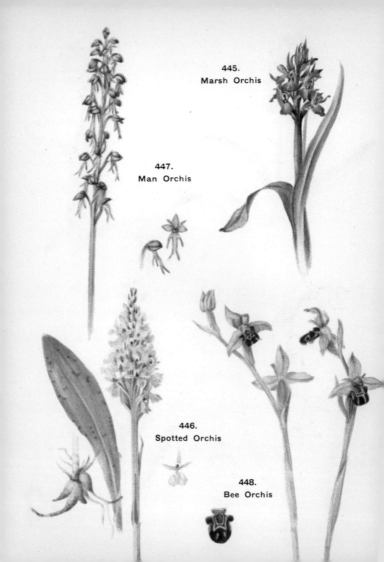

445.
Marsh Orchis

447.
Man Orchis

446.
Spotted Orchis

448.
Bee Orchis

445. *Orchis latifo'lia.* Marsh Orchis.

Perennial, $\frac{1}{2}$–$1\frac{1}{2}$ ft., common in moist meadows and marshes throughout Britain; I. Flowers dull purple, early summer. Root tubers forked. Stem hollow, leafy. Leaves broadly strap-shaped, blunt, sometimes spotted. Spike dense; bracts green, longer than the flowers; side sepals spreading; lip rounded, very slightly notched; spur shorter than the ovary.

446. *Orchis macula'ta.* Spotted Orchis.

Perennial, 1–2 ft., common in meadows and pastures throughout Britain; I. Flowers pink-purple, early summer. Root tubers lobed. Stem solid, leafy. Leaves oval or lance-shaped, usually spotted. Spike crowded, with many flowers; sepals spreading; bracts green, about as long as the ovary; lip 3-lobed, the middle lobe small and pointed; spur narrow, rather shorter than the ovary. There are several other rare species. As in other species, no nectar is formed and insects pierce and suck the juicy cells lining the spur. An insect, pushing its head into the throat of the corolla, comes in contact with the base of the stalks of the pollen masses, and these stick to its head and are removed. As the insect flies the stalks bend downwards so that, when the next flower is visited, the pollen mass is pushed against the receptive stigma. The process may be imitated by pushing a pencil point into a flower. Bees are the principal visitors. The mechanism is similar, with variation in details, in most other members of the family.

A'CERAS

447. *Aceras anthropo'phora.* Man Orchis.

Perennial, $\frac{1}{2}$–1 ft., rare in calcareous pastures of south-eastern England. Flowers greenish-yellow, early summer. Root tubers ovoid. Leaves oval oblong. Spike loose, slender; sepals and side petals form a close green hood over the column; lip long, with 2 narrow lobes at the base, deeply forked at the tip.

O'PHRYS

448. *Ophrys api'fera.* Bee Orchis.

Perennial, $\frac{1}{2}$–1 ft., locally common in calcareous pastures, especially in southern England; I. Flowers pink and brown, summer. Leaves elliptical, pointed. Flowers few, in a loose spike; bracts large, green; sepals pinkish, spreading; lip as broad as long, rounded, puffed out, velvety brown with yellow markings, resembling a bee settled on the flower. O. SPHEGO'DES, the *Spider Orchis*, is a similar plant with greenish sepals and a dark brown lip. O. MUSCI'FERA, the *Fly Orchis*, has green sepals and an elongated, 4-lobed lip, reddish-brown. Many attempts have been made to assign a use to the remarkable resemblance of these flowers to insects; in fact the resemblance seems to be disadvantageous, as the flowers are very seldom visited and are usually self-pollinated.

HERMI'NIUM

449. Herminium Mono'rchis. **Musk Orchis.**

Perennial, 3-6 in., a rare plant of calcareous pastures in southern England; Flowers green, summer. Leaves oval, pointed. Spikes slender, flowers small, scented at night; lip with 3 pointed lobes. A new tuber is formed at the end of a sucker and the plant that grows from it is at some little distance from its parent. Pollinated by small flies and beetles.

HABENA'RIA

450. Habenaria cono'psea. **Fragrant Orchis.**

Perennial, $\frac{1}{2}$-$1\frac{1}{2}$ ft., of marshy ground, heaths, and pastures throughout Britain, common in the north; I. Flowers rose-purple, summer. Root tubers lobed. Leaves strap- or lance-shaped, pointed. Spike dense, many-flowered. Bracts green, about the length of the ovary; lip broad, 3-lobed; spur very slender, much longer than the ovary. The flowers are very fragrant, form nectar, and are visited by moths and butterflies which can probe the slender spur, sometimes over 1 in. long.

451. Habenaria vi'ridis. **Frog Orchis.**

Perennial, 3-12 in., of upland meadows and pastures throughout Britain, not uncommon in the north; I. Flowers greenish, summer. Leaves oblong or lance-shaped. Spike loose; bracts green, longer than the ovary; sepals and side petals forming a hood; lip strap-shaped, with 2 or 3 teeth at the tip, brownish-green; spur much shorter than the ovary. H. A'LBIDA, the *Small White Orchis*, is a less frequent plant of upland pastures, with a slender spike of small, whitish flowers; lip about as long as the sepals, with 3 pointed lobes; spur very short; scented.

452. Habenaria bifo'lia. **Butterfly Orchis.**

Perennial, $\frac{1}{2}$-$1\frac{1}{2}$ ft., not uncommon in moist pastures, heaths, and open woods throughout Britain; I. Flowers large, white, summer. Root tubers 2, tapering below. Leaves usually 2, oval, blunt. Spike loose, elegant; bracts green, about the length of the ovary; side sepals spreading; lip long, narrow, entire; spur slender and very long. The sweetly scented flowers form abundant nectar and are visited and pollinated by moths.

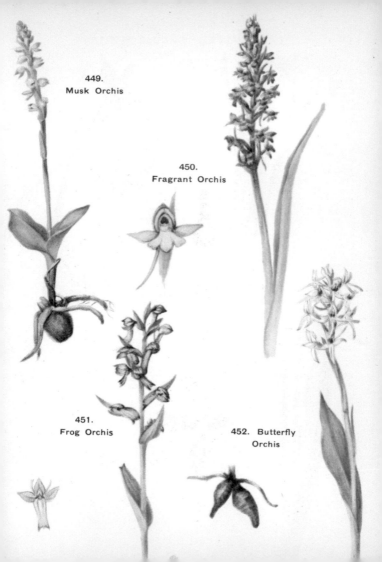

449.
Musk Orchis

450.
Fragrant Orchis

451.
Frog Orchis

452. Butterfly
Orchis

454. Daffodil

455.
Black Bryony

453. Gladdon

IRIDACEAE. IRIS FAMILY
I′RIS

453. *Iris foetidi′ssima*. **Gladdon.**

Perennial, 1–2 ft., of copses on calcareous soils in England, especially in the south; I. Flowers dull purple, with yellow markings, summer. Leaves and flowering shoots rise from a branching rhizome. Leaves sword-shaped, rather limp, evergreen, over-topping the flowers. The fruit opens by 3 valves, displaying numerous, bright orange seeds. When crushed the leaves have a peculiar smell from which the plant gets the names of *Stinking Iris* and *Roast-beef Plant*. I. PSEUDA′CORUS, the *Yellow Flag*, is common along streams, with brilliant yellow flowers overtopping the stiff leaves. The receptive region of the stigma is on the underside below a small flap; a bee pushing between the stigma and sepal first deposits pollen on the stigma, then it touches the stamen, from which it receives pollen; on withdrawing it closes the flap which prevents pollen from the same flower reaching the receptive surface.

AMARYLLIDACEAE. DAFFODIL FAMILY
NARCI′SSUS

454. *Narcissus Pseu′do-narci′ssus*. **Daffodil, Lent Lily.**

Perennial, ½–1 ft., of open woods and pastures throughout England, probably not native in Scotland; I. Flowers yellow, spring. Leaves long, narrow, bluish-green, fleshy. Flowers solitary on long stalks, crown darker than petals. The bulb is formed of the swollen bases of the leaves of the previous year. Nectar is produced at the base of the tube and is reached by long-tongued bees, which touch the stigma before the stamens.

DIOSCOREACEAE. YAM FAMILY
TA′MUS

455. *Tamus commu′nis*. **Black Bryony.**

Perennial, twining extensively through hedges throughout England, common in the south; I. Flowers inconspicuous, greenish, summer. The twining stems come up every year from a large, underground tuber. Leaves stalked, heart-shaped, pointed, glabrous, dark glossy green. Flowers in racemes in the leaf axils, male and female on different plants. Berry bright scarlet. This plant is interesting as the only European representative of the important tropical family which includes the yam.

LILIACEAE. LILY FAMILY

RU'SCUS

456. Ruscus aculea'tus.   **Butcher's Broom.**

Evergreen shrub, 1–2 ft., of shady places in southern England. Flowers greenish-white, spring. The plant spreads by a branching rhizome. Shoots erect, bearing, in the axils of small alternate scales, flattened, leaf-like shoots, ovate, sharply pointed, leathery, evergreen. Male and female flowers mostly on separate plants. Berries bright crimson in the middle of the flattened shoots.

POLYGONA'TUM

457. Polygonatum multiflo'rum.   **Solomon's Seal.**

Perennial, 1–3 ft., an uncommon woodland plant in England. Flowers white, tinged green, summer. The apical bud of the rhizome grows up into the erect, arched, flowering stem, the growth of the rhizome being continued by a side bud. Leaves alternate, sessile, oval, glabrous, glossy. Flowers in small, drooping racemes in the leaf axils. Fruit a black berry, rarely seen. The flowers are visited for nectar by humble-bees and may also be self-pollinated as the anthers lie close to the stigma. CONVALLA'RIA MAJA'LIS, the *Lily-of-the-Valley*, occasionally found in woods, but usually introduced, has 2 broad leaves and a raceme of small, drooping, scented flowers in summer. MAIA'NTHEMUM BIFO'LIUM, the *May-lily*, is a rare plant of woods in Yorkshire. The stem bears 2 heart-shaped leaves and ends in a raceme of small, white flowers.

A'LLIUM

458. Allium vinea'le.   **Crow Garlic.**

Perennial, 1–2 ft., not uncommon in dry places from mid-Scotland southwards; I. Flowers pinkish, summer. Leaves long, narrow, rounded, hollow, grooved, often twisted. Umbel small, dense, rounded; bract 1, with a short point. Flowers pinkish-green, mixed with, or entirely replaced by, little bulbils. A. OLERA'CEUM, the *Field Garlic*, is an uncommon plant of dry places distinguished by the narrow, flat leaves and the 2 bracts with very long points. There are several other rare species.

459. Allium ursi'num.   **Wild Garlic, Ramsons.**

Perennial, 1–1½ ft., of woods, hedgerows, and copses, except in northern Scotland, common in England; I. Flowers white, early summer. The long, flat bulbs send up 1–3 stalked, broadly lance-shaped leaves, dark green, shining, and smelling of garlic when crushed. Flowering stem 3-angled, with a dense umbel enclosed, when in bud, in 2 broad, membranous bracts. Nectar is formed at the base of the ovary and the flower is visited by bees.

456.
Butcher's Broom

458.
Crow Garlic

457.
Solomon's Seal

459.
Wild Garlic

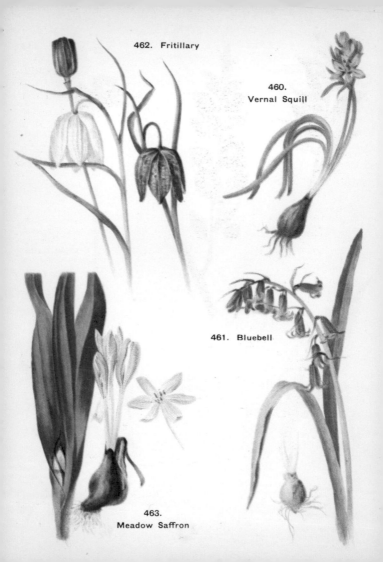

462. Fritillary

460.
Vernal Squill

461. Bluebell

463.
Meadow Saffron

SCI'LLA

460. *Scilla ve'rna.*   **Vernal Squill.**

Perennial, 2–4 in., occasionally found in abundance in dry pastures round the coast; I. Flowers light blue, spring. Leaves very narrow, recurved. Flowers in a small corymb, each flower with a thin bract. S. AUTUMNA'LIS, the *Autumn Squill*, is a rare plant of the coast in southern England, with racemes of purplish flowers, without bracts, in late summer.

461. *Scilla nonscri'pta.*   **Bluebell.**

Perennial, ½–1½ ft., common in woods, hedges, and copses, except in northern Scotland; I. Flowers blue, early summer. Leaves long, strap-shaped, fleshy, glossy. Raceme long, arched; flowers drooping, bell-shaped, each with 2 coloured bracts. Seeding profusely and multiplying by offshoots from its bulbs, the bluebell usually occurs in masses; it tolerates shade because of its early leaf production.

FRITILLA'RIA

462. *Fritillaria Melea'gris.*   **Fritillary, Snake's-head.**

Perennial, ½–1 ft., a rare plant of moist meadows in southern England. Flowers mottled maroon, sometimes almost white, early summer. Leaves narrow, tapering to both ends, pointed. Flowers solitary, drooping, cup-shaped. Nectar is secreted at the base of the perianth segments and the flowers are pollinated by humble-bees.

COL'CHICUM

463. *Colchicum autumna'le.*   **Meadow Saffron, Autumn Crocus.**

Perennial, ½–1 ft., locally abundant in meadows through most of England; I. Flowers lilac, autumn. The broadly lance-shaped, smooth, dark-green leaves come up in early summer. After the leaves have died away the flowers appear, several in succession from a corm. The base of the flowering stem produces the leaves in the following year and forms the new corm. The flowers resemble those of the crocus, but are readily distinguished from true autumn crocuses by possessing 6 instead of 3 stamens. Nectar is formed at the base of the stamens and the flowers are pollinated by bees, butterflies, and flies. The leaves are poisonous to stock.

NARTHE'CIUM

464. *Narthecium ossi'fragum*.   **Bog Asphodel.**

Perennial, ½–1 ft., locally common on wet moors throughout Britain; I. Flowers golden yellow, summer. The branching rhizome sends up tufts of sheathing, sword-shaped leaves and flowering shoots, with a few scale-like leaves. Flowers star-shaped. The fruiting shoots turn a bright brown-red. The flowers are visited for pollen by a variety of insects.

TOFIE'LDIA

465. *Tofieldia borea'lis*.   **Scottish Asphodel.**

Perennial, 3–6 in., not uncommon in mountain bogs in northern England and Scotland. Flowers greenish, summer. The rhizome sends up tufts of short, grass-like leaves and leafless flowering stems. Raceme short, dense; flowers small. Visited by flies for nectar.

PA'RIS

466. *Paris quadrifo'lia*.   **Herb Paris.**

Perennial, about 1 ft., rare, but locally abundant, in woods throughout Britain. Flowers greenish-yellow, early summer. The branching rhizome sends up a shoot, bearing near the top a whorl of 4 leaves, broadly reverse ovate, pointed, glabrous. Above these is a stalk terminating in a single, star-shaped flower; sepals green, lance-shaped; petals very narrow, yellowish; stamens with long, pointed heads.

JUNCACEAE.   RUSH FAMILY

JU'NCUS

467. *Juncus bufo'nius*.   **Toad Rush.**

Annual, 1–6 in., common in wet places throughout Britain; I. Flowers greenish, late summer. Growth tufted; stems slender, ending in points. Leaves and bracts sheathing, narrow, grooved, pointed, pale green. Flowers in loose panicles; perianth leaves lance-shaped, pointed, longer than the capsule, the outer longer than the inner. Pollinated by wind, and also forming flowers which do not open and are self-pollinated.

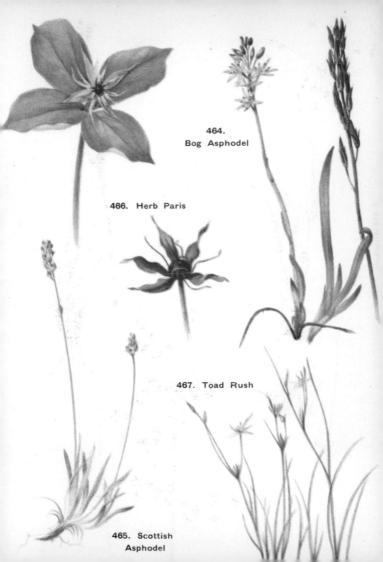

464.
Bog Asphodel

466. Herb Paris

467. Toad Rush

465. Scottish Asphodel

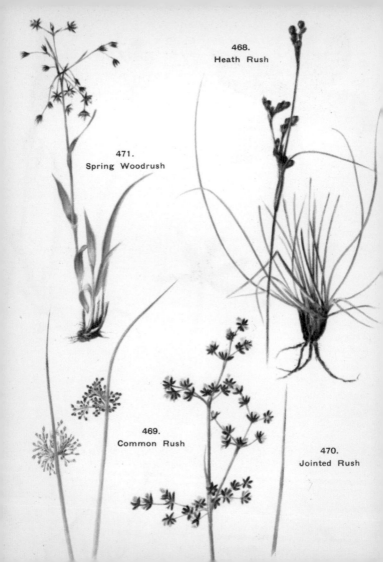

468.
Heath Rush

471.
Spring Woodrush

469.
Common Rush

470.
Jointed Rush

468. *Juncus squarro'sus*. Heath Rush.

Perennial, ½–1 ft., common on moist heaths and moors throughout Britain; I. Flowers pale brown, summer. Leaves and flowering stems in dense, matted tufts. Stems flattened, nearly leafless. Leaves very narrow, stiff, spreading, grooved, pointed. In autumn the plants take on a brownish orange colour and lend a characteristic hue to the moorland.

469. *Juncus commu'nis*. Common Rush.

Perennial, 1½–3 ft., common in marshy ground throughout Britain; I. Flowers greenish brown, summer. The rhizome sends up tufts of slender, cylindrical, green stems, ending in sharp points; these are filled with a continuous white pith (formerly used as lamp-wick); they are clothed below with brown leaf sheaths, sometimes having a green tip. The inflorescence appears from the side of the stem, some distance from the tip, in some forms as a dense head, in others as a loose panicle; becoming brown in the fruit. Perianth segments lance-shaped, longer than the reverse ovoid capsule. Like other rushes this species is wind-pollinated; the flowers open in the early morning and the stigmas protrude; a few hours later the stamens shed their pollen, and by evening the flower closes.

470. *Juncus articula'tus*. Jointed Rush.

Perennial, 1–2 ft., common in moist places throughout Britain; I. Flowers brown, summer. The branched rhizome throws up tufts of slender, flowering stems and long, pointed, stem-like leaves. The leaves have white pith in short blocks with intervening, hollow spaces, so that, when they are dried or pressed, they appear jointed. Flowers in loose, false corymbs; perianth segments oval, shorter than the dark brown, shining capsules. J. GERA'RDI is a slender, erect, smaller plant, common in marshes near the sea; leaves not jointed.

LU'ZULA

471. *Luzula pilo'sa*. Spring Woodrush.

Perennial, ½–1 ft., common in pastures and shady places throughout Britain; I. Flowers pale brown, early summer. Leaves soft, grass-like, sheathing, with fine white hairs about the edges. Flowers usually solitary at the ends of the slender branches of a very loose panicle; branches bending down in the fruit. Perianth leaves pointed, rather shorter than the blunt capsule. Like the other species this is wind-pollinated; the stigmas are receptive and exposed for several days before the stamens shed their pollen. Seeds sought for and dispersed by ants.

472. *Luzula sylva'tica*. Great Woodrush.

Perennial, 1–2 ft., common, where the shade is not too great, in upland woods throughout Britain; I. Flowers pale brown, summer. The stout rhizome sends up tufts of leaves and flowering shoots. Leaves rather broad, shining green, with silky hairs at the edges. Flowers clustered in a large, loose panicle.

473. *Luzula campe'stris*. Field Woodrush.

Perennial, 3–9 in., common in pastures and heaths throughout Britain; I. Flowers brown, early summer. Leaves and flowering shoots in tufts from the rhizome. Leaves narrow, hairy, sheathing. Flowers in small ovoid heads, of which a few are grouped in a panicle, sometimes close, sometimes rather loose. Perianth leaves just longer than the capsule. L. SPICA'TA, with flower-heads in a spike, and L. ARCUA'TA, a dwarf species with glabrous leaves, are found only on high mountains, especially in Scotland.

TYPHACEAE. REED-MACE FAMILY
TY'PHA

474. *Typha latifo'lia*. Reed-mace.

Perennial, 4–7 ft., not uncommon on the margins of lakes and streams in England, rare in Scotland; I. Flowers yellow and brown, summer. Leaves in tufts from the rhizome, long, sword-shaped, ½–1 in. broad, bluish green. Flowering stems, with a few short leaves, terminating in a close, yellowish spike of male flowers; immediately below this is a cylindrical, chocolate-brown, almost solid spike of female flowers; when ripe the female spike breaks up into innumerable plumed nutlets dispersed by wind. T. ANGUSTI-FOLIA is a very similar plant with narrower leaves; male and female spikes separated by about an inch of bare stem. Pollinated by wind. These plants are often called 'bulrush', a name applied properly to *Scirpus lacustris*.

SPARGANIACEAE. BUR-REED FAMILY
SPARGA'NIUM

475. *Sparganium si'mplex*. Bur-reed.

Perennial, 1–2 ft., not uncommon along pools and streams throughout Britain; I. Flowers green, summer. Leaves sheathing, long, strap-shaped, 3-angled at the base, soft, bright green, sometimes floating. Female flowers in globular heads, sessile or solitary on short stalks, in the axils of leafy bracts; male flowers in smaller, sessile heads at the top of the inflorescence. S. ERE'CTUM, the *Great Bur-reed*, is a taller plant with several female heads on each stalk. S. MINIMUM, the *Floating Bur-reed*, has limp leaves floating on the surface of the water. Pollinated by wind.

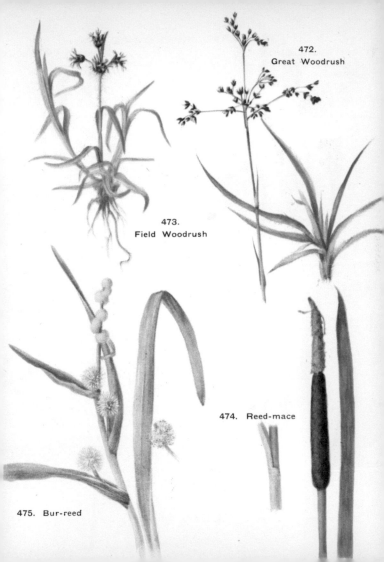

472.
Great Woodrush

473.
Field Woodrush

474. Reed-mace

475. Bur-reed

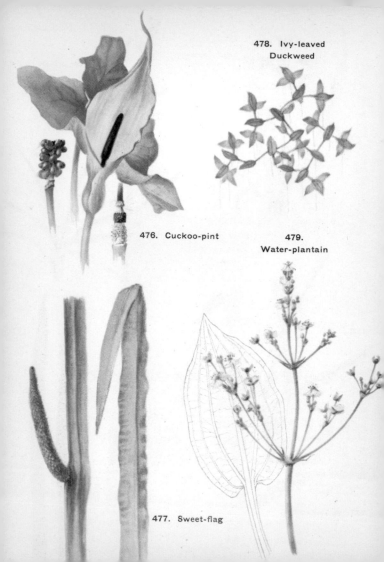

478. Ivy-leaved
Duckweed

476. Cuckoo-pint

479.
Water-plantain

477. Sweet-flag

ARACEAE. ARUM FAMILY
A'RUM

476. *Arum macula'tum.*　　　Cuckoo-pint, Lords-and-Ladies, Jack-in-the-Pulpit.

Perennial, ½–1 ft., common in hedgerows in England and occasionally found in Scotland; I. The inflorescences, with pale green hood and purple club, appear in spring, and the leaves expand fully later. Leaves stalked, arrow-shaped, dark glossy green, often spotted. In autumn the leaves, bracts, and club wither away, leaving a stalked head of scarlet berries. Small flies and beetles are attracted to the inflorescence by a faint, unpleasant smell and are trapped in the bottom of the hood, by the ring of hairs and by the slippery sides up which they cannot climb; there they pollinate the female flowers; a day later the male flowers shed their pollen, the hairs wither, and the insects escape and visit another inflorescence.

A'CORUS

477. *Acorus Ca'lamus.*　　　Sweet-flag.

Perennial, 3–4 ft., not uncommon along streams in south-eastern England, occasionally introduced elsewhere. Flowers yellowish green, summer. Leaves long, sword-shaped, with wavy margins. Flowering stem leaf-like, terminating in the thick spike, but continued by a leafy bract. Fragrant when crushed. The plant is a doubtful native and never sets seed; it is propagated and spread by the vigorously branching rhizome.

LEMNACEAE. DUCKWEED FAMILY
LE'MNA

478. *Lemna trisu'lca.*　　　Ivy-leaved Duckweed.

Perennial, common in ponds and ditches in England, rare in Scotland; I. Blades about ½ in. long, 3-lobed, with a fine root hanging down. The blade is propagated by the side lobes which grow outwards till they are attached only by a thin stalk, and, finally, become free: in their turn they form lobes; the process is repeated indefinitely and so rapidly that the whole surface of a pool is soon covered. In autumn minute buds are formed which sink in the mud and hibernate there. L. MI'NOR, the *Common Duckweed*, found throughout Britain, has oval blades, the new ones formed one at a time, without stalks. L. POLYRRHI'ZA, with several roots, and L. GIBBA, with a half-spherical blade, are less common. L. ARRHI'ZA, found in south-eastern England, has blades like little grains $\frac{1}{10}$ in. diam., without roots.

ALISMACEAE. WATER-PLANTAIN FAMILY
ALI'SMA

479. *Alisma Planta'go-aqua'tica.*　　　Water-plantain.

Perennial, 1–2½ ft., along the margins of pools and slow streams throughout Britain, commonest in the south; I. Flowers white or pale lilac, summer. Stock swollen, rooting in the mud. First leaves submerged, strap-shaped;

later leaves long-stalked, ovate, pointed, base sometimes heart-shaped, glabrous. Flowers in a loose panicle, the smaller groups of which are umbels; petals delicate and silky. Pollinated by hover-flies visiting the flowers for nectar formed at the base of the stamens.

480. *Alisma ranunculoi'des.*   Lesser Water-plantain.

Perennial, ½–1½ ft., uncommon along the margins of ponds and ditches, except in northern Scotland; I. Flowers pale lilac, summer. Leaves narrowly lance-shaped. Flowers in an umbel, sometimes with a second above it. In one variety the stems bend over and root at the base of the umbels. A. NA'TANS is a rare plant of north-western England and Wales with floating stems and leaves; flowers in groups of 1–3.

SAGITTA'RIA

481. *Sagittaria sagittifo'lia.*   Arrowhead.

Perennial, 1–2 ft., not uncommon in ditches and slow streams in England, not native in Scotland; I. Flowers white, late summer. Spreads by runners which form corms at the tip and rest over winter. First formed leaves submerged and narrow; later leaves rising above the water on long stalks, arrow-shaped, glossy. Flowers in small whorls on a naked stem, those near the tip male, those lower female. Petals white with a purple blotch; stamens purple; female flowers smaller and less showy than the male. Insect visits are rare and little seed is set.

BU'TOMUS

482. *Butomus umbella'tus.*   Flowering-rush.

Perennial, 3–4 ft., local in ditches and rivers in England and Wales; I. Flowers rose, summer. The rhizome sends up very long, narrow, 3-angled leaves, with sheathing bases, and a naked flowering stem which terminates in an umbel with 3 membranous bracts at its base. Flowers rather large; stamens and carpels red. Nectar is formed at the base of the carpels, and the flowers are pollinated chiefly by bees.

JUNCAGINACEAE. ARROW-GRASS FAMILY
TRIGLO'CHIN

483. *Triglochin palu'stre.*   Arrow-grass.

Perennial, ½–1 ft., frequent in wet heaths and marshes throughout Britain; I. Flowers greenish brown, summer. Stock swollen, giving off suckers. Leaves in tufts round the flowering stem, sheathing, 3-angled, long, linear, rather limp. Flowers small, in a slender raceme which elongates in the fruit. Carpels 3, separating in the long fruit. T. MARI'TIMUM, the *Sea Arrow-grass*, is a taller, fleshier plant, common in marshes near the sea, with 6 carpels and a short, ovoid fruit.

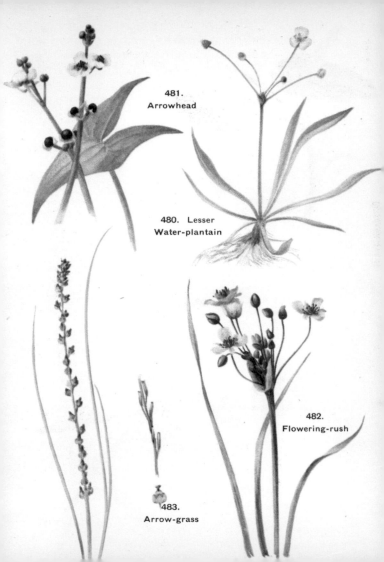

481.
Arrowhead

480. Lesser
Water-plantain

482.
Flowering-rush

483.
Arrow-grass

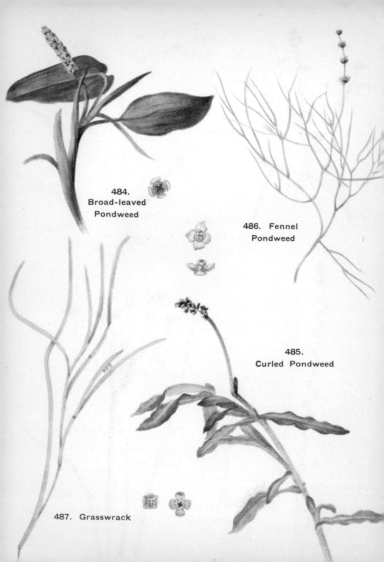

484.
Broad-leaved
Pondweed

486. Fennel
Pondweed

485.
Curled Pondweed

487. Grasswrack

NAIADACEAE. PONDWEED FAMILY

POTAMOGE'TON

484. *Potamogeton na'tans*.   **Broad-leaved Pondweed.**

Perennial, common in ponds and ditches throughout Britain; I. Flowers inconspicuous, brownish green, summer. Leaves floating on the surface on long, limp stalks to which the blades are jointed, broadly elliptical, rounded at the base, brownish green and shining above. The flowers are borne on a short spike above water. Pollination is by wind, the stigmas maturing before the stamens. P. POLYGONIFO'LIUS is a similar common plant, with the lower leaves submerged and the blades not jointed to the stalk. P. COLO-RA'TUS is a less widely spread plant, with all the leaves submerged, thin and translucent.

485. *Potamogeton cri'spus*.   **Curled Pondweed.**

Perennial, common in ponds and ditches throughout Britain; I. Flowers green, summer. Leaves thin, submerged, sessile, alternate, oblong, with wavy margins, very finely toothed. P. DE'NSUS, a common plant of southern Scotland and England, has submerged leaves, opposite, sessile, short, and broadly lance-shaped.

486. *Potamogeton pectina'tus*.   **Fennel Pondweed.**

Perennial, common in pools and ditches of fresh and brackish water throughout Britain; I. Flowers greenish, late summer. Stems very slender, much branched with numerous linear leaves, giving the effect of much divided foliage. The plant usually grows in dense masses. P. PUSI'LLUS is a similar common species, distinguished by the presence of a membranous stipule in the leaf axil.

ZOSTE'RA

487. *Zostera mari'na*.   **Grasswrack.**

Perennial, locally abundant on sandy or muddy shores round the coasts. Flowers greenish, summer. Leaves about ¼ in. broad and 1–3 ft. long. The plant is rooted about low-water mark, but is often torn off and cast up in masses. One of the few plants pollinated under water. Z. NA'NA is a rare plant with very narrow leaves, less than 1 ft. long.

CYPERACEAE. SEDGE FAMILY
SCI'RPUS

488. *Scirpus palu'stris*. Marsh Club-rush.

Perennial, $\frac{1}{2}$–1 ft., common in marshy places and the borders of pools throughout Britain; I. Flowers chocolate, summer. The branched rhizome sends up dense tufts of slender, green, pointed stems, some of which terminate in a single spike about $\frac{1}{2}$ in. long. Leaves reduced to reddish sheaths at the base of the stems. Like all other members of the family, pollination is by wind; the stigmas mature before the stamens.

489. *Scirpus caespito'sus*. Deer's-grass.

Perennial, $\frac{1}{2}$–1 ft., common on moors throughout Britain; I. Flowers light brown, summer. Stock branched, giving rise to dense tufts of wiry, green stems; base of stem enclosed in leaf sheaths, the outer brown and leafless, the inner green and with a leaf-point about $\frac{1}{4}$ in. long. Spikes about $\frac{1}{4}$ in. long, at the tips of the stems, almost enclosed by 2 scaly bracts.

490. *Scirpus flu'itans*. Floating Club-rush.

Perennial, up to $1\frac{1}{2}$ ft., common, floating in masses in moorland pools throughout Britain; I. Flowers greenish, summer. The slender, flattened, branched stem bears numerous, short, linear, pointed leaves. Spikes about $\frac{1}{10}$ in. long, solitary at the branch tips.

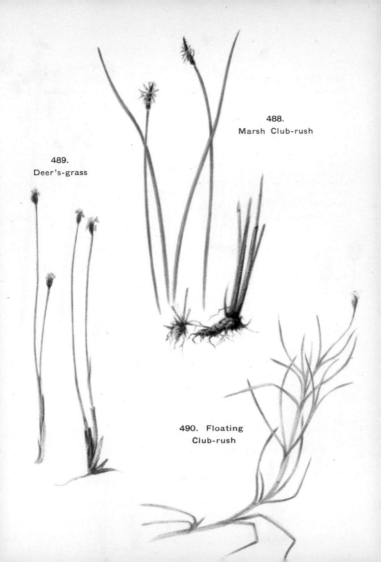

489.
Deer's-grass

488.
Marsh Club-rush

490. Floating
Club-rush

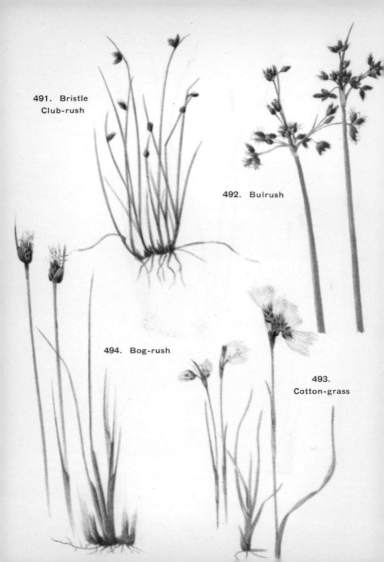

491. Bristle Club-rush

492. Bulrush

494. Bog-rush

493. Cotton-grass

491. *Scirpus seta'ceus*.   **Bristle Club-rush.**

Perennial, 2–6 in., local in wet, sandy places throughout Britain; I.
Flowers greenish brown, summer. Stems very slender, tufted. Leaves
wiry, shorter than the stems, pointed. Spikes about ⅛ in. long, in clusters
of 2–3, with a green bract prolonging the line of the stem, so that the cluster
appears to be lateral.

492. *Scirpus lacu'stris*.   **Bulrush.**

Perennial, up to 8 ft., common along the margins of streams and lakes
through most of Britain; I. Flowers bright brown, summer. The rhizome,
branching and rooting in the mud, gives rise to stout, erect stems, spongy
inside, with a few leaf-sheaths at the base; the uppermost of these may
have a short blade; there are also barren, leafy tufts which may be floating
in running water. Spikes oval and numerous, in a loose, irregular, terminal
umbel; bracts large, brown or greenish. S. MARI'TIMUS, the *Sea Club-rush*,
a common plant of marshes and estuaries near the sea, 2–4 ft., has a leafy
stem, leafy bracts, and 4–8 spikes in the inflorescence.

ERIO'PHORUM

493. *Eriophorum angustifo'lium*.   **Cotton-grass, Cannoch.**

Perennial, ½–1½ ft., common on wet moors and bogs throughout Britain; I.
Flowers brown, early summer. Stems erect, 3-angled, solid. Leaves with
sheathing base, slender, grooved. At the tip of the stem is an umbel of
spikes, some nearly sessile, some on arching stalks, each with 2–3 membranous bracts. Fruiting head conspicuous. E. LATIFO'LIUM is a very similar
plant with hollow stems and flat leaves. E. VAGINA'TUM, the *Harestail
Cotton-grass*, occurs over most of Britain, but is commonest in the north;
it has tufted stems, stiff, wiry leaves with an inflated sheath and a single,
apical spike.

SCHOE'NUS

494. *Schoenus ni'gricans*.   **Bog-rush.**

Perennial, ½–1½ ft., local in wet moors through most of Britain; I.
Flowers dark brown, summer. Stems and leaves in dense tufts. Leaves
wiry, with broad, blackish sheaths. Stems stiff, longer than the leaves, with
a dense head of small spikes at the tip; below the head is a bract with a broad,
brown base and a green tip, overtopping the head.

CA'REX

495. *Carex pulica'ris*.   **Flea Sedge.**

Perennial, 3–8 in., common in marshy places throughout Britain; I. Flowers light brown, summer. Stems very slender, with a single loose apical, few-flowered spike; lower flowers female, upper male. Leaves wiry, shorter than the stem.

496. *Carex arena'ria*.   **Sand Sedge.**

Perennial, ½–1 ft., common in sandy places near the coast throughout Britain; I. Flowers greenish brown, summer. The rhizome branches extensively through sand, which it helps to bind, and sends up many shoots. Stem stiff, 3-angled, rough. Leaves stiff, rough, bright green. Spikes in a terminal spike, upper male, lower female; in fruit the latter are broadly ovoid and chaffy, while the male drop off. Utricles shorter than the bracts.

497. *Carex Goodenovii*.   **Common Sedge.**

Perennial, 1–1½ ft., common in damp, grassy places throughout Britain; I. Flowers black and green, summer. Stem slender, stiff. Leaves narrow, bright green. Spikes few; 1–2 at the top male, those lower down female, erect, sessile or shortly stalked, almost cylindrical; bracts almost black, contrasting with the green utricle which shows round their edges; stigmas 2.

498. *Carex fla'cca*.   **Glaucous Sedge.**

Perennial, ½–1 ft., common in pastures throughout Britain; I. Flowers brown and green, early summer. Rhizome branching. Stems, and the long, tapering leaves, stiff, blue-green in colour. Female spikes 2–3, cylindrical, on slender stalks about half their own length, erect or drooping in the fruit; male spikes shortly stalked or sessile. Bracts brown, with a green midrib and margin. Utricle with a short beak.

498.
Glaucous Sedge

495.
Flea Sedge

496.
Sand Sedge

497.
Common Sedge

499.
Carnation Sedge

501.
Bladder Sedge

500.
Wood Sedge

499. *Carex pani'cea*.   Carnation Sedge.

Perennial, $\frac{1}{2}$–$1\frac{1}{2}$ ft., common in damp, grassy places throughout Britain; I.
Flowers brown, summer. The rhizome spreads by runners and gives rise to
tufts of stems and leaves. Stems 3-angled, arched above. Leaves short, flat,
blue-green. Female spikes rather loose, stalked, erect; bracts dark brown
with a green midrib; male spike solitary, terminal; utricle with a short beak.

500. *Carex sylva'tica*.   Wood Sedge.

Perennial, 1–2 ft., common in moist, shady places from mid-Scotland southwards; I. Flowers green, summer. A slender plant, with smooth, 3-angled
stems arched at the tip. Leaves long, flat, rather limp. Female spikes drooping, on long stalks, rather loose; utricle with a long beak.

501. *Carex vesica'ria*.   Bladder Sedge.

Perennial, 1–2 ft., occasional in marshy places and the margins of ponds,
except in northern Scotland; I. Flowers green and brown, early summer.
Stem stout, rough, 3-angled. Leaves long and broad. Male spikes several,
slender, at the tip of the stem. Female spikes large, green tinged brown,
pendulous when in fruit; bracts brown, with a green midrib, much smaller
than the inflated utricles, which taper into a forked beak. C. ROSTRA'TA, the
Bottle Sedge, is a similar, commoner plant which may be distinguished by
the abrupt narrowing of the utricle into the long beak.

GRAMINEAE. GRASS FAMILY

The leaf has a split sheath surrounding the stem and at its junction with the narrow blade there is a scale, the ligule. The inflorescence is a spike or panicle composed of a large number of ears or spikelets. The spikelet bears at its base 2 scales, the glumes, within which are 1, 2, or several flowers. Each flower is enclosed by 2 scales, the pales, and consists of 3 stamens and an ovary with 2 stigmas. The glumes and pales frequently bear bristles called awns.

DIGRA'PHIS

Inflorescence a close panicle. Spikelets with 1 flower and 1 or 2 minute rudiments. Glumes nearly equal, boat-shaped, enclosing the flower. Greek, dis, twice, and graphis, a style, from the two hairy tufts at the base of the pale.

502. Digraphis arundina'cea.　　　　　　　**Reed-grass.**

Perennial, 3–4 ft., often growing in masses along streams and lakes throughout Britain; I. Flowers in summer. A tall, coarse grass spreading by a creeping rhizome. Leaves broad and flat with a prominent ligule. Panicle long, shortly branched, purplish or pale green; glumes 3-nerved, sharply pointed, hairless.

ANTHOXA'NTHUM

Inflorescence a very close panicle or loose spike. The spikelet consists of 2 pointed glumes, the upper larger than the lower, 2, awned, sterile pales and 2 pales enclosing the single flower, which has only 2 stamens. Greek anthos, a flower, and xanthos, yellow, from the tint of the inflorescence.

503. Anthoxanthum odora'tum　　　　　　**Sweet Vernal Grass.**

Perennial, ½–1 ft., common in meadows, pastures, and open woods throughout Britain; I. Flowers in early summer. A grass of tufted growth; leaves flat, finely hairy. Inflorescence a spike-like panicle, brownish-green in colour; stamens often purple. When crushed or dried the whole plant has a pleasant aromatic odour.

ALOPECU'RUS

Inflorescence a close cylindrical spike. Spikelets 1-flowered. Glumes equal, boat-shaped, pointed; there is only 1 pale and from its back springs a long awn. The Greek name, alōpecouros, from alopex, a fox, and oura, a tail, from the form of the inflorescence.

504. Alopecurus prate'nsis.　　　　　　　**Meadow Foxtail.**

Perennial, 1–2 ft., common in meadows and pastures throughout Britain; I. Flowers in early summer. Stems erect spreading by suckers; upper leaves rather inflated, with short, rough blades; ligule short. Spike 2–3 in. long, dense, cylindrical, greyish-green; awns projecting beyond the spikelets. A. GENICULATUS, the *Marsh Foxtail*, a more slender plant, with the stem prostrate at the base and then bent upwards, is common in moist places.

PHLE'UM

Inflorescence a close, cylindrical spike. Spikelets 1-flowered. Glumes boat-shaped, pointed or tipped with an awn; pales 2, small, without awns. Greek phleos, the name of a grass.

505. Phleum prate'nse.　　　　　　　**Cat's-tail, Timothy.**

Perennial, ½–1½ ft., common in meadows throughout Britain; I. Flowers

502 Re'ed-grass

503 Sweet Vernal Grass

504 Meadow Foxtail Grass

505 Cat's-tail, Timothy

in summer. Stems prostrate below, then erect, tufted; leaves flat, rough; ligule long. Inflorescence a slender cylindrical spike 1½–6 in. long; glumes with a prominent, hairy keel and apical awns. P. ARENA'RIUM, the *Sand Cat's-tail* is a smaller plant, not uncommon on sandy coasts.

AGRO'STIS

Inflorescence a delicate open panicle. Spikelets very small, 1-flowered. Lower glume rather larger than upper; pales smaller than the glumes, the lower with or without a slender awn. The Greek name of a grass.

506. Agrostis te'nuis.   **Bent-grass.**

Perennial, ½–1½ ft., common on heaths and dry pastures throughout Britain; I. Flowers in summer. The grass is more or less tufted and spreads by runners; leaves short, narrow, and flat; ligule short. Inflorescence an elegant open panicle, often purplish in colour. A. PALU'STRIS, the *Fiorin* is a coarser grass, common in moist fields, waste places, and woods, with the branches of the panicle closed together. A. CANI'NA, a not uncommon grass of upland pastures and downs, has an awn on the back of the lower pale.

PSA'MMA

Inflorescence a dense, thick spike. Spikelets large, 1-flowered. Glumes nearly equal, boat-shaped, pointed; pales nearly as long as the glumes. Greek, psammos, sand, as the plant grows in dunes.

507. Psamma arena'ria.   **Marram-grass.**

Perennial, 2–3 ft., abundant on sand dunes on nearly all our coasts; I. Flowers in summer. The plant spreads vigorously by very long, branching rhizomes which can throw up shoots though deeply buried; these rhizomes have a most important action in binding sand and leading to the formation of dunes. Leaves bluish-green, stiff, sharp-pointed, ridged, and rough on the upper surface; when dry they roll into narrow cylinders. Spike long, dense, pale greenish-brown.

AI'RA

Inflorescence a loose or, sometimes, rather close panicle. Spikelets small, 2-flowered. Glumes nearly equal, as long as the pales; lower pale toothed at the tip and with a slender awn springing from the back. Greek name of a grass.

508. Aira prae'cox.   **Early Hair-grass.**

Annual, 2–6 in., common in dry heaths and sandy places throughout Britain; I. Flowers in early summer, then dies off. A small, tufted grass with narrow leaves and small, close panicles. A. CARYOPHY'LLEA, the *Silver Hair-grass*, is a similar, but larger, plant with more open panicles of a greyish-green, and usually purplish stems.

509. Aira cae'spitosa.   **Tufted Hair-grass.**

Perennial, 1–3 ft., common in moist pastures and woods throughout Britain; I. Flowers in summer. A rather coarse grass, growing in tussocks; leaves stiff and rough. Inflorescence a large, elegant panicle with widely spreading branches when mature; spikelets shining and often purplish; awn of the lower pale short.

506 Bent-grass

507 Marram-grass

508 Early Hair-grass

509 Tufted Hair-grass

510. Aira fle'xuosa.   Wavy Hair-grass.

Perennial, 1–2 ft., common on heaths, moors, and in open woods throughout Britain; I. Flowers in late summer. A tufted grass; the very fine and narrow, rich green leaves form dense cushions. Stem slender, terminating in a rather small, delicate, open panicle the branches of which are wavy; spikelets shining, often purple and with the awn of the lower pale protruding.

HO'LCUS

Inflorescence an open panicle. Spikelets 2-flowered, the upper flower with stamens only. Glumes hairy, boat-shaped, the upper rather larger, 3-veined; lower pale of the upper flower with a short awn. Greek, holkos, the name of a grass.

511. Holcus lana'tus.   Yorkshire Fog.

Perennial, 1–3 ft., common in meadows, pastures, and waste places throughout Britain; I. Flowers in summer. A tufted grass with limp, softly hairy leaves and inflated sheaths; ligule short. Panicle 2–4 in. long, of a pinkish-grey colour; awn short. H. MO'LLIS, the *Soft-grass*, is a very similar but less common plant which may be distinguished by the longer awn, projecting from the spikelet. It grows in dry woods, hedgerows, and heaths.

AVE'NA

Inflorescence a very loose panicle. Spikelets large, 2–6 flowered, the upper flowers usually rudimentary. Glumes unequal, or nearly equal, pointed, nearly as long as the pales; lower pale toothed at the tip with a conspicuous, long, bent, and twisted awn on the back. Latin, avena, the oat.

512. Avena pube'scens.   Oat-grass.

Perennial, 1–3 ft., occasionally found in dry places throughout Britain; I. Flowers in summer. Stems erect, in loose tufts; leaf-blades rather short; ligule pointed; sheaths softly hairy. Inflorescence a very open, little-branched panicle, often violet; spikelets few, very large, erect or spreading; awns very conspicuous. A. FA'TUA, the *Wild Oat*, a common annual field-weed, has drooping spikelets.

ARRHENA'THERUM

Characters of Avena, but the spikelets are 2-flowered; the lower flower is male and it alone has an awn. Greek, arren, male, ather, a bristle.

513. Arrhenatherum avena'ceum   False-oat.

Perennial, 2–3 ft., very common as a field weed and in waste places throughout Britain; I. Flowers in summer. The plant spreads vigorously by a branching rhizome which makes it a difficult weed to eradicate; in one variety the rhizome forms small hard tubers. Stem slender and erect; leaves flat; ligule blunt. Inflorescence a loose, narrow panicle of a pale yellowish-green, with more or less erect branches; spikelets few, large, each with a single prominent awn.

510 Wavy Hair-grass

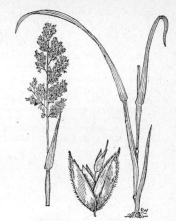

511 Yorkshire Fog

512 Oat-grass

513 False-oat

ARU'NDO

Inflorescence a dense panicle inclined to one side. Spikelets very numerous, 2–5 flowered. Glumes unequal, pointed; lower pale with a long point. Flower surrounded at the base with long silky hairs. Latin, arundo, a reed.

514. Arundo Phragmi'tes. Reed.

Perennial, 5–6 ft. or more in height, common along streams, swamps, and lakes throughout Britain; I. Flowers in late summer. Our tallest grass; it spreads by deep-seated, branching rhizomes and grows in dense thickets. The stout, erect stem bears broad, flat leaves tapering gradually to a sharp point and with rough, cutting edges. Panicle large, flag-like, purplish-brown, with a grey sheen when mature from the silky hairs.

CYNOSU'RUS

Inflorescence a narrow, spike-like panicle or head with the spikelets turned to one side. The spikelets are in small clusters of which the outer spikelet is flat and consists of 2 ranks of narrow, sterile pales. The inner spikelets have 2 somewhat unequal, pointed glumes and 2–5 flowers. There are no awns. Greek, kuon, a dog, and oura, a tail, from the appearance of the spike.

515. Cynosurus crista'tus. Crested Dog's-tail.

Perennial, ½–1½ ft., common in pastures throughout Britain; I. Flowers in summer. A tufted grass, spreading by suckers; stem tough, erect; leaves narrow; ligule short. Spike narrow; easily recognized by the spikelets pointing to one side and the finely toothed appearance given by the sterile outer spikelets.

MOLI'NIA

Inflorescence a narrow panicle with erect branches. Spikelets 2–3 flowered, the upper flower sterile. Glumes nearly equal, sharply pointed, 1-veined, much shorter than the spikelets; no awns. Called after the naturalist Molin.

516. Molinia caeru'lea. Purple Moor-grass.

Perennial, 1–3 ft., common on damp moors, heaths, and open woods throughout Britain; I. Flowers in summer. A tufted grass, often forming huge, dense tufts or tussocks; stems stiff, wiry, erect; leaves from the base of the stem, flat, rough, bluish-green. Panicle narrow, often over 6 in. long, usually purplish, sometimes green.

ME'LICA

Inflorescence a very loose panicle with few spikelets. Spikelets 2-flowered, with a small, terminal, club-shaped, sterile flower. Glumes nearly equal; no awns. Etymology doubtful.

517. Melica uniflo'ra. Wood Melick.

Perennial, 1–2 ft., often found in open woods and shady banks in England, rare in Scotland; I. Flowers in early summer. Spreads by runners; stems slender; leaves long, narrow, limp, slightly hairy. Panicle slender with erect branches; glumes purplish-brown. M. NUTANS, the *Mountain Melick*, is a rarer plant of the North and Wales with the branches of the panicle drooping to one side.

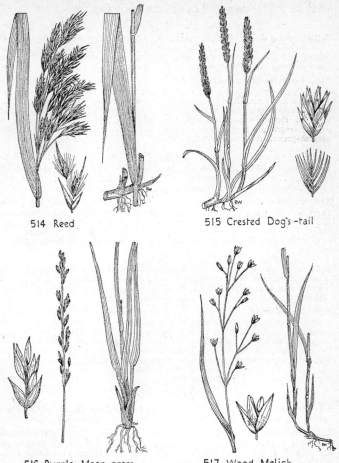

514 Reed

515 Crested Dog's-tail

516 Purple Moor-grass

517 Wood Melick

DA'CTYLIS

Inflorescence a dense, ovoid or triangular panicle. Spikelets in clusters, pointing to one side, 2–3 flowered. Glumes hairy, sharply pointed, shorter than the spikelets; pales with short terminal bristles. Greek, dactylos, a finger, from the shape of the inflorescence.

518. Dactylis glomera'ta.   **Cock's-foot.**

Perennial, 1–3 ft., very common in pastures, meadows, and roadsides throughout Britain; I. Flowers in summer. A tufted grass with stiff, erect stems; leaves long, flat, bright green, folded together when young; ligule pointed. Panicle sometimes little branched, and forming a small head, but usually larger and more open; spikelets in dense clusters turned to one side, greyish-green. A valuable pasture grass.

BRI'ZA

Inflorescence a very open panicle, with solitary spikelets hanging on slender stalks. Spikelets 7–9 flowered. Glumes boat-shaped, blunt, membranous, much shorter than the spikelets. Greek, brizein, to nod.

519. Briza me'dia.   **Quaking Grass.**

Perennial, ½–1½ ft., common in meadows, pastures, and heaths throughout Britain; I. Flowers in early summer. Leaves flat, short and narrow; ligule short. Inflorescence an elegant, purplish, very open panicle; spikelets ovoid or bluntly triangular, solitary, nodding and trembling on hair-like stalks.

POA

Inflorescence an open panicle. Spikelets numerous, small, 3–9 flowered. Glumes unequal, pointed, shorter than the lowest pales; lower pale pointed, 5–7 veined; upper pale with a blunt, toothed tip, 2-veined; no awns. Greek, poa, fodder grass.

520. Poa a'nnua.   **Annual Meadow-grass.**

Annual, ½–1 ft., very common as a weed throughout Britain; I. Flowers spring to autumn. A tufted grass; stems somewhat flattened; leaves rather limp, flat, often crinkled at the base, folded together when young, rich green. Panicle open, whitish-green. There are several common perennial species important as meadow-grasses and in forming turf; the commonest is POA PRATE'NSIS, the *Smooth Meadow-grass*, which spreads vigorously by runners and often has purplish panicles.

GLYCE'RIA

Characters of Poa, but the spikelets are very long and narrow, usually with more than 9 flowers; lower pale blunt; grasses of wet places. Greek, glykeros, sweet.

521. Glyceria flu'itans.   **Flote-grass.**

Perennial, 1–3 ft., common in ditches, slow streams, and wet places throughout Britain; I. Flowers in late summer. The stem creeps on mud or floats, with the leaves, in water; leaves limp, broad, flat, long when floating. Panicle long, narrow, very little branched; spikelets long, narrow on slender stalks. G. AQUA'TICA, the *Reed Meadow-grass*, is a tall (3–5 ft.) stout grass of wet places, with long broad leaves and a much branched, yellowish panicle.

518 Cock's-foot

519 Quaking Grass

520 Annual Meadow-grass

521 Flote-grass

FESTU'CA

Inflorescence a panicle, sometimes spike-like, sometimes open, usually little-branched, sometimes 1-sided. Spikelets with 3 or more flowers. Glumes unequal, keeled, pointed; lower pale tipped by a bristle or awn, upper pale toothed at the tip. The Latin name for straw.

522. Festuca ovi'na. **Sheep's Fescue.**

Perennial, 3–12 in., common, especially in upland pastures, throughout Britain; I. Flowers in summer. A tufted grass with short, stiff, bristle-like leaves. Panicle usually little-branched, greyish-purple. Many varieties of this grass are described; it is an important constituent of fine turf.

BRO'MUS

Inflorescence usually a rather close panicle. Spikelets very large, 5–10 flowered. Glumes unequal, pointed, shorter than the lowest pale; lower pale with a long awn; upper pale toothed at the tip. Greek, bromos, a kind of grass.

523. Bromus mo'llis. **Soft Brome-grass.**

Annual, ½–2 ft., common in waste places, roadsides, and meadows throughout Britain; I. Flowers in summer. Leaves flat, soft, bluish-green. Panicles little-branched; spikelets large, ovoid, inclined. The long awns give the inflorescence a hairy appearance. There are several other widespread species.

BRACHYPO'DIUM

Inflorescence a loose spike of very long, almost sessile, spikelets. Spikelets 6–10 flowered. Lower pales awned at the tip. Greek, brachys, short, and podion, a foot, from the short stalks of the spikelets.

524. Brachypodium sylva'ticum **False Brome-grass.**

Perennial, 1–3 ft., common in thickets and hedgerows throughout Britain; I. Flowers in summer. A tall, slender grass with limp, flat, bright-green leaves. Spike slender, inclined; spikelets long; lower pale with a long awn.

LO'LIUM

Inflorescence a flattened spike. Spikelets flattened, sessile, edge-on in notches of the stem. There is only 1 glume which stands outside the spikelet. Latin, lolium, the darnel.

525. Lolium pere'nne. **Perennial Rye-grass.**

Perennial, ½–1½ ft., common in meadows, pastures, and waste places throughout Britain; I. Flowers in summer. Leaves flat, rather rough. Spike long with the spikelets well separated, brownish-green. Glume shorter than the spikelet; lower pale sometimes with a bristle. A very valuable fodder grass; the *Italian Rye-grass* is an annual, cultivated variety with many-flowered spikelets, the lower pale long-awned; L. TEMULE'NTUM, the *darnel*, is occasionally found as a weed; its glume is as long as the spikelet.

522 Sheep's Fescue

523 Soft Brome-grass

524 False Brome-grass

525 Perennial Rye-grass

AGROPY'RUM

Characters of Lolium, *but with 2 glumes which are sometimes awned. Greek,* agros, *a field, and* puros, *wheat.*

526. Agropyrum re'pens. **Couch-grass, Twitch.**

Perennial, 1–3 ft., common in waste places and as a weed throughout Britain; I. Flowers in summer. This troublesome weed spreads by long, much-branched rhizomes which make it extremely difficult to eradicate. Leaves flat, bright-green, rather limp. Spike long, with close-set spikelets; glumes pointed or awned.

NA'RDUS

Inflorescence a very thin spike with the spikelets all on one side. There are no glumes. Lower pale larger than upper, and ending in a bristle. Greek, nardos, *spikenard.*

527. Nardus stri'cta. **Mat-grass.**

Perennial, ½–1 ft., common on heaths and moors throughout Britain; I. Flowers in summer. A tufted grass, forming dense tussocks; base of stem clad in broad, membranous sheaths; leaves like bristles, the lower spreading outwards, pale green, white in winter. Spike stiff, very slender, 1-sided, purplish.

HO'RDEUM

Inflorescence a dense spike; spikelets flattened, set edge-on to the stem. The spikelets occur in groups of 3; the 2 outer are generally sterile and consist of narrow, awn-like glumes; the central spikelet has 2, awned glumes and a single flower with an awned pale; the spike has a very bristly appearance. The Latin name for barley.

528. Hordeum muri'num. **Wall Barley, Waybent.**

Annual, ½–1 ft., common in dry waste places and roadsides throughout Britain; I. Flowers in summer. Plant tufted; stems bent at the base; leaves flat, hairy, rather limp. Spike very dense, bluish-green.

E'LYMUS

Inflorescence a dense spike. Spikelets 3–5 flowered, flattened, set broad-side on in notches of the stem. Glumes large, ending in points or bristles. Greek, elumos, *a sheath, the grain being covered by the pale.*

529. Elymus arena'rius. **Lyme-grass.**

Perennial, 2–4 ft., locally common on sandy shores of most of the maritime counties of Britain; I. Flowers late summer. Spreads by extensive branching rhizomes which bind the sand; stem stout, erect; leaves stiff, rough, bluish-green. Spike long and dense; spikelets very large.

526 Couch-grass, Twitch

527 Mat-grass

528 Wall Barley, Waybent

529 Lyme-grass

INDEX

The numbers in ordinary type refer to pages, those in heavy type to the serial number of the species and illustrations.

PRINTED IN
GREAT BRITAIN
AT THE
UNIVERSITY PRESS
OXFORD
BY
JOHN JOHNSON
PRINTER
TO THE
UNIVERSITY